C0-AOE-704

PRAEGER INTRODUCTORY GEOGRAPHIES

Turkey

Praeger Introductory Geographies

HUMAN GEOGRAPHY
Emrys Jones

FRANCE
E. Estyn Evans

SPAIN
W. B. Fisher and H. Bowen-Jones

GERMANY
T. H. Elkins

ITALY
J. P. Cole

EAST-CENTRAL EUROPE
R. H. Osborne

TURKEY

An Introductory Geography

J. C. DEWDNEY

PRAEGER PUBLISHERS
New York · Washington

BOOKS THAT MATTER

Published in the United States of America in 1971
by Praeger Publishers, Inc., 111 Fourth Avenue,
New York, N.Y. 10003

Library of Congress Catalog Card Number: 79–101658

Printed in Great Britain

CONTENTS

MAPS AND DIAGRAMS

PREFACE

Study of the Middle East by British geographers has intensified over the last twenty years and a number of excellent texts have been written covering the area as a whole. There has, however, been no single volume in English devoted entirely to a geography of Turkey. It is hoped that the present volume will to some extent remedy this deficiency by assembling, under a single cover, a fairly wide range of information, description and discussion which could otherwise only be obtained from scattered and in many cases somewhat inaccessible sources. Turkey, in contrast to the Arab lands, has so far received relatively little attention from British geographers, a fact which stems largely from Britain's much greater involvement in the political and economic affairs of the Arab world. It is hoped that this book will help to acquaint a wide audience with the character of the Turkish landscape, people and economy, and will be of value not only to teachers and their students at various levels but also to businessmen, tourists and others who are now visiting Turkey in increasing numbers.

In common with other authors in this series, I have presented my material under three heads—physical, human and economic—with a concluding regional section in which I have attempted to integrate the various parts. I make no apology for this approach which, in my opinion, remains the most satisfactory method for an introductory text of this sort. Inevitably, in a country where farming still occupies more than 70% of the population, such matters as climate, soils and agriculture itself are treated at considerable length.

Place names are given in their modern Turkish forms throughout. While Antioch, Smyrna or Trebizond, for example, may be more familiar to western ears, they have long since fallen out of use in Turkey itself and Antakya, Izmir and Trabzon are now taking their place in non-Turkish as well as in Turkish writings. It was less easy to discard the classical regional names such as Phrygia, Galatia, Cilicia, Pamphylia, etc., since they often retain a certain geographical significance and have no direct Turkish equivalents. However, these too are rarely used in modern Turkish and I have replaced them, wherever possible, by references to the appropriate Turkish provinces. The use of modern Turkish place-names presents certain difficulties of orthography, grammar and pronunciation which it is hoped the reader will be able to overcome by reference to the notes on pages 8–11.

The reading list on pages 205–8 is not intended as even a partial bibliography of relevant works. The titles included have been selected for their general availability as well as for their quality and content and a great deal of valuable material published in Turkey in English, French and German, as well as in the Turkish language, has been omitted.

My thanks are due to a variety of organisations and individuals. In particular, I owe a debt of gratitude to the officials of *Topraksu* (Soil Conservation and Farm Irrigation Division, Ministry of Agriculture), who did so much to assist me in my travels, to the State Institute of Statistics for the regular supply of numerous publications, and to many other Turkish official agencies. I also wish to thank the cartographic and secretarial staff of the Department of Geography, University of Durham for their assistance in preparing the book for publication, especially Miss Christine Hill and Mr A. Corner who drew most of the maps and Mrs J. Abbott, Mrs S. Eckford and Miss A. Yeates, who did the typing.

I wish to express my thanks to my Turkish colleague, Professor Sirri Erinç, for permission to reproduce from the *Atlas of Turkey* the area-height diagrams in Fig. 7, to the American Geographical Society for permission to base Fig. 32 on a map which appeared in the *Geographical Review*, Volume 42, 1952, and to Professor Erhard Winkler for permission to use maps from his article 'Die Wirtschaft von Zonguldak, Türkei' in the preparation of Fig. 46.

I am greatly indebted to my colleagues in Durham and particularly to Professor H. Bowen-Jones for help and encouragement both at home and in the field. Finally, I would like to express my gratitude to my wife for bearing without complaint my lengthy absences in Turkey and my constant pre-occupation with this book.

John C. Dewdney
Durham

INTRODUCTION

Compared with most European countries Turkey covers a large area but has a relatively small population for its size. Its total area, including lakes, of 780 576 square km (302 169 square miles) is greater than that of any European state outside the Soviet Union. Turkey is two and a half times as big as Italy, more than twice the size of Germany,

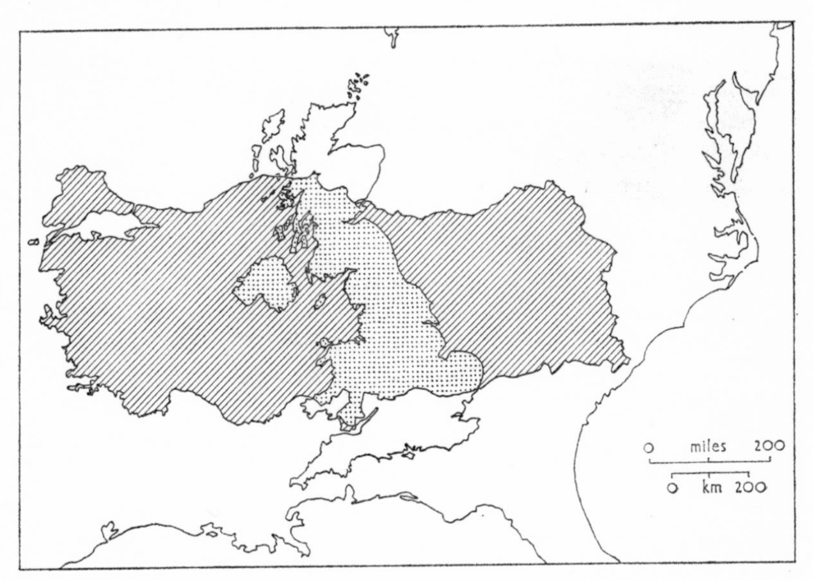

Fig. 1. Turkey, the United Kingdom and the eastern U.S.A.

one and a half times the size of Spain and about three times as big as the United Kingdom (Fig. 1). Turkey is also one of the larger states of the Middle East, where she is exceeded in area only by Saudi Arabia, Iran and Egypt. A second simple, yet highly significant fact is the elongated shape of the country: while the distance from the Aegean coast to the eastern boundary is more than 1600 km (1000 miles), that from the Black Sea to the Mediterranean nowhere exceeds 800 km (500 miles). The attenuated shape of the country has presented considerable difficulties in its economic development, particularly of the remote, eastern regions.

The population of Turkey according to the census of 1965 was 31 391 207, the largest of any Middle Eastern country, but well below those of Britain, West Germany, Italy and France. The overall population density in 1965 was 41 per square km (107 per square mile) and in this respect, as in so many others, Turkey occupies an intermediate position between her more densely settled Balkan neighbours to the west and north-west (Bulgaria 191, Greece 168 per square mile) and the more thinly populated countries of the Middle East (Iran 37, Iraq 48, Syria 76 per square mile). The Turkish population is growing at a very rapid rate. Between 1960 and 1965 it increased by about 13%, an annual growth rate of some 2·5%, which is among the most rapid in the world for a population of such a size (Fig. 2).

Only about 3% of the area and 8% of the population are in the European part of the country which is known as Trakya (Thrace). The remainder of the territory, Anadolu (Anatolia), is, according to the usual convention, in Asia, forming part of that very distinctive region known variously as South-West Asia or the Middle East. Asia Minor is another geographical term used by many authors to describe an area virtually identical with that of present-day Turkey. Turkey is thus, in a sense, peripheral to both Europe and Asia, lying at the extreme south-eastern limit of the former and on the western margin of the latter. In such a position it has inevitably functioned as a bridgeland between the two continents and in particular between the Balkans and the Middle East. Turkey draws its geographical characteristics from both these regions, having some features which are clearly European and others which are equally clearly Middle Eastern. From the days of the 11th and 12th-century Crusaders to those of the 20th-century 'Berlin–Baghdad' Railway, Turkey has been a routeway from Europe into the Moslem world. The converse is also true: when Islam was pressing hard on Christendom and Moslem armies were at the gates of Vienna, this situation had been brought about by a north-westward expansion of the Turkish domain into the Balkans, where relict Moslem groups remain to this day just as there are relict Christian groups in the Moslem-dominated Middle East.

The bridgeland or contact-zone character of Turkey remains a dominant feature and the country stands poised between east and west in matters other than its mere geographical location. With a cultural tradition almost entirely Islamic and Asiatic, though superimposed on earlier classical and Christian cultures derived from the Aegean, modern Turkey has striven with considerable success to adopt essentially European forms of culture and economic development. While the mass of the Turkish peasantry follows modes of life very similar to those of other Middle Eastern lands, the more educated Turk, at least, feels himself

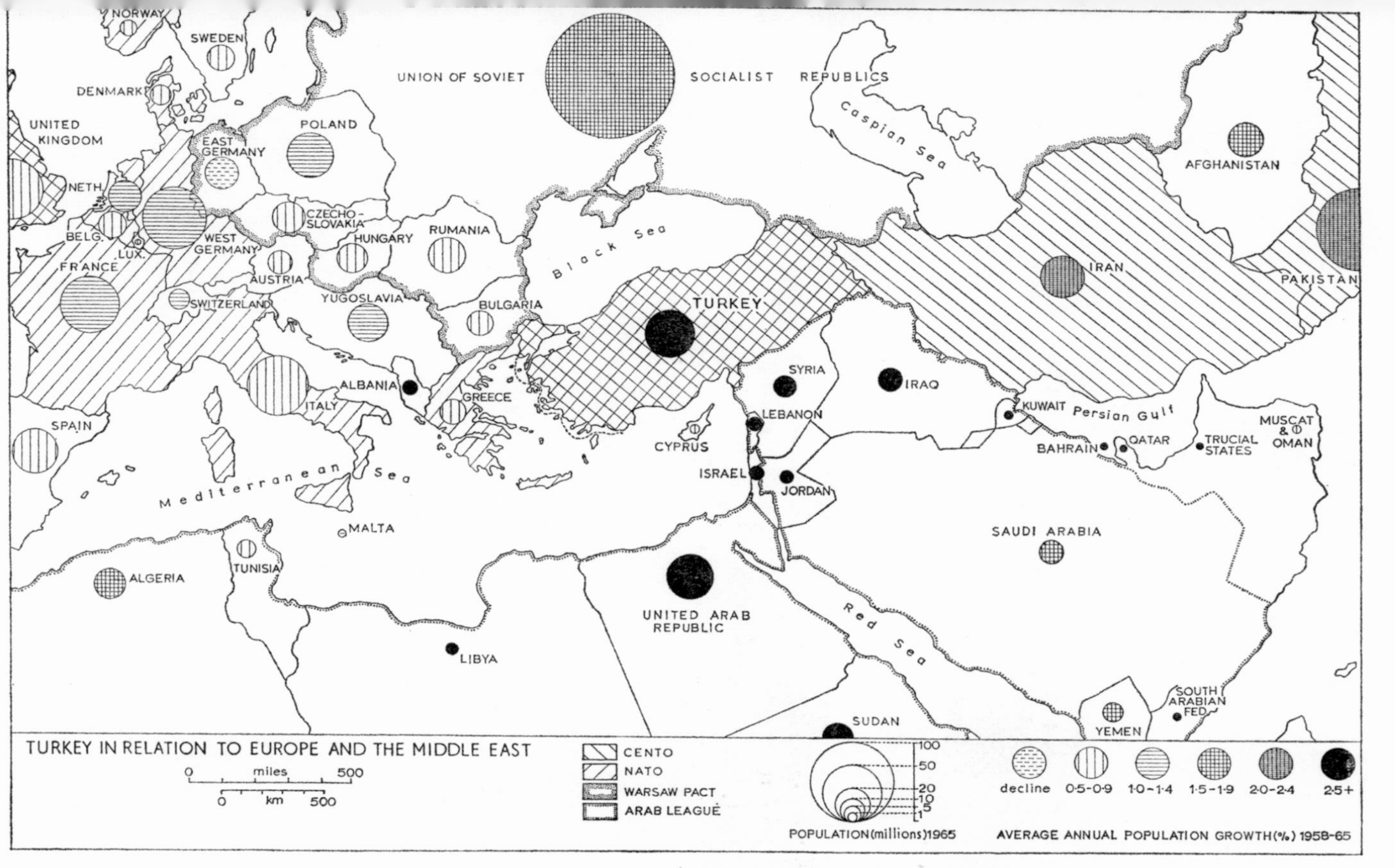

Fig. 2. Turkey in relation to the countries of Europe and the Middle East

more akin to his European, indeed his west European contemporaries than to his Arab neighbours to the south, an attitude exemplified by Turkey's membership of O.E.C.D. and the Council of Europe. In addition Turkey, like Iran, stands somewhat aloof from the politics of the rest of the Middle East, maintaining, for example, friendly relations with both Israel and the Arab states. Traditional hostility to her northern neighbour, Russia, had much to do with her accession to the NATO and CENTO alliances, and Turkey's link function is again emphasised by the fact that, apart from Britain and the United States, she is the only country belonging to both these organisations. Her membership of NATO, incidentally, brings Turkey into uneasy partnership with Greece, another traditionally hostile state, relations with which have been exacerbated in recent years by the conflict over Cyprus.

Much of Turkey's past and present importance in world affairs stems from its position, which is one of great strategic significance exemplified by the crossing, within Turkish territory, of major north-east to south-west and north-west to south-east routeways. The former are the maritime routes between the Black Sea, the coasts of which are, with the exception of the Turkish sector, entirely in the hands of the communist powers, and the Mediterranean. The narrows of the Bosphorus and Dardanelles lie in Turkish territorial waters and although the Black Sea powers have special rights of passage these could easily be denied. From this situation springs Russia's traditional interest in the control of these straits and her attempts, continued in Soviet times, to obtain a greater influence over their use. Turkey's position as a bridge between Europe and Asia has already been mentioned and had important implications during both World Wars. Her alliance with Germany during the First World War was a serious threat to Britain's interest in the Middle East as a link with India, and the abortive attack on Gallipoli (Gelibolu) was an attempt to put Turkey out of the war and, by forcing the Straits, to open up communications between the western allies and Russia. Turkey's neutrality during the Second World War prevented the full development of an axis 'pincer movement' towards Suez, the other arm of which was driven along the North African coast and only checked at Alamein, within 200 miles of the canal. Today, Turkey's membership of NATO and CENTO is a vital link in the containing ring around the communist world.

Internally, Turkey has achieved a considerable degree of political and cultural unity. It is true, as later chapters will show, that there is a great deal of regional diversity in most aspects of the country's physical and human geography. In particular there is a wide economic and social gulf between the peasantry and the largely westernised town-dweller, but Turkish nationalism is a strong unifying force which tends to override internal differences, at least where major international issues are involved. Large minority groups are still present and prevent the full attainment of the nation–state ideal but these are being slowly assimilated and present a much smaller threat to internal stability than they do, for example, in Iraq. At the same time there is still recurrent tension within Turkey between progressive and conservative elements, the former intent upon pressing Atatürk's reforms to their logical conclusion of a completely secular state, the latter concerned lest all the values of traditional Islamic–Turkish culture should be lost.

The Turks have close linguistic and cultural affinities with many of the peoples of inner Asia: Turkic languages are spoken over much of Soviet Central Asia and in parts of Siberia and western China. Turkey has also had a long history as an imperial power, controlling large parts of the Balkans and the Middle East. However, neither of these facts has much influence on present-day Turkish policies. 'Pan-Turkism' no longer attracts significant support and the Turkish Republic has renounced the imperialist ambitions of its predecessors. These are aspects of that complete break with the past which has been the dominant aim of most Turkish leaders since the establishment of the Republic in 1923.

Just as Turkey stands geographically at the meeting point of Europe and Asia, with some of the attributes of each and belonging fully to neither, so she also stands on the economic borderline between 'developed' and 'developing' territories. Whereas over large rural areas conditions are primitive and standards of living are low, certain districts are plainly outliers of the 'developed' European world. The economy as a whole is dominated by agriculture, much of it still at a low level of efficiency, but Turkey's industrial base is the strongest of all Middle Eastern economies. Twenty years ago Turkey was clearly part of the under-developed world: today she is at or very close to the 'take-off' stage of economic growth.

In conclusion, it is instructive to note the many similarities which exist between Turkey and the Iberian peninsula and in this connexion it is relevant to quote, in slightly amended form, from a companion volume in this series.*

> Nowadays, the geographer might be tempted to regard Turkey as a mirror-image of the Iberian peninsula. In the two regions there is the same physical pattern of daunting topography, unexpectedly varied and severe climates, and a wide range in ways of life. Both have been the centres of large empires now in eclipse; and both have remained

* Fisher, W. B., and Bowen-Jones, H., *Spain: A Geographical Background* (Chatto & Windus), 1958, p. 11.

partly secluded from the main currents of European affairs, with interests away from Europe; both have impinged politically, for limited periods but with profound effect, on the course of history in Europe, as centres of invasion outwards and as zones of weakness that have attracted predatory neighbours. Finally, both include in their territory sea straits that are regarded as vital spheres of influence by more northerly powers.

To this one might add a further point of similarity. In Turkey, as in the Iberian peninsula, regional contrasts are of two kinds. Predominant over all is the fundamental dichotomy between the interior and the periphery: subsidiary to this basic division are the contrasts which exist between the various parts of the periphery. Thus a division of Turkey into regions which can legitimately be described as 'north', 'west', 'south', 'east' and 'centre' becomes a recurrent feature of this book.

B

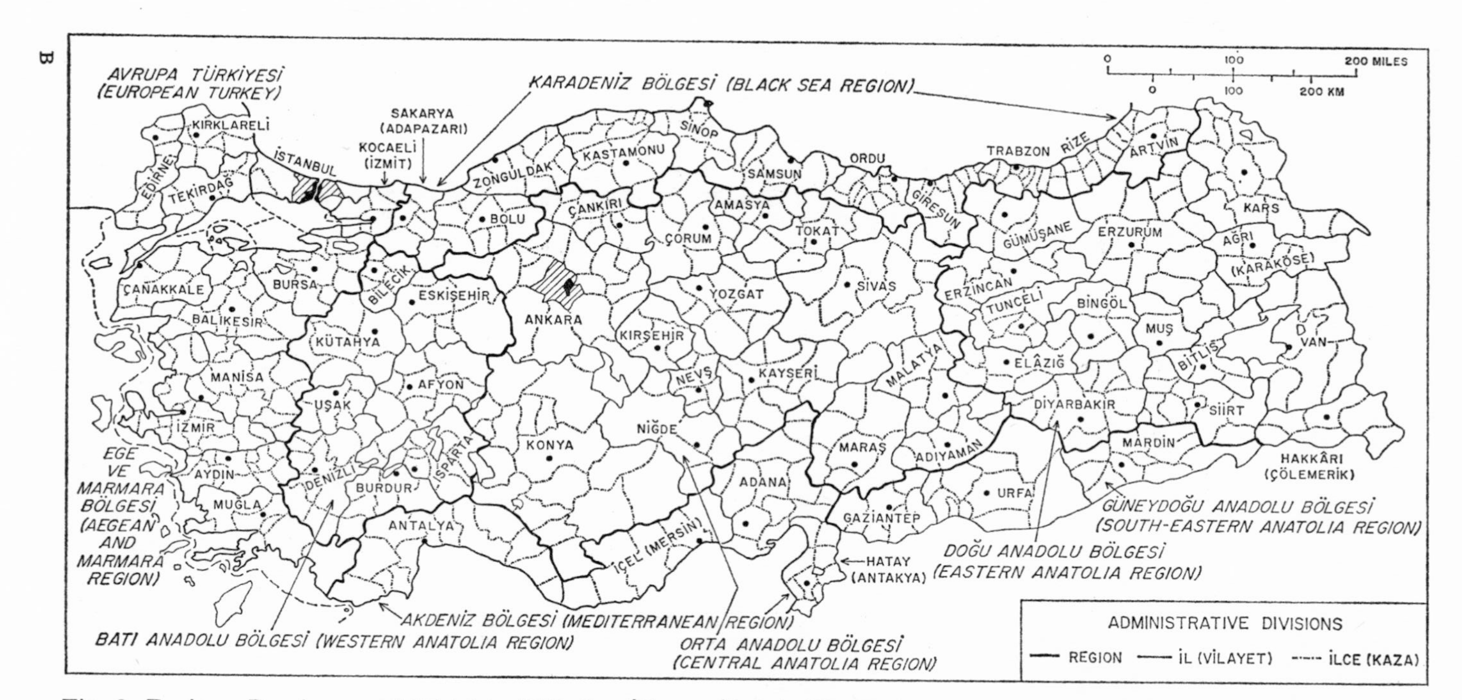

Fig. 3. Regions, Provinces and Districts (*Bölgeler, İller* ve *İlceler*). The Regions shown are those used in censuses and other official publications

TURKISH ORTHOGRAPHY AND PRONUNCIATION

The Turkish language belongs to the Turkic subdivision of the Ural–Altaic language family and is thus quite distinct from the languages spoken in Europe, most of which belong to the Indo-European family. Turkish is also quite different in origin and construction from the other major languages of the Middle East, though it does contain a large number of loan words derived from both Arabic and Persian. Languages of the Turkic group are spoken over large parts of the interior of Asia, including Persian and Soviet Azerbaijan, Soviet Central Asia and much of Siberia.

Prior to the establishment of the Republic, Turkish was written in Arabic characters but Atatürk's reform of 1928 replaced these by a modified version of the Roman alphabet. Over the past forty years, there has been a conscious attempt to replace Arabic and Persian loan words by their Turkish equivalents, but at the same time there has been a large-scale introduction of new loan words, particularly technical terms, from European languages, especially French and English.

The Turkish alphabet consists of 28 characters. The main differences from the standard English alphabet are the absence of q, w and x and the introduction of five additional letters: ö, ü, ı (undotted), ç and ş. Turkish characters also include ğ which is not normally regarded as a separate letter, and a circumflex accent ^ which modifies the pronunciation of certain vowels. The majority of letters common to the Turkish and English alphabets are pronounced very much as in standard English, a notable exception being the letter c, which in Turkish is pronounced like the j in English 'jam'. The apostrophe ' is sometimes used to denote a break in pronunciation but most commonly occurs when a suffix is attached to a proper name, e.g. *Ingiltere'den* = from England, *Ankara'da* = in Ankara.

Table A is intended to indicate the pronunciation of the Turkish alphabet.

A few grammatical notes are necessary for an understanding of Turkish place-names. It should be realised that the language is 'suffix-agglutinative' which means that tenses, cases, prepositions, etc., are all

TABLE A

TURKISH CHARACTERS AND THEIR PRONUNCIATION

a	As in English
b	As in English
c	As English j in 'jam', e.g. *Ceyhan* pronounced Jeyhan
ç	As ch in English 'church', e.g. *Çorum* pronounced Chorum
d	As in English
e	As in English 'get'
f	As in English 'far'
g	As in English 'go'
ğ	Does not occur at the beginning of words: usually mute or a very slight glottal stop, indicating a break in pronunciation, e.g. *Boğaz* pronounced Bo-az
h	As in English
i	As in English 'bit'. The capital letter is also written with a dot, e.g. *İzmir*
ı	Similar to the English i in 'first'
j	As French j; used rarely, for the most part in loan-words from French, e.g. *jambon* = ham, *garaj* = garage
k	As in English
l	As in English
m	As in English
n	As in English
o	As English o in 'god'
ö	As German ö
p	As in English
r	As English r in 'red', slightly rolled
s	As in English 'sit'
ş	As sh in English 'ship', e.g. *Şehir* = city, pronounced Shehir
t	As in English
u	As in English 'bull'
ü	As German ü or French u in *tu*
v	As in English
y	At beginning of words, or before vowels, as English y in 'yet'; also used in place of i in the second half of diphthongs, e.g. *Kayseri*
z	As in English 'zebra'
^	The circumflex ^ appears most frequently in â. It is sometimes used, mainly at the beginning of a word, to lengthen the vowel and to distinguish the word from a similar one without accent, e.g. *Ali* (personal name), *âli* = exalted. It also occurs in â and û after g, l or k, where it gives a slight y sound, e.g. *Hakkâri*, pronounced Hakkyarı; *lûtfen* (= please), pronounced lyutfen. Its use on a final i as in Şarkî (= eastern) has largely been dropped.

rendered by suffixes added to the word stem. Thus, for example, we have: *dağ* = mountain, *dağlar* = mountains, *dağlarda* = in the mountains, *dağlara* = to the mountains, *dağlardan* = from the mountains, etc. A second point, of particular significance where place-names are concerned is the possessive form in which the suffixes -ı, -i, u, ü or -sı, -si, su, sü-, after a final vowel, are added to the object possessed. Thus we have

Marmara Denizi = Sea of Marmara, *İmroz Adası* = Island of Imroz, *İzmir Körfezi* = Gulf of Izmir, *Toros Dağları* = Taurus Mountains, *Van Gölü* = Lake Van, *Konya ovası* = Konya Basin, etc. There is one irregular form in this group, *suyu* from *su* = water or river, e.g. *Çakit Suyu* = Çakit River. The existence of so many alternative possessive suffixes is a result of the rules of vowel harmony, another characteristic feature of the Turkish language. The eight vowels are divided into two groups of four, the 'hard' vowels, *a, ı, o* and *u*, and the 'soft' vowels *e, i, ö* and *ü*. The vowel in the suffix must be from the same group as the final vowel in the word stem. Thus, for example, there are two plural forms, *-lar* after a hard vowel and *-ler* after a soft one, e.g. *dağ, dağlar*; *göl, göller*. As a result, a word may have different possessive suffixes in the singular and plural, e.g. *dağ, dağlar* (*-lar* after *a*), *dağı, dağları* (*-ı* after *a* in both cases), but *göl, göller* (*-ler* after *ö*), *gölü* (*-ü* after *ö*), *gölleri* (*-i* after *e*).

Many Turkish place-names are compounds, consisting of an adjective or adjectival noun and a noun. These are nearly always written as one word, e.g. *Karadeniz* = Black Sea (contrast *Marmara Denizi*), *Bozcaada* = Grey Island (contrast *İmroz Adası*), *Eskişehir* = Old City, *Taşköprü* = Stone Bridge. Note that, in compound words of this sort, the rules of vowel harmony do not always apply. Finally it should be noted that there are often a number of alternative Turkish words for a particular topographical feature, e.g. *çay, su, nehir, ırmak* (possessive forms *çayı, suyu, nehri, ırmağı*) are all used to denote watercourses. Like the English words stream, brook, river, water, etc., these terms bear no formal relationship to the size of the feature named.

Following are some of the more important topographical terms, many of which are used in this book, either in the text or on the maps. Where appropriate, plural and/or possessive forms are indicated. In addition, several common place-name elements are included.

acı	bitter (*Acıgöl* = Bitter Lake)
ada, pl. *adalar*, poss. *adası, adaları*	island
afyon	opium
ak	white (*Akdeniz* = lit. White Sea = Mediterranean)
altın	gold (*Altındağ* = Golden Mountain)
Anadolu	Anatolia
batı	west (*Batı Anadolu* = Western Anatolia)
boğaz, poss. *boğazı*	strait (*Marmara Boğazı* = Bosphorus)
burun, poss. *burnu*	headland, point
büyük	big (*Büyük Menderes*)
cami, poss. *camii*	mosque

cumhuriyet, poss. *cumhuriyeti*	republic (T.C. = *Turkiye Cumhuriyeti* = Republic of Turkey)
çay, poss. *çayı*	brook, stream
dağ. pl. *dağlar*, poss. *dağı*, *dağları*	mountain
demir	iron
dere, poss. *deresi*	valley, stream
doğu	east
eski	old
göl, poss. *gölü*	lake
gümüş	silver
güney	south
hisar, poss. *hisarı*	castle
ırmak, poss. *ırmağı*	river (*Kızılırmak* = Red River, *Köprü Irmağı* = Bridge River)
il, poss. *ili*	province (*Ankara ili* = Ankara Province)
ilce, poss. *ilcesi*	district (*Tarsus ilcesi* = Tarsus District)
kale, poss. *kalesi*	fortress
kara	black (*Karadağ* = Black Mountain)
kaza, poss. *kazası*	district (now replaced by *ilce*)
kilise, poss. *kilisesi*	church
kıyı, poss. *kıyısı*	shore (*Karadeniz kıyısı* = Black Sea coast)
köprü	bridge
körfez, poss. *körfezi*	gulf (*İzmit Körfezi* = Gulf of Izmit)
Küçük	small (*Küçük Menderes*)
kuzey	north
mahalle, poss. *mahallesi*	settlement, city quarter
meydan, poss. *meydanı*	open space, city square
nehir, poss. *nehri*	river (*Ceyhan Nehri* = Ceyhan River)
ova, pl. *ovalar*, poss. *ovası*, *ovaları*	plain, basin
pazar, poss. *pazarı*	market (*Adapazarı* = Island Market)
saray, poss. *sarayı*	palace
su, poss. *suyu*	water, stream
sark	east (now replaced by *doğu*)
şehir, poss. *şehri*	town, city
taş	stone
tepe, poss. *tepesi*	hill
Trakya	Thrace
tuz	salt
uzun	long
vilayet, poss. *vilayeti*	province (now replaced by *İl*)
yaylâ, poss. *yaylâsı*	plateau, upland pasture
yeni	new
yeşil	green
yol, pl. *yollar*, poss. *yolu*, *yolları*	road, route (*Demir Yolları* = Railways, *Hava Yolları* = Airways)

STATISTICAL SOURCES

A considerable volume of statistical material is published by the State Institute of Statistics in Ankara (*Deviet İstatistik Enstitüsü, Başbakanlık, Ankara*). The publications of the Institute include a number of regular series as well as special reports on a variety of topics. Almost all these works are published in Turkish and one European language, which in recent years has been either English or French. Some of the more important items are listed below, with each title given in the language of publication.

Aylik İstatistik Bülteni: Monthly Bulletin of Statistics
Türkiye İstatistik Yıllığı: Annuaire Statistique de la Turquie
Genel Nüfus Sayimi: Census of Population

Censuses were held in 1927, 1935, and thereafter at five-year intervals. Recent census results have been published in two main volumes:

İdari Bolunus: By Administrative Division
Nüfusun Sosyal ve Ekonomik Nitelikleri: Social and Economic Characteristics of the Population

Diş Ticaret Yıllık İstatistik: Annual Foreign Trade Statistics
Tarımsal Yapı ve Üretim (formerly *Zirai Bünye ve Istihsal*): *Agricultural Structure and Production.* Published at irregular intervals but covers every year since 1947 and a number of earlier years.

Part One

PHYSICAL GEOGRAPHY

Chapter 1

STRUCTURE, RELIEF AND DRAINAGE

Structure and Relief

The structure of Turkey is highly complex and, although in broad outline there is a general correspondence between the larger structural units and the major relief zones, the relationship between the two is by no means simple or direct. Detailed research on the country's tectonics, geology and geomorphology is still in a rather early stage: small areas have been studied closely and broad hypotheses have been advanced for the country as a whole. As the process of detailed investigation continues, the generalisations made by earlier workers become progressively less tenable, and it is now apparent that matters are far more involved than was at one time believed.

Until a few decades ago the picture given by most authors was a simple one. The south-eastern part of Turkey was a northern continuation of the rigid Arabian foreland block, while the remainder of the country lay within the Alpine fold zone, where sedimentaries laid down in the Tethys Sea had been compressed between a southward-moving European block and the stationary block of Gondwanaland. Within the folded zone, smaller rigid blocks or median masses were present, and these affected the detailed arrangement of the fold ranges. One such median mass underlay the area commonly referred to as the Anatolian Plateau and the fold ranges diverged on either side of this, giving a northern Pontic and southern Taurus system which reunited in western and eastern Turkey.

Such a concept was descriptive rather than explanatory. It is true that the interior of Turkey shows a predominance of plateau-like topography; it is equally true that east–west-trending mountain ranges enclose the central area on all four sides. However, a number of features invalidate the simple picture of a resistant block surrounded by folded ranges implicit in the preceding paragraph. In the first place, the east–west ranges which run transverse to the Aegean coast, and account for the latter's discordant character, are a series of *horsts* and *graben* rather than true fold ranges. Secondly, the Anatolian 'plateau' is by no means the single block feature which the name suggests. It is criss-crossed by a complex system of faults, and contains numerous uplifted blocks and sunken basins and trenches which give it a considerable amplitude of relief. Furthermore, where broad expanses of flat or gently sloping terrain do occur, these are often developed on very recent sedimentary materials which conceal planated folds of Mesozoic and Tertiary age, similar to those of the Pontic and Taurus systems. Again, the Pontic and Taurus mountains form zones in which fold ranges are the predominant feature, but in many cases the present height of the mountains is due more to recent block uplift than to the original folding, there are numerous down-faulted troughs, and the mountain ranges themselves enclose small median masses, where rocks of Paleozoic or earlier age are exposed.

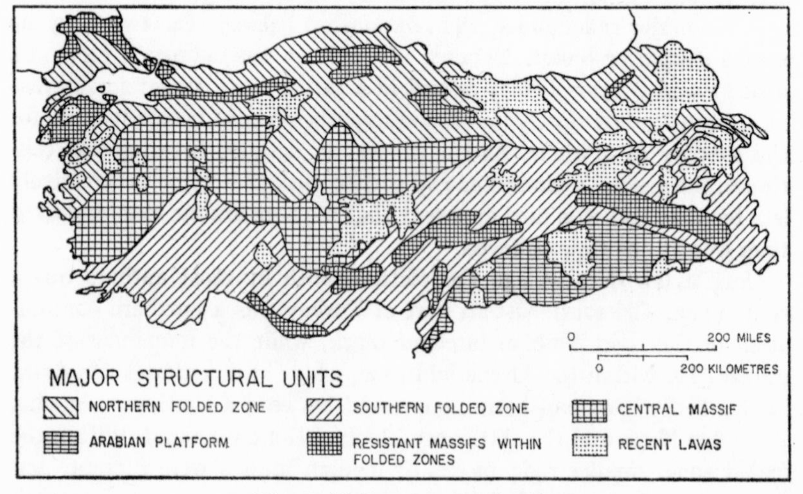

Fig. 4. Major structural units

Further variety results from the widespread occurrence of large areas of Tertiary lavas. These are most extensively developed in the east but are also common in central Anatolia where they add further diversity to the relief of the 'plateau'.

With these points in mind, however, it is still possible to discuss the structure and relief of Turkey under the following headings (Fig. 4):

(i) The Northern Folded Zone
(ii) The Central Massif
(iii) The Southern Folded Zone
(iv) The Arabian Platform

(i) The Northern Folded Zone

This quite clearly defined zone occupies the whole of northern Turkey for distances of 150–200 km (90–125 miles) inland from the Black Sea.

In the west, the zone curves round to run approximately north-east to south-west from the Sea of Marmara to the Aegean and it also includes the whole of Thrace. Problems of nomenclature arise when discussing this area. Most English texts use the term Pontic Ranges or Pontic Mountains (cf. German: *Pontische Gebirge,* French: *Chaînes Pontiques*) but there is no Turkish equivalent and the terms Kuzey Anadolu dağları (North Anatolian Mountains) or Karadeniz dağları (Black Sea Mountains) are preferred. In this text the word Pontic will be used for the system as a whole and the structural distinction made by some authors between a more northerly Pontide and southerly Anatolide fold system will be ignored.

Surface outcrops over the region as a whole are predominantly of Mesozoic and Lower Tertiary age: Cretaceous flysch and volcanic materials are the most widespread types but there is also a great variety of clays, shales, sandstones and limestones. Set into these folded materials are a number of uplifted blocks — often fault-bounded and usually carrying a planated upper surface — composed of Paleozoic and intrusive rocks. There are also large spreads of Neogene (late Tertiary) lavas, particularly in the extreme east and in the provinces of Ordu and Giresun.* The last two formations usually make up the highest parts of the mountain chains but this is not a universal rule: high peaks also occur on relatively weak rocks.

Dissection of the northern folded zone has served to emphasise the general east–west structural grain. Long, narrow mountain chains alternate with deep-set, trough-like valleys and basins, typified by the valleys of the Kelkit and Çoruh rivers (Fig. 5). These longitudinal inland corridors are connected to the coast by short gorge sections cut across the mountain ranges as in the lower reaches of the Kızılırmak, Yeşilırmak and Çoruh valleys.

There is a general tendency for the whole system to become more elevated and to show increasingly vigorous relief towards the east. Thus around the Sea of Marmara, in Thrace and in the provinces of Çanakkale, Bursa, Kocaeli and Sakarya, relief is subdued and heights rarely exceed 1000 m (3281 feet). The area bordering Marmara was in fact down-faulted during the late Tertiary so that in Thrace the northern folded zone consists mainly of the lowlands of the Ergene basin, where the fold structures are buried beneath Neogene deposits. Higher land comprises the low upswelling of the Tekirdağ range, which reaches only 945 m

* In Turkey there are few local regional names on the style of the French *pays*. Many English authors make use of classical names such as Bithynia, Paphlagonia, Pontus, etc., but these mean little to the modern Turk and are avoided here save when dealing with earlier times. Recourse must be to the modern provincial names which are indicated in Fig. 3.

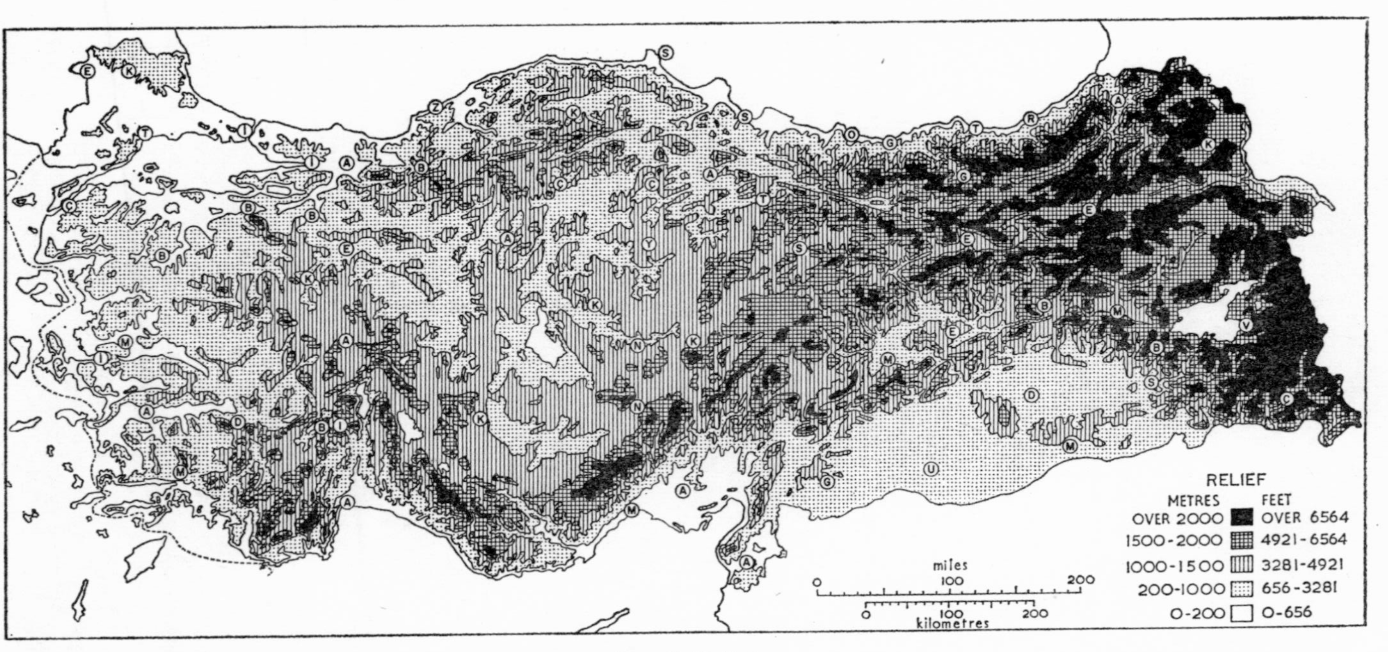
RELIEF
METRES
FEET
OVER 2000
OVER 6564
1500-2000
4921-6564
1000-1500
3281-4921
200-1000
656-3281
0-200
0-656
miles
0
100
200
kilometres
0
100
200

Fig. 5. Relief

(3100 feet) and the ancient massif of the Istranca dağları (1018 m/3340 feet). The lowlands of Balıkesir and Bursa provinces, with their alluvial and young sedimentary cover, are another area in which the fold structures are completely buried.

East of the Sakarya river, there is a fairly abrupt rise in altitude and the mountain barrier is broad and high as far as the Kızılırmak. In this section, there are three roughly parallel ranges. Immediately behind the Black Sea coast, the Baba dağları of Zonguldak province rise to 1500 m (4900 feet) and are continued through Kastamonu and Sinop provinces by the İsfendiyar dağları, which reach a maximum elevation of 2018 m (6620 feet). These ranges are separated by the upland basins of the Filyos and Gökırmak rivers from the Bolu (1828 m/5995 feet) and Ilgaz dağları (2588 m/8490 feet) the latter developed on a large block of Paleozoic materials. South again, beyond the Gerede and Devrez basins, lie the Koroğlu dağları (2400 m/7870 feet), developed largely on resistant volcanics. It is in this section that the northern folded zone has a marked protuberance towards the south, fold structures running through Ankara almost as far as the Tuz Gölü. Thus the northern part of Ankara province, between the Sakarya and Kızılırmak rivers, comprises a number of broken ranges with a general north-east to south-west trend, such as the Ayaş dağları (1668 m/5470 feet) and the Elmadağ range (1855 m/6084 feet).

Between the Kızılırmak and Yeşilırmak rivers, the rocks are relatively weak and the relief much more broken, though even here a number of short mountain ranges have peaks as high as 2000 m (6560 feet). By cutting back through this zone of weakness, the two rivers have succeeded in tapping the drainage of a large part of the northern folded zone and the central massif, from Çankırı province in the west to Gümüşhane in the east and southwards to the foot of the Taurus ranges. One result has been the development of large deltas at the mouths of these two rivers which are unique on the Black Sea coast along most of which there is only a very narrow coastal plain.

Beyond the Yeşilırmak, relief again becomes much stronger and more clearly defined and continues so, right to the Soviet frontier. Throughout this section, a single, near-continuous range runs parallel to the coast at a distance of about 50 km (30 miles) inland. This has a variety of local names including, from west to east, the Çanık dağları (2070 m/6790 feet), Giresun dağları (3200 m/10 500 feet) and Rize dağları (3937 m/12 900 feet). The range is developed mainly on Neogene volcanics to the west of Gümüşhane and on Cretaceous volcanics to the east. The highest peaks generally occur on intrusions. To the south of this formidable barrier, the valleys of the westward-flowing Kelkit and the eastward-flowing Çoruh form a long, narrow trench with its floor at 1000–1500 m (3200–5000 feet) above sea level. South of this corridor, as far as the line Sivas–Erzincan–Erzurum, which marks the limit of the northern folded zone and its junction with the Taurus system, is a further series of east–west-trending ranges, generally less continuous than the coastal range but containing a number of major ridges, of which the most important are the Köşedağı (3577 m/11 733 feet), Keşiş dağları (3537 m/11 600 feet), Çimen-Kop dağları (3100 m/10 168 feet) and Allahüekber dağları (3111 m/10 204 feet). There is a much greater variety of rock-type and structure here than in the area further north. Folded Mesozoics and Tertiaries, small Paleozoic blocks and igneous intrusions all occur; in addition there are a number of well-defined down-faulted basins with a cover of recent sedimentaries, as for example around Erzincan. In Kars and Erzurum provinces, where the surface is largely composed of recent volcanics, the terrain takes on the form of a high-standing, dissected lava plateau which is continued across the frontier into Soviet Armenia.

Taken as a whole, the Pontic ranges form a major barrier to movement and contact between the Black Sea coast and the interior, particularly in the eastern section. Road and rail routes across it are few; indeed, the latter are wholly absent beyond the Yeşilırmak, and movement along the coast is also made difficult since much of the coastal plain is extremely narrow. However, the region is by no means wholly negative from the point of view of human occupance. Steep slopes abound, but there are considerable areas of plateau and high valley land between the ranges as well as numerous enclosed basins and corridors. These features provide a variety of sites for human settlement, while the coastal strip, largely by reason of its favourable climate and agricultural productivity, is among the most densely populated parts of Turkey.

(ii) The Central Massif

This structural unit extends inland from the Aegean coast south of İzmir, passes well to the south of Ankara, between the Tuz Gölü and Konya, and culminates near Sivas, where the northern and southern folded zones come together. Its generalised S-shape reflects the trends of the Taurus mountain system to the south. Throughout the massif, fold structures, though not entirely absent, are very rare. Nevertheless this is a zone with considerable variety of relief and is much more diversified than reference to the Anatolian 'plateau' would lead one to expect. This diversity is best illustrated by considering the central massif in a series of subdivisions from west to east.

From the Aegean coast inland to a line running roughly from Bursa to

Denizli, the structure comprises a series of particularly well-defined east–west dislocations, giving a north–south sequence of block mountains and rift valleys. Between the Marmara lowlands, which are developed on a faulted basin within the northern folded zone, and the Bakır valley, the picture is confused by the presence of young volcanics and folded Mesozoic and Tertiary rocks, together forming an upland which rises to some 1300 m (4250 feet), but south of the Bakır valley the *horst* and *graben* structure is clearly visible. The Gediz and Büyük Menderes valleys are broad, flat-floored troughs extending more than 150 km (93 miles) inland. The alluvial plains along these rivers, often as much as 10 or 12 km (6–7½ miles) wide, are among the few extensive lowlands in Turkey. Between the Gediz and Büyük Menderes, the Küçük Menderes valley is a similar feature about 75 km (47 miles) long. Rising abruptly above the valley troughs are hill masses developed almost entirely on metamorphic materials, mainly mica-schists and gneisses. These include the Bozdağları (2160 m/7085 feet) between the Gediz and Küçük Menderes valleys, Aydın dağları (1732 m/5681 feet) between the Küçük and Büyük Menderes, and the Menteşe ranges (1792 m/5878 feet) which occupy the area between the Büyük Menderes and the northern edge of the southern folded zone which occurs along the line Mandalya körfezi–Muğla–Denizli. The valley troughs in this area have long been important route-ways from the Aegean coast to the interior.

East of the Bursa–Denizli line and as far as a line from Eskişehir to Afyon, is an area of more complex structure and relief. The general surface level rises eastwards from 500 to 1000 m (1600–3200 feet) and much of the area is gently sloping with a cover of Neogene materials. These recent deposits, however, mask a great variety of rock type. A number of faulted basins are set into this surface, while above it rise numerous islands of metamorphic and Paleozoic rocks which give mountains of 2000 m (6500 feet) or more (e.g. Murat dağı: 2224 m/7295 feet). Some of the highest peaks of all in this region are associated with intrusions as in the case of Ulu dağ (2543 m/8341 feet) and Eğrigöz dağı (2181 m/7154 feet) or with young volcanics as in the case of the Türkmen dağı (1829 m/6000 feet).

The section of the central massif bounded on the west by the Eskişehir–Afyon line and on the east by a line from Ankara through the Tuz Gölü to Niğde shows most clearly those features associated with the term 'Anatolian plateau'. Here are vast expanses of flat or very gently sloping land covered with Neogene deposits and standing at heights in the region of 1000 m (3200 feet) above sea level. These plains are divided by low upswellings in the surface into three main sectors. In the west is the basin of the Sakarya river, bounded on the north and south respectively by the

Paleozoic ranges of the Sundiken dağları (1768 m/5800 feet) and the Emir dağları (2241 m/7350 feet) and broken in the centre by the metamorphic Sivrihisar dağları (1820 m/5970 feet). Away from these mountain ranges, slopes are gentle, save where the Sakarya and its tributaries are incised into the surface. The Sakarya basin is bounded on its eastern side by the plateaux of Haymanı yaylâsı and Cihanbeyli yaylâsı, whose gentle slopes, developed entirely on Neogene deposits, rise to a general level of 1200–1400 m (4000–4600 feet). Beyond these plateaux are two extensive basins, the Tuz Gölü havzası and the Konya ovası, separated by the Obruk yaylâsı (1200 m/4000 feet). Both these basins are areas of internal drainage (see page 33) and carried extensive lakes in Pliocene times. The Tuz Gölü (Salt Lake) is a shrinking remnant of one of these lakes and there are numerous swampy areas which, after heavy rain, may be temporarily covered with water.

Beyond this central Anatolian heartland, relief and structure again become extremely complex in the triangular eastern part of the massif, which has its apex near Sivas. The great plains described in the preceding paragraph are closed in on the east by a series of uplands which have a general north–south alignment. In the north and centre, that is from the north-eastern corner of Ankara province to the eastern side of Tuz Gölü, these uplands are developed on a series of intrusive massifs which give rise to peaks at 1700–2000 m (5500–6500 feet). The southernmost of these massifs, the Kochisar yaylâsı, rises abruptly above the Tuz Gölü plains along a well-marked fault-line scarp. Further south, however, the eastern side of the Konya ovası is closed in by a particularly extensive spread of recent volcanics, which occupy much of Niğde, Nevşehir and Kayseri provinces. Here a number of volcanic peaks rise above 3000 m (9800 feet), notably Erciyas (3916 m/12 844 feet) south of Kayseri, and Hasandağı (3258 m/10 686 feet) to the north-west of Niğde. The large area of relatively gentle relief which occurs inside the curve of the Kızılırmak is developed across a great variety of structures. Paleozoic and intrusive massifs, planated Mesozoic and Tertiary folds and extensive spreads of Neogene sediments are all found within this zone, which is terminated on its eastern side by the metamorphic mass of the Akdağlar range (2245 m/7364 feet), which runs parallel to the Kızılırmak on its north-western side. This in turn gives way to the broad depression of the upper Kızılırmak, bounded on its south-eastern side by the outer ranges of the southern folded zone.

Thus the interior massif as a whole is by no means a single, uniform block, but consists of a series of high-level plains separated by mountain ranges of varied origin and rock type. While parts of the massif are characterised by centripetal, inland drainage with swamps and ephemeral lakes, others have become connected to the external drainage systems of the Sakarya and Kızılırmak which are generally incised deeply into the surface. As a result, steep slopes occur in many parts of the region. Nevertheless, by comparison with the mountain zones to the north, south and east, the central massif is a zone of relatively easy movement. Its disadvantages are climatic rather than physiographic.

(iii) The Southern Folded Zone

As Fig. 4 shows, this is a well-defined and continuous zone, which occupies the southern third of the country from the Aegean to the Gulf of İskenderun, whence it swings first north-eastwards and then eastwards around the northern side of the Arabian platform. Problems of nomenclature again arise when discussing this region as a whole. It has long been the practice of English writers to refer to this mountain system as the Taurus, a title originally derived from the Turkish Toros dağı, one of the highest peaks in the system, which stands due north of Mersin and overlooks the Cilician Gates. This usage has been adopted by Turkish authors, who now speak of Toros dağları when referring to the mountain system as a whole. Other conventions in common use include a subdivision into western Taurus and eastern Anti-Taurus (or Kurdish Taurus), and a structural distinction between northerly Tauride and southerly Iranide folds. Neither of these conventions is adopted in this book, where the southern folded zone as a whole will be described as the Taurus, divided for purposes of description into western, central and eastern sections.

The Western Taurus are the ranges which enclose the Gulf of Antalya and lie mainly in the provinces of Antalya, Isparta and Burdur. West of the gulf, the dominant structural trend is almost due north–south. The mountain ranges rise abruptly from the western shore and are equally abruptly terminated by fault structures along the Mediterranean coast on either side of Finike. The Tahtahlı dağları reach 2375 m (7790 feet) within 15 km (10 miles) of the sea and are succeeded westwards first by the deep-set Alakır valley and then by the main range of the Bey dağları (3086 m/10 122 feet). To the west of this range are a number of enclosed basins (*ovalar*) at heights around 1000 m (3200 feet) above sea level, closed in on the west by the Elmalı dağları (3024 m/9919 feet). A succession of similar high ridges and enclosed basins continues as far as a line from Denizli to Muğla, which represents the western edge of the Taurus system. Throughout this section, limestones, mainly of Cretaceous age, are dominant, and karstic features are very widely developed. The whole constitutes a formidable barrier to movement between the Aegean and Mediterranean coastlands and the numerous basins have until recently been very isolated from the outside world.

Inland from the head of the Gulf of Antalya, north–south fold axes meet others running from north-west to south-east in the region sometimes referred to as the Turkish Lake District (Göller Bölgesi). Here, there is a rather confused assemblage of short fold ranges, faulted blocks and sunken basins. The highest peaks in this area, Barla dağı (2734 m/8968 feet) and Davras dağı (2635 m/8643 feet), both occur on folded Cretaceous limestones immediately west of Eğridir Gölü. From this complex area, a series of roughly parallel ridges, of which the highest are the Dedegöl (2980 m/9774 feet), Seytan (2403 m/7882 feet) and Küpe (2350 m/7708 feet) ranges, run in a general north-west to south-east direction to link with the Paleozoic massif of the Geyik dağları (2890 m/9479 feet). To the north-east of these ranges, which are again developed mainly on limestones, is a down-faulted trough containing Lakes Beyşehir and Suğla, drained by the Çarşamba river into Konya ovası. Beyond this trough a further mountain barrier is formed by the Paleozoic block of the Sultan dağları (2520 m/8266 feet) and the volcanic Alacadağ (2203 m/7226 feet).

The Central Taurus begin at the Geyik dağları and extend as far east as the upper reaches of the Seyhan river. In the western part of the central Taurus, in a zone roughly coincident with the basin of the Göksu, mountain ridges are much less clearly marked, the terrain is more broken and the peaks are much lower than elsewhere. Here, the main fold systems have been covered by a great thickness of Miocene material, the whole being recently uplifted and vigorously dissected by the Göksu and other streams. East of the Göksu relief again becomes stronger in the great Permo-Carboniferous limestone massif of the Bolkar dağları (3585 m/11 759 feet) and the Cretaceous limestones of the Aladağlar (3726 m/12 221 feet). Between these two is the narrow defile of the Cilician Gates, cut 1000 m (3200 feet) into the local surface which, apart from its significance as a routeway, provides strong evidence for antecedent drainage in this area.

Attention should be drawn at this stage to the character of the coastal plain to the south of the western and central Taurus. In the triangular lowland at the head of the Gulf of Antalya, true alluvial plain is confined to a narrow fringe, often marshy, behind a belt of coastal dunes and the bulk of the lowland is in fact composed of a series of infertile, karstic platforms. This situation, combined with the isolation of the area, does much to explain its rather underdeveloped and thinly populated character. Between Alanya and Silifke Paleozoic massifs rise abruptly from the sea and much of the coast is lined with cliffs, but beyond Silifke, where the Göksu delta forms a small, fertile lowland, the coastal plain widens out into the plains of the lower Seyhan and Ceyhan. Here, although there are extensive poorly drained stretches, there are also large areas of deep-soiled fertile land, particularly in the Seyhan delta south of Adana. This is one of the most productive and densely populated parts of Turkey.

The Eastern Taurus run in an arc around the northern side of the Arabian platform, abutting on to the northern folded zone within 50 km (30 miles) of a line through Erzincan, Erzurum and Kars. Here again structure involves all three major elements: ancient massifs, folded sedimentaries and recent volcanic effusions. From the point of view of relief, two main mountain systems may be discerned. The more northerly rises from the Seyhan–Ceyhan plains, runs northwards between the upper courses of those two rivers and then curves round to the east, crossing the Fırat (Euphrates) south of Erzincan and eventually passing to the north of Lake Van. West of the Fırat the main ranges are the Tahtalı dağları (3054 m/10 017 feet) and Munzur dağları (3449 m/11 316 feet), developed on Paleozoic and Mesozoic strata respectively, while to the east the line is continued by the predominantly volcanic Karasu–Aras dağları (3124 m/10 247 feet) which terminate, near the Soviet frontier, in Büyük Ağri daği (Ararat: 4165 m/16 941 feet), the highest peak in Turkey.

The more southerly system, which runs along the northern edge of the Arabian platform, stands out on the geology map (Fig. 6) as a well-defined series of Paleozoic blocks. In Hatay one such block forms the north–south-trending Amanos dağları (2262 m/7419 feet) bounded on the west by the Gulf of İskenderun and the Ceyhan plains and on the east by a down-faulted corridor containing the Amık Gölü, a northward extension of the Levant rift valley. Beyond Maraş the Nuhurak (3060 m/10 037 feet) and Malatya (2620 m/8594 feet) dağları run north-eastwards to the Fırat river, beyond which the line is continued eastwards and south-eastwards by the Maden, Genç and Bitlis ranges, all of which exceed 2000 m (6500 feet), south of Lake Van into Hakkârı province. Here a, tangled mass of mountain ranges with no single dominant direction rise in many places above 3500 m (11 500 feet) and reach a maximum elevation of 4168 m (13 671 feet) in Çilo dağ some 30 km (20 miles) south-west of Çölemerik.

Between the two major mountain systems which go to make up the eastern Taurus are a series of high-standing plateaux and lesser mountain ranges. The terrain is generally very broken, but there are occasional pockets of relatively level land as, for example, around Malatya, Elâzığ and Muş.

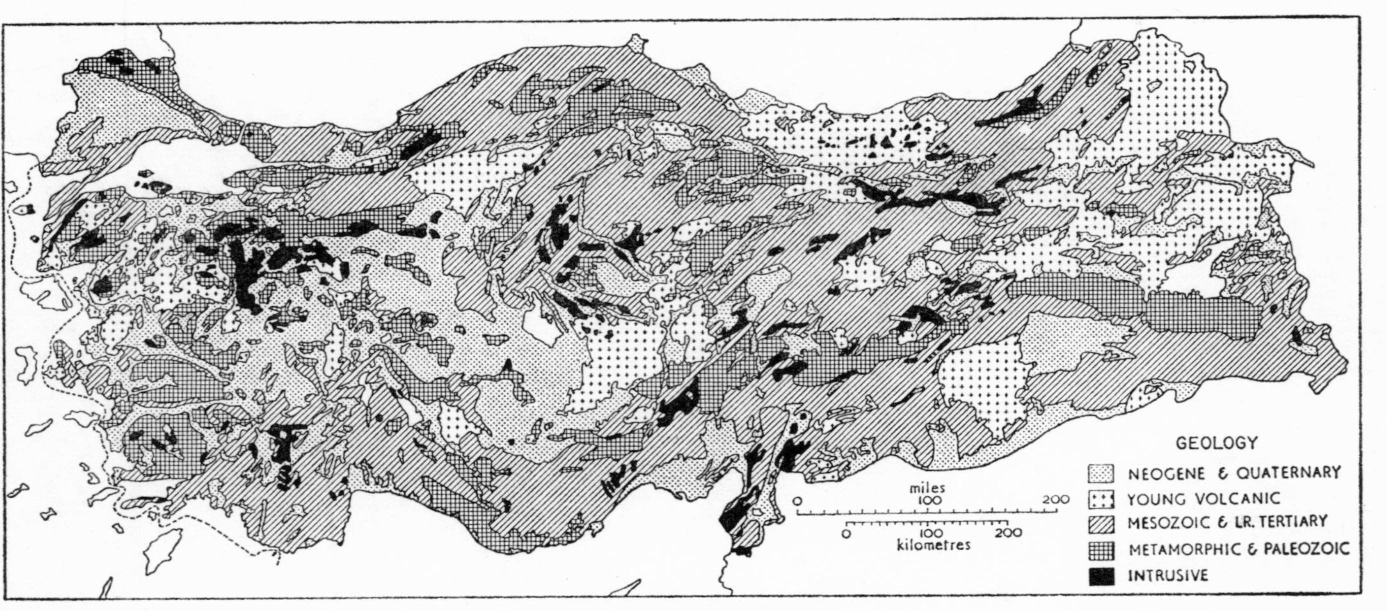

Fig. 6. Geology, simplified

(iv) The Arabian Platform

The northern edge of this stable massif is defined by a line running through Antakya, Adıyaman and Siirt and passing about 75 km (45 miles) north of Diyarbakır. The relief of this region is, when compared with the mountainous areas to the north, quite gentle, consisting of a series of broad plateau surfaces which fall away southwards to below 400 m (1200 feet) along the Syrian border. There are broad expanses of Neogene deposits, as in the Diyarbakir and Adıyaman basins, but there are also large areas of Eocene rocks which give hill country rising above the general level, as to the north of Urfa and Mardin. The highest points occur on the large area of recent lavas to the west of Diyarbakır, where Karacadağ rises to 1919 m (6294 feet).

The structure of Turkey, in which faults and folds of recent origin are such widespread features and where earth movement is still going on along innumerable lines of tectonic weakness, is particularly conducive to the occurrence of earthquakes and Turkey is one of the areas of the world most frequently and most seriously affected. Literally dozens of major shocks have been experienced in historical times and few towns of any size have escaped damage. The most serious earthquake of recent decades was that which took place in 1939 with its epicentre near Erzincan, in which more than 20 000 people were killed. Within the past two years major earthquakes, fortunately with smaller loss of life, have occurred at Varto in Muş province and at Adapazarı. No part of the country can be considered free from this danger and modern buildings are now constructed in such a way as to lessen the risk of their destruction by earthquakes.

Altitude and Slope

The patterns of structure and relief discussed in the preceding pages produce two characteristic features of the land surface of Turkey, its high altitude and the widespread occurrence of steep slopes. Turkey is a country in which true lowland is very restricted in extent, being confined almost entirely to the coastlands which are themselves extremely narrow. Only in the west, in Thrace and along the rivers draining into the Sea of Marmara and the Aegean, do lowlands extend inland for any considerable distance. As Fig. 7 shows, only about 17·5% of the land surface is less than 500 m (1640 feet) above sea level. As much as 55% lies between 500 and 1500 m (1640–4920 feet) and a further 22% between 1500 m and 2500 m (4920–8200 feet). The median altitude is 1132 m (3713 feet), land at about this level being particularly widespread in central Anatolia.

Secondly, Turkey is a country in which flat or gently sloping land is at a premium, as the data in Table I illustrate:

TABLE I

SLOPE/AREA ANALYSIS*

	Slope	*square km*	*square miles*	%
I	3% (1:33)	73 535	28 358	9·8
II	3–8% (1:33–1:12½)	48 111	18 554	6·4
III	8–15% (1:12½—1:6)	16 189	6 243	2·1
IV	Rough, broken land	264 862	102 142	35·1
V	Rough, mountainous land	351 813	135 360	46·6
	Total land area	754 510	290 657	100·0
	Water bodies	8 453	3 263	—
	Total area	762 963	293 920	—

* *Note:* These data have been tabulated from information given in Oakes (1957), pp. 46–7. Areas were derived from map measurement and the total differs by 17 613 square km (7102 square miles) from the standard used by the Central Statistics Office.

Fig. 8 shows the distribution of land in these five categories. Level or gently sloping land (I) occurs in a variety of situations. These include the valley troughs of the Gediz, Menderes and other rivers flowing to the Marmara and Aegean, the deltas of the Kızılırmak and Yeşilırmak on the north coast and the Antalya and Seyhan–Ceyhan plains on the south, together with the Ası valley in Hatay. The largest expanses, however, are found in the interior high plains of Anatolia, notably in the Konya and Tuz Gölü basins. Elsewhere, gently sloping land occurs in narrow strips along the floors of the main valleys and in isolated basins in mountain areas. Moderately sloping land (II) is typical of two regions, the lowlands of Thrace and parts of the Arabian foreland. Rough, broken land (IV), where actual gradients have not been mapped but where steep slopes (>8%) abound, occupies most of the remainder of western and central Anatolia and the south-east. This category, together with rough, mountainous land (V), which occurs not only in the main folded zones but also in scattered patches throughout the central massif, occupy more than four-fifths of the total land area of Turkey. These two features—the restricted development of lowlands and the dominance of steep slopes—are major factors in determining the nature of land use and the distribution of agricultural activities.

Drainage

Such matters as river flow, groundwater and hydrology in general are of vital significance to agriculture in Turkey and will be discussed in the appropriate chapters. At this stage, attention will be confined to a brief consideration of the drainage patterns illustrated in Fig. 9.

The greater part of the country drains into the Mediterranean, either

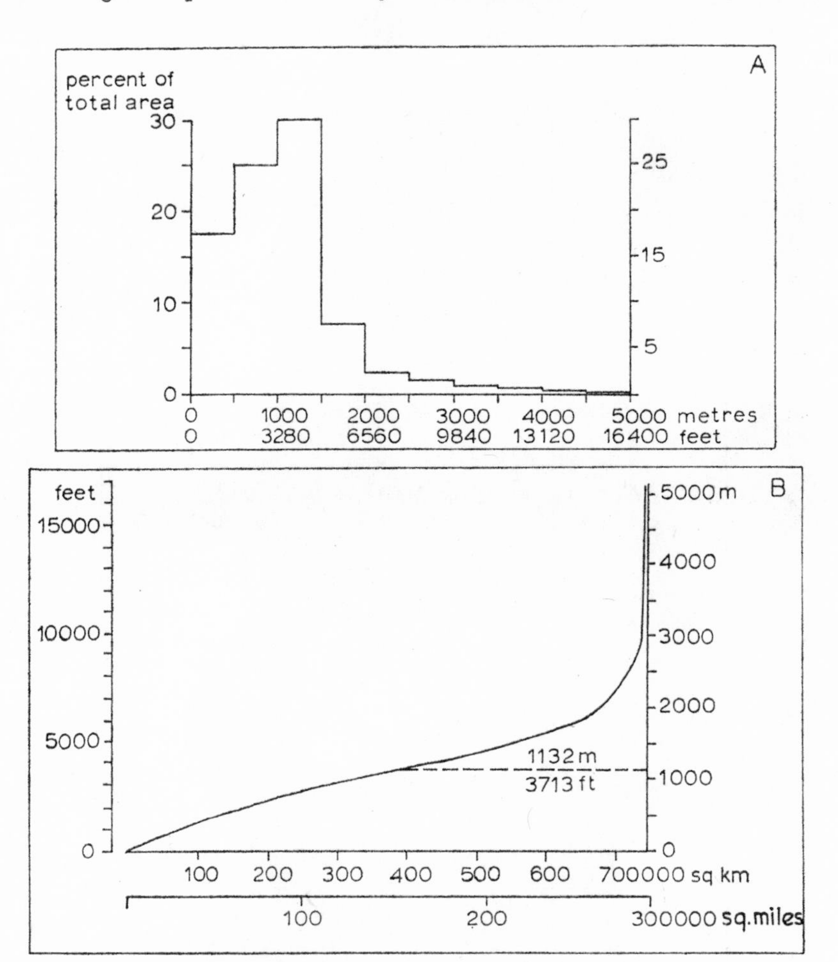

Fig. 7. Area–height diagrams. Based on diagrams in Tanoğlu, A., Erinç, S. and Tümertekin, E. *Turkiye Atlası*, İstanbul, 1961. A: Proportions of the land surface of Turkey at various heights above sea level; B: Hypsographic Curve for Turkey

directly or by a more circuitous route through the Black Sea and Sea of Marmara. A large area in the east, however, drains through Iraq to the Persian Gulf, while the smaller Aras catchment eventually drains to the Caspian. In addition, there are two areas of inland drainage, the relatively

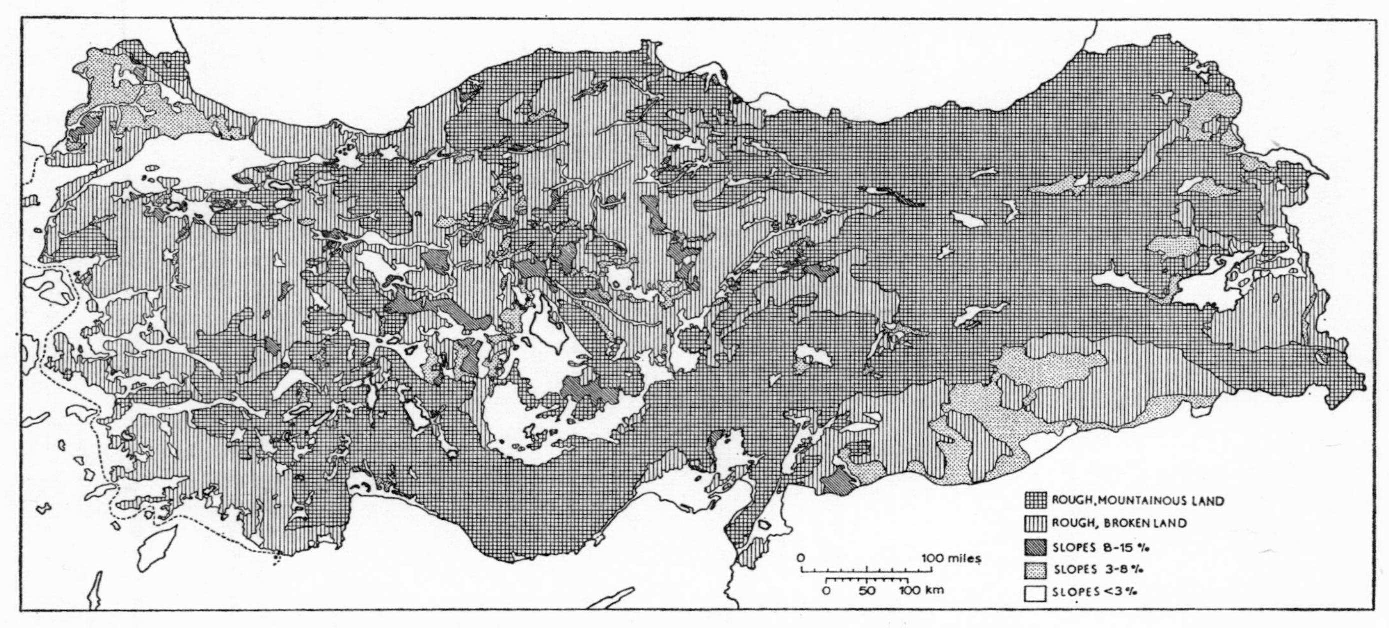

Fig. 8. Steepness of slope. For explanation, see text pages 27–8

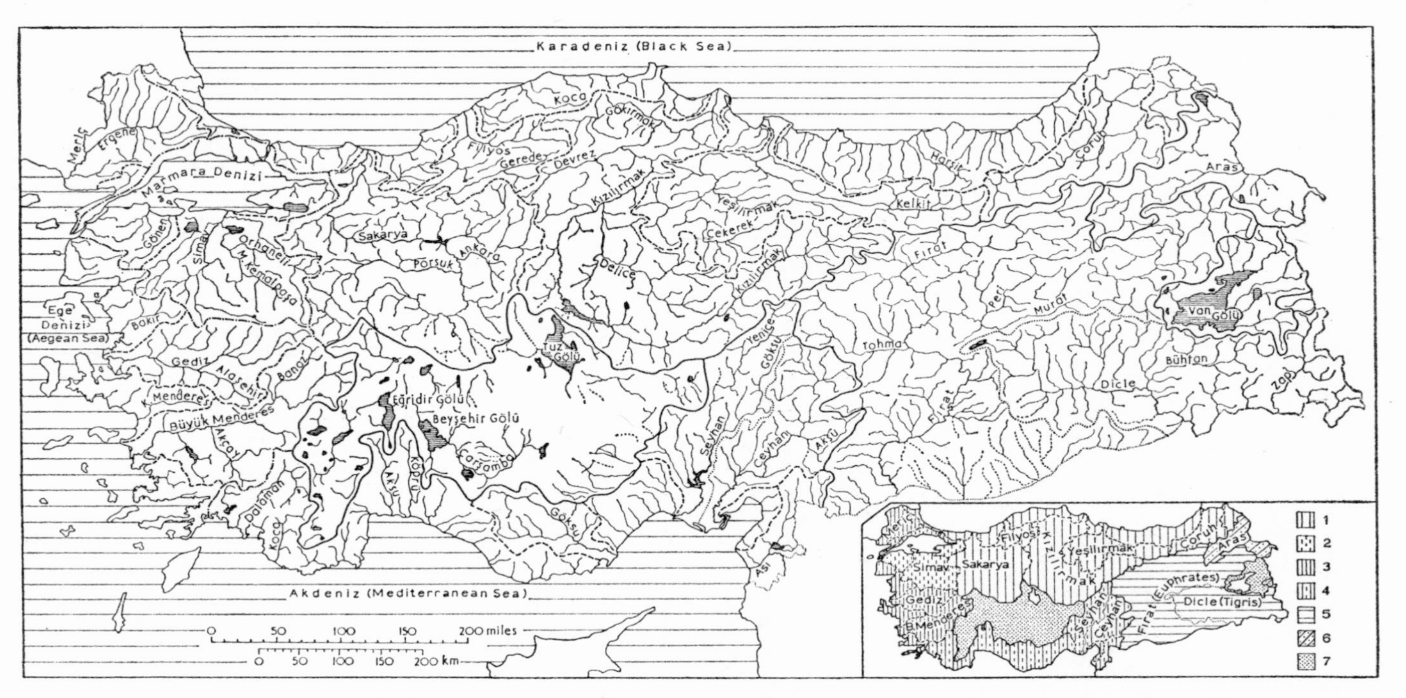

Fig. 9. Drainage. Inset: major drainage basins—1. Black Sea; 2. Sea of Marmara; 3. Aegean Sea; 4. Mediterranean Sea; 5. Persian Gulf; 6, Caspian Sea; 7. Areas of inland drainage

small Lake Van basin and a much larger one comprising the southern part of central Anatolia and adjacent sections of the Taurus.

Black Sea drainage. The majority of rivers which flow into the Black Sea are short, torrential streams whose steep courses are transverse to the structural grain of the northern coastal ranges into which they have been sharply incised. A few of them, like the Filyos, have developed tributaries parallel to the structure and this characteristic is particularly well marked in the larger river systems of the Sakarya, Kızılırmak and Yeşilırmak. These three have cut back through the coastal ranges to develop large catchment areas in the interior, their headwaters extending almost as far south as the Tuz Gölü.

Marmara drainage. The areas draining directly into the Sea of Marmara are quite small and the valleys, in their lower reaches at least, are relatively open and gentle. A coastal ridge along the southern shore tends to impede the flow of the Simav and its tributaries, giving rise to Lakes Manyas and Apolyont and associated areas of marshland.

Aegean drainage. Practically the whole of Thrace is drained by the Meriç and its tributary the Ergene which forms one of the largest lowlands in Turkey. These rivers are broad and slow-moving, and marshland is extensively developed along the lower Meriç. The part of Asia Minor which drains directly to the Aegean is highly distinctive in possessing broad, flat-floored river valleys which extend a considerable distance inland. Such rivers as the Bakır, Gediz, Küçük Menderes and Büyük Menderes have very gentle gradients and flow in broad meanders across their terrace-lined floodplains. Indeed, so distinctive are these rivers that the classical name Meander (Menderes) has found its way into English as a standard descriptive term.

Mediterranean drainage. Along the Mediterranean, as along the northern coast of Turkey, much of the drainage is by short, torrential streams transverse to the structural grain. Somewhat larger rivers have developed in the west (Dalaman, Koca) where the mountain ranges themselves are aligned in a north–south direction, in the Antalya lowland (Aksu, Köprü) and in the Miocene-covered zone of the central Taurus where the Göksu has carved out an extensive drainage basin. Where the Taurus ranges turn away northwards from the Gulf of İskenderun, the Seyhan and Ceyhan have large catchment areas with extensive alluvial lowlands and deltas, sometimes marshy, in their lower parts.

Fırat–Dicle (Euphrates–Tigris) drainage. Within Turkey these two rivers are separate but, in a broader sense, they are parts of a single catchment area draining southwards to the Persian Gulf. The general alignment of these rivers is therefore transverse to the structural grain and there are numerous gorge sections where they cut through successive ranges of the eastern Taurus system. At the same time there are lengthy longitudinal sections parallel to the structural trend as, for example, the upper Dicle and its tributary the Buhtan and the upper Fırat and its tributaries the Tohma and Murat. Across the Arabian platform the Fırat and Dicle are incised well into the surface.

Inland drainage. The main area of inland drainage in central Anatolia has been progressively reduced in size during recent geological times by the encroachment of the Sakarya and Kızılırmak river systems. As a result, inland drainage is now confined to the southern half of central Anatolia and adjacent parts of the Taurus. The two main centres are the Tuz Gölü and Konya basins but there are also a number of smaller, independent catchments, often containing lakes. These are most common in the area immediately north of the Sultan dağları and in the western Taurus. From the latter there is probably a good deal of underground seepage through the predominantly limestone mountains into the Antalya basin. It is believed, for example, that Lake Eğridir drains underground to the Aksu. The eastern basin of inland drainage comprises Lake Van and the rivers flowing into it. Here again there is probably a subterranean outflow, in this case to the upper Dicle.

The great majority of Turkish rivers have steep gradients along much of their courses and are sharply incised. Where this is not the case, as in the west, they are slow-moving and meandering, with swampy deltas. Furthermore, over much of the country and particularly in the Aegean and Mediterranean regions there are large-scale seasonal fluctuations in the volume of flow. Consequently, inland waterways have never been of any real significance as a means of transport but the rivers do have a large hydro-electric potential which is now being fairly vigorously developed.

Chapter 2

CLIMATE

The climates of Turkey are the product of a variety of factors which include the country's geographical position within the northern hemisphere, its relation to the land and water masses of that hemisphere and its own size, shape and relief. In this connexion we must note that Turkey lies between latitudes 36° and 42° north, at the eastern end of the Mediterranean basin. It is bounded on the north and south by the contrasting Black Sea and Mediterranean (Turkish: Akdeniz = White Sea) beyond which lie respectively the great plains of eastern Europe and the subtropical deserts of North Africa and the Middle East. At the same time, Turkey may be viewed as a western extension of the high mountains and plateaux of the Asian interior. Thus a great variety of influences affect the climate of the country. In addition, variations in climatic conditions within Turkey also clearly reflect internal variations in relief, particularly the presence of a high-standing interior separated by bordering mountain ranges from restricted coastal lowlands. The existence, already emphasised in the preceding chapter, of a predominant contrast between the interior and periphery, together with subordinate contrasts within each of these main divisions is particularly clear with respect to climate.

In general terms, the climate of most of Turkey can be described as a dry, semi-continental variant of the mediterranean type or alternatively as transitional between the mediterranean and temperate continental régimes. Several areas have the winter rainfall maximum characteristic of mediterranean climates and summer drought is very widespread, but over much of the country winter temperatures are much lower and total precipitation smaller than in the true mediterranean régime. Continental influences are to be seen in the large temperature range experienced over wide areas and the frequent occurrence of spring rainfall maxima.

Pressure and winds. In winter Turkey, in common with the Mediterranean lands, lies within the zone of eastward-moving cyclonic disturbances which originate over the Atlantic and eventually reach the Persian Gulf and western Pakistan. However, intense cooling of the high-standing interior of Turkey and Iran gives rise to pronounced high pressure over those areas and the presence of this high-pressure cell, protruding westwards between the Black Sea and the Mediterranean, causes depressions approaching from the west to follow two divergent tracks along the north and south coasts respectively, bringing heavy rainfall to both. Winter winds over the interior high-pressure zone are, of course, weak and variable, but the predominant directions are outwards towards the coast. These outblowing winds are strongest during the passage of depressions along the coast, but adiabatic warming during their descent

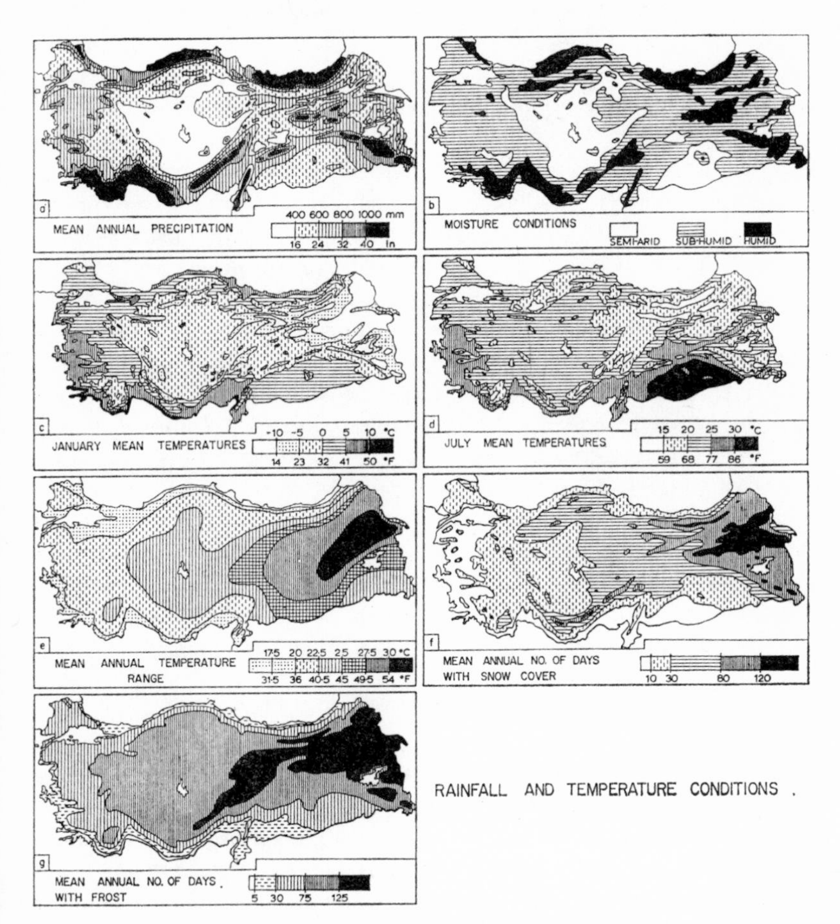

Fig. 10. Rainfall and temperature conditions

from the high interior (the föhn effect) ensures that coastal temperatures rarely fall to the low levels experienced in the interior.

Temperature conditions are illustrated in Fig. 10(*c*), (*d*) and (*e*) and need not be described at length. In January, means below freezing are recorded throughout the interior, conditions becoming progressively colder towards the east where there is a considerable area with means below −10°C (14°F). At times, very intense cold is experienced, extreme minima ranging from −20°C (−4°F) in the west to −40°C (−40°F) in the east. The peripheral coastal areas are characterised by mild winters, January means above 5°C (41°F) occurring along the Black Sea coast, in Thrace and throughout the Aegean and Mediterranean coastlands. The highest winter temperatures are recorded in the Antalya and Adana lowlands, though even here minima below −4°C (25°F) have occurred.

In the summer months, temperature differences are much less marked and all but the higher mountain areas may be described as hot. July means above 20°C (68°F) occur over the whole country, rising above 25°C (72°F) in western and central Anatolia and above 30°C (86°F) in the south-east, where maxima of more than 40°C (104°F) have been recorded.

Annual rainfall (Fig. 10(*a*)). Here again, the effects of relief are clearly marked. Totals between 300 and 400 mm (12–16 inches) are recorded over a large area of western and central Anatolia and in parts of the south-east. In eastern Anatolia there is a pronounced contrast between the low rainfall amounts received by the sheltered valleys and the much higher totals on the mountains. The wettest areas are, of course, the coastlands, particularly the coastal mountain ranges. The annual average exceeds 2000 mm (80 inches) in the Rize area and amounts between 1000 and 1500 mm (40–60 inches) occur widely not only in the Pontic ranges but also on the higher parts of the Taurus.

A considerable proportion of the annual precipitation in most areas falls in the form of snow and a fairly prolonged snow cover is typical of the interior. This is particularly true of the colder, higher east where, as Fig. 10(*a*) shows, snow cover lasts for four months or more.

Climatic Regions (see also Table II and Fig. 11)

(i) *The Black Sea Coastlands.* This region is particularly strongly affected by maritime influences. In the winter months, the passage of depressions along the coast gives plentiful rainfall and the winter maximum is well marked at coastal stations. However, summers are by no means dry: the northerly winds of that season pick up moisture in their passage across the Black Sea and give heavy orographic rainfall in the coastal ranges. Over the year as a whole, north-westerly winds are the most common and the result is a noticeable variation in total rainfall along the coast. North-west-facing sections (Zonguldak, Rize) have a much higher rainfall than those facing north-east (Samsun). Precipitation amounts increase rapidly with height above sea level in the coastal ranges but there is a pronounced rain-shadow effect and the coastal régime gives way fairly abruptly to that of the interior with its spring maximum and much lower total (e.g. Merzifon: 341 mm/13·6 inches).

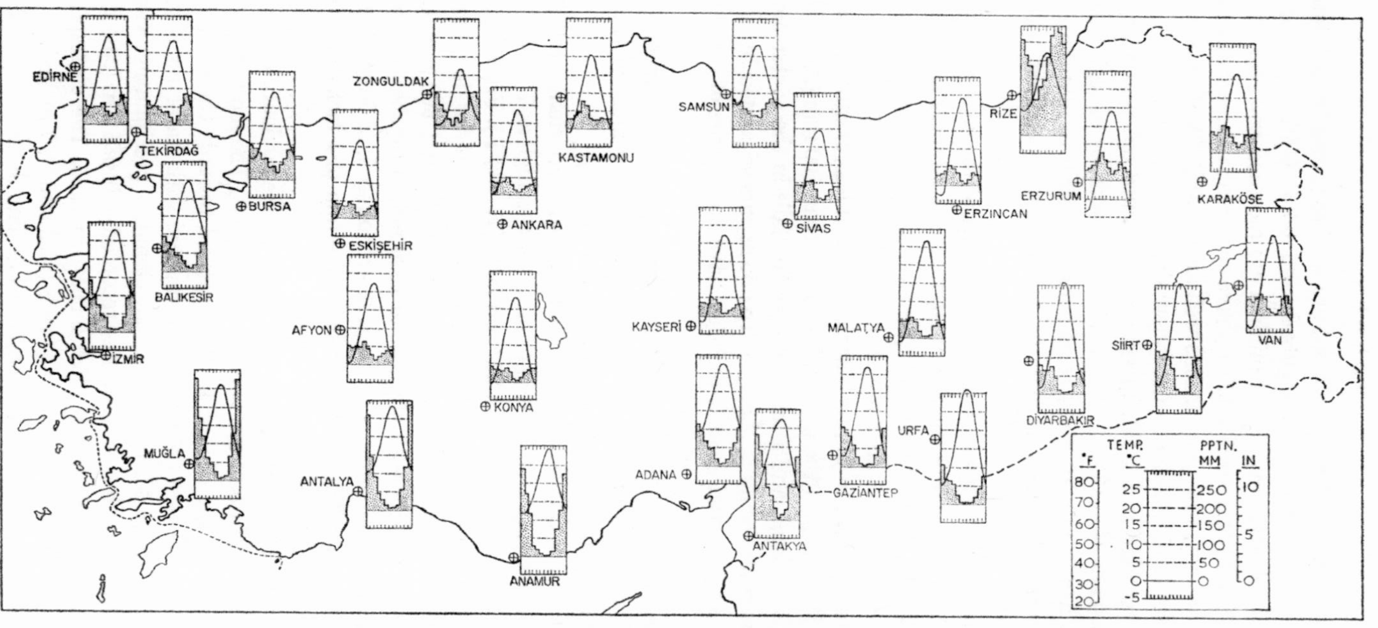

Fig. 11. Mean monthly temperature and precipitation at selected climatic stations

Winters along the Black Sea coast are mild as shown by the January means of 6·0°C (43°F) at Zonguldak and 6·9°C (44°F) at Rize. On occasions, however, much lower minima are recorded and temperatures of −8·0°C (17°F) and −6·6°C (20°F) have occurred at these two stations. Summers are hot, with July means well above 20°C (68°F) at sea level, though considerably lower in the mountains.

Altogether this is a mild, moist climate, quite different from that experienced anywhere else in Turkey. The combination of high temperatures and heavy rainfall gives conditions conducive to luxuriant vegetation growth and thus favourable for certain specialised forms of agriculture.

(ii) *Thrace and Marmara.* The European part of the country, together with the Asiatic shores of the Sea of Marmara are strongly influenced by winter depressions which pass frequently through the Straits, but the northerly winds of summer are much drier than along the Black Sea coast. Consequently, total precipitation is much less, ranging from some 900 mm (36 inches) in the mountains to less than 600 mm (24 inches) in the Ergene lowland, and a larger proportion falls in the winter months. Summer rainfall occurs in short, sharp downpours separated by lengthy dry periods: July and August together have an average of only eleven days with rain.

There is a considerable temperature range, with January means below 2°C (36°F) and July means above 25°C (77°F) over most of the area. Extremes range from −22°C (−8°F) to 35°C (95°F).

(iii) *The Aegean Coastlands.* Conditions here are very similar to those of other mediterranean areas. January means are as high as 7° or 8°C (45°–47°F) and July means between 25° and 30°C (77°–86°F). Frosts are very rare but occasional outbursts of cold air from the interior do occur. The annual rainfall at low levels varies between 600 and 800 mm (24–32 inches), rising rapidly with altitude to 1000 mm (40 inches) or more in the mountains. The summer drought is pronounced, at least along the coast, where İzmir has on average only 13·6 mm (5·4 inches) of rain in the three months June–August.

(iv) *The Mediterranean Coastlands.* There can be no doubt of the truly mediterranean nature of the climate in this zone. The most noteworthy local variation is the decline in total rainfall towards the east, Adana receiving only 611 mm (24·4 inches) compared with Antalya's 1030 mm (41·2 inches). As in all mediterranean climates, precipitation varies a great deal from year to year: Antalya recorded only 584 mm (23·4 inches) in 1964 as against 1376 mm (55·0 inches) in 1965. The corresponding figures for Adana were 531 and 667 mm (21·2 and 26·7 inches).

(v) *South-eastern Turkey.* The eastward decline in annual rainfall continues into this region which lies between the Syrian frontier and the southern slopes of the Taurus. Totals range from 600 to less than 300 mm (24–12 inches), and there is marked summer drought. This region also has a particularly large temperature range: while winters are quite cold, with January means below freezing, July means are generally above 30°C (86°F) making this the hottest as well as one of the driest parts of the country.

(vi) *The Anatolian Interior.* This large region is characterised by a semi-continental type of climate. There is a large temperature range between the sub-zero (centigrade) means of January and the heat of summer which is somewhat alleviated by the altitude. Rainfall totals are small over most of the region and are strongly influenced by relief. Thus the Konya *ova* and the Malatya basin are the driest areas in Turkey with annual totals of less than 300 mm (12 inches). The rainfall régime shows a pronounced spring maximum followed by a rather dry summer and autumn and a cold, damp winter. The spring rainfall, however, comes largely in thunderstorms so that the number of rain-days is much smaller than in the winter months.

Moisture conditions. In a country such as Turkey, where agriculture is still the dominant activity and where the great majority of the population depend directly on agriculture for their livelihood, climate is most significant for its effects on agricultural production. In this connexion, the most important elements are temperature and precipitation, the simple distributions of which have already been described but which assume a much greater significance when they are discussed in combination. It is well known that the important aspect of rainfall in any area is not the total amount but its 'effectiveness', that is to say the proportion of the total which becomes available to support plant growth. Put in its simplest terms, the effectiveness of a given amount of rainfall diminishes as temperatures rise and evaporation losses increase. Numerous measures of precipitation effectiveness and definitions of dry and humid climates have been made: of these one of the simplest is de Martonne's aridity index, expressed in the formula $\frac{P}{T} \times 10$, where $P =$ annual precipitation in centimetres, $T =$ mean annual temperature in degrees centigrade. Indices of 20 or below indicate dry climates, indices between 20 and 40 are described as sub-humid and those over 40 indicate humid conditions. Fig. 10(*b*) identifies these three categories and shows semi-arid climates in two areas, the larger covering much of central Anatolia and the smaller occurring in the south-east. At the other end of the scale, humid climates are found over most of the northern and

TABLE

CLIMATIC DATA FOR

(i) *Black Sea*

		J	F	M	A	M
ZONGULDAK	°C	6·0	6·3	7·0	10·5	15·0
41°, 27′ N.	°F	42·8	43·0	44·6	50·9	59·0
31°, 48′ E.	mm	146	114	94	74	53
136 m/415 ft	in.	5·8	4·5	3·7	2·9	2·1
SAMSUN	°C	6·9	6·8	7·5	11·0	15·4
41°, 17′ N.	°F	44·4	44·2	45·5	51·8	59·7
36°, 20′ E.	mm	81	71	75	56	42
44 m/13 ft	in.	3·2	2·8	3·0	2·2	1·7
RİZE	°C	6·9	6·9	7·8	11·4	15·7
41°, 02′ N.	°F	44·4	44·4	46·0	52·5	60·3
40°, 30′ E.	mm	259	214	187	97	97
4 m/13 ft	in.	10·2	8·4	7·4	3·8	3·8

(ii) *Thrace*

		J	F	M	A	M
EDİRNE	°C	2·0	3·8	6·8	12·6	17·7
41°, 40′ N.	°F	35·6	38·8	44·2	54·7	63·9
27°, 33′ E.	mm	65	48	43	48	48
48 m/157 ft	in.	2·6	1·9	1·7	1·9	1·9
BURSA	°C	5·4	6·1	8·0	12·6	17·4
40°, 11′ N.	°F	39·7	43·0	46·4	54·7	63·3
29°, 04′ E.	mm	92	83	71	62	61
100 m/328 ft	in.	3·7	3·3	2·8	2·4	2·4

(iii) *Aegean*

		J	F	M	A	M
İZMİR	°C	8·6	9·2	11·0	15·3	20·2
38°, 24′ N.	°F	47·5	48·6	51·8	59·5	68·4
27°, 12′ E.	mm	141	100	72	43	39
25 m/82 ft	in.	5·6	3·9	2·8	1·7	1·5
MUĞLA	°C	5·4	6·0	8·0	12·6	17·5
37°, 12′ N.	°F	41·7	42·8	46·4	54·7	62·5
28°, 21′ E.	mm	276	170	120	60	44
646 m/2120 ft	in.	10·9	6·7	4·7	2·4	1·7

II

SELECTED STATIONS

Coastlands

J	J	A	S	O	N	D	YR
19·2	21·7	21·6	18·4	15·0	11·5	8·5	—
68·6	71·1	70·9	65·1	59·0	52·7	37·3	—
79	65	92	97	150	151	132	1245
3·1	2·6	3·6	3·8	5·9	5·9	5·2	49·1
20·0	23·0	23·3	19·9	16·3	12·6	9·3	—
68·0	73·4	73·9	67·8	61·3	54·7	48·7	—
39	39	33	56	74	85	79	731
1·5	1·5	1·3	2·2	2·9	3·3	3·1	28·8
19·8	22·4	22·6	19·7	16·3	11·9	8·9	—
67·6	72·3	72·7	67·5	61·3	53·4	48·0	—
131	150	211	270	300	278	246	2440
5·2	5·9	8·3	10·7	11·8	11·0	9·7	96·1

and Marmara

J	J	A	S	O	N	D	YR
21·9	24·6	24·1	19·7	14·4	9·0	4·4	—
71·4	76·3	75·4	67·5	57·9	48·2	39·9	—
57	34	23	30	60	79	73	609
2·2	1·3	0·9	1·2	2·4	3·1	2·9	24·0
21·6	24·2	24·0	19·9	15·6	11·2	7·2	—
70·8	63·8	63·6	67·8	60·1	52·1	44·9	—
31	41	20	50	64	76	89	740
1·2	1·6	0·8	2·0	2·5	3·0	3·5	29·6

Coastlands

J	J	A	S	O	N	D	YR
24·8	27·6	27·3	23·2	18·5	14·0	10·2	—
76·6	81·7	81·1	73·8	65·3	57·2	50·4	—
8	3	3	11	41	93	141	693
0·3	0·1	0·1	0·4	1·6	3·7	5·6	27·3
22·6	26·1	25·8	21·6	15·9	10·7	7·1	—
72·7	79·0	78·4	70·9	60·6	51·3	42·8	—
22	6	9	10	64	126	273	1180
0·9	0·2	0·4	0·4	2·5	5·0	10·8	46·5

TABLE

(iv) *Mediterranean*

		J	F	M	A	M
ANTALYA	°C	10·0	10·6	12·6	16·2	20·5
36°, 53′ N.	°F	50·0	51·1	54·7	61·7	68·9
30°, 42′ E.	mm	255	143	86	41	26
43 m/141 ft	in.	10·0	5·6	3·4	1·6	1·0
ADANA	°C	9·1	10·2	12·7	16·9	21·2
36°, 59′ N.	°F	48·4	50·4	54·9	60·8	70·2
35°, 18′ E.	mm	111	93	66	45	47
20 m/66 ft	in.	4·4	3·7	2·6	1·8	1·9

(v) *South-eastern*

		J	F	M	A	M
URFA	°C	5·0	6·7	10·0	15·7	21·8
37°, 08′ N.	°F	41·0	44·1	50·0	60·3	71·0
38°, 46′ E.	mm	104	67	61	53	22
547 m/1794 ft	in.	4·1	2·6	2·4	2·1	0·9

(vi) *Interior*

		J	F	M	A	M
ANKARA	°C	−0·2	1·1	4·9	11·0	16·0
39°, 57′ N.	°F	28·4	34·0	40·8	51·8	60·8
32°, 53′ E.	mm	37	36	36	37	49
903 m/2963 ft	in.	1·5	1·4	1·4	1·5	1·9
KONYA	°C	−0·2	1·6	5·0	11·0	15·9
37°, 52′ N.	°F	28·4	34·9	41·0	51·8	60·6
32°, 30′ E.	mm	41	32	31	31	39
1026 m/3366 ft	in.	1·6	1·3	1·2	1·2	1·5
SİVAS	°C	−4·2	−2·9	1·4	8·3	13·2
39°, 45′ N.	°F	24·4	26·8	34·5	46·9	57·8
37°, 01′ E.	mm	44	42	42	56	59
1285 m/4216 ft	in.	1·7	1·7	1·7	2·2	2·3
ERZURUM	°C	−8·6	−7·0	−3·1	5·0	10·9
39°, 55′ N.	°F	16·5	19·4	26·4	41·0	51·6
41°, 16′ E.	mm	29	32	41	53	78
1893 m/6211 ft	in.	1·1	1·3	1·6	2·1	3·1

II—*Continued*

Coastlands

J	J	A	S	O	N	D	YR
25·0	28·2	28·1	24·9	20·3	15·5	11·6	—
77·0	82·8	82·6	76·8	68·5	59·9	52·9	—
10	2	3	10	53	115	284	1030
0·4	0·1	0·1	0·4	2·1	4·5	11·2	40·6
25·0	27·6	28·0	25·2	20·8	15·5	10·9	—
77·0	81·7	82·4	77·4	69·4	59·9	51·6	—
18	4	5	17	42	62	102	611
0·7	0·2	0·2	0·7	1·7	2·4	4·0	24·0

Turkey

J	J	A	S	O	N	D	YR
27·7	31·7	31·4	26·8	20·0	13·0	7·4	—
81·9	89·0	88·5	80·0	68·0	55·4	45·3	—
3	1	1	1	18	42	78	452
0·1	0·04	0·04	0·04	0·7	1·7	3·1	17·8

Anatolia

J	J	A	S	O	N	D	YR
20·0	23·3	23·3	18·4	12·9	7·3	2·1	—
68·0	73·9	73·9	65·1	55·2	45·1	35·8	—
30	14	9	17	24	30	43	360
1·2	0·6	0·4	0·7	0·9	1·2	1·7	14·2
19·8	23·1	22·9	18·2	12·5	6·5	1·6	—
67·6	73·6	73·2	64·8	54·5	43·7	34·9	—
26	6	4	11	27	31	37	315
1·0	0·2	0·2	0·4	1·1	1·2	1·5	12·4
16·6	19·5	19·7	15·7	10·6	4·6	−1·5	—
61·9	67·1	67·5	60·3	51·1	40·3	29·3	—
32	8	5	16	31	40	40	413
1·3	0·3	0·2	0·6	1·2	1·6	1·6	16·3
15·0	19·1	19·6	15·1	8·7	1·7	−5·5	—
59·0	66·4	67·3	59·2	47·7	35·1	22·1	—
55	31	19	27	49	38	25	476
2·2	1·2	0·7	1·1	1·9	1·5	1·0	18·8

southern mountain zones and on the higher ranges of the east. Between these extremes is a broad area described as sub-humid, within which there is a good deal of variation in moisture conditions. The drier parts of this area include the Adana lowland, much of western Anatolia and most of lowland Thrace. From this brief discussion it is apparent that moisture shortage is a major problem for Turkish agriculture since semi-arid or sub-humid climates occur over the greater part of the settled and farmed areas of the country. The only exceptions to this general rule are the narrow coastal lowlands along the Black Sea and parts of the Aegean coastal zone, both of which have consequently become areas of specialised and highly productive agriculture.

From the point of view of farming practice it is important to consider not only the moisture balance over the year as a whole but also the availability of moisture in each season. When more sophisticated methods of analysis, such as Thornethwaite's measure of evapotranspiration, are applied, it is seen that very few areas indeed avoid aridity in the summer months when maximum temperatures and minimum rainfall coincide. Only along parts of the Black Sea coast is there a moisture surplus throughout the year. Over most of the semi-arid zone the period of moisture deficiency lasts from mid-May to late October, and even in the sub-humid zone it runs from early June to late September. Furthermore, annual variations in precipitation can lead to much longer periods of drought. Consequently, over most of Turkey irrigation is a major factor in increasing agricultural productivity.

Chapter 3

SOILS AND VEGETATION

Soils

Detailed knowledge of the characteristics of Turkish soils is still lacking for many areas and the amount of material published on this subject remains small. Close studies have been made of a number of districts in connexion with specific development projects in various parts of the country but only one general survey has appeared, that of Harvey Oakes (1957) and this, as Oakes himself points out, is of a reconnaissance nature. However, this publication includes a soil map of Turkey on a scale of 1 : 800 000, the only one of its kind, and the present author wishes to acknowledge his debt to Oakes' work, on which the following summary account is largely based.

The basic pattern of soils in Turkey is of course largely influenced by climate: therefore we must, once again, expect to find contrasts between the interior and the various peripheral areas. At the same time, Turkey is a country in which relief is of particular significance since, as we have seen, steep slopes are dominant over large areas and the proportion of level or gently sloping land is small. Thus, in addition to representatives of a number of major, climatically determined zonal soil types, we should expect to find numerous azonal and intrazonal types resulting from local conditions of slope, drainage and parent material. In his survey, Oakes recognised 18 main soil types, which have been reduced to nine major categories in the map (Fig. 12) accompanying this chapter.

(i) *Red and grey-brown podsolic soils, with brown forest soils.* These three types occur together under approximately similar climatic conditions in the more humid parts of the country. The red and grey-brown podsolic soils, as their name suggests, are moderately leached and thus somewhat acid, the red type tending to occur in the warmer, wetter areas. The brown forest soil is an intrazonal type, generally developed on calcareous material and thus neutral in its chemical reaction. As Fig. 12 shows, this group of soils, which covers rather more than one-third of the country, is found mainly in mountain areas, occurring in a broad belt around the northern, southern and western sides of the Anatolian interior. The dominant characteristic of these areas is the thin, immature nature of the soils resulting from the predominance of steep slopes. Thus the area as a whole is one of limited agricultural value. The natural vegetation is

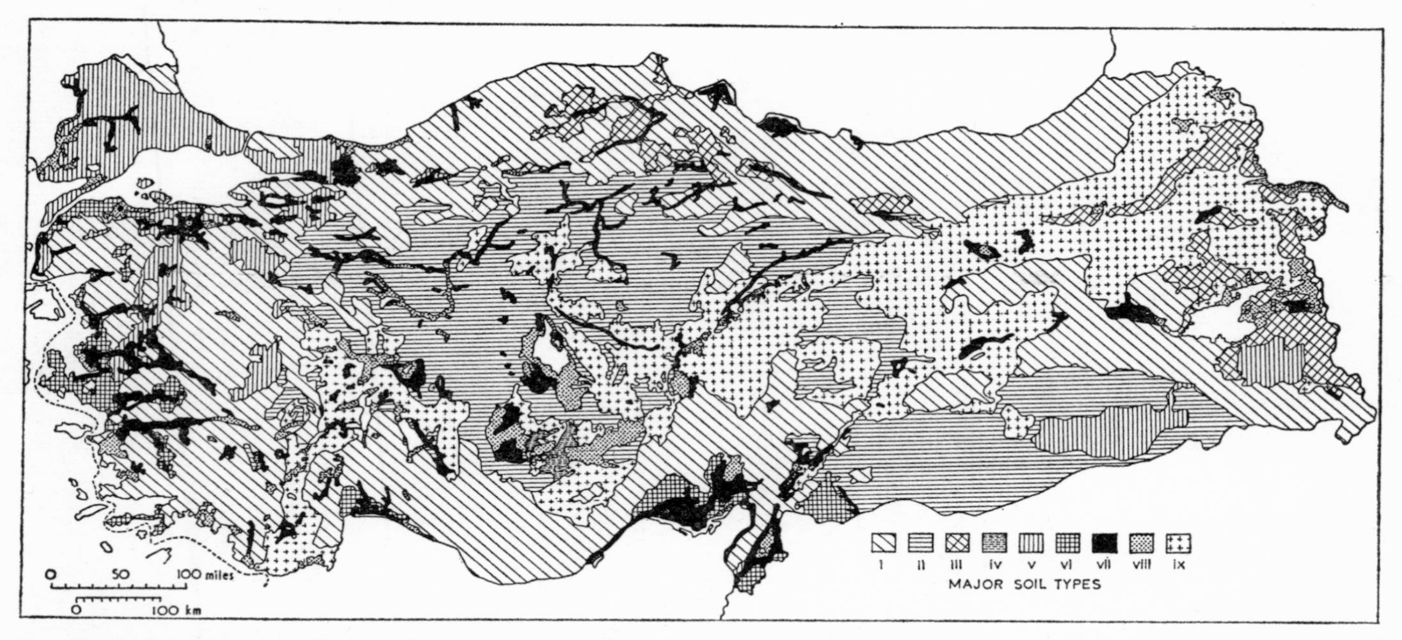

Fig. 12. Major soil types: (i) Red and grey-brown podsolic soils, with brown forest soils; (ii) Brown and reddish-brown soils; (iii) Chestnut soils; (iv) Sierozems; (v) Non-Calcic brown soils with rendzinas and grumsols; (vi) Terra rossas and red prairie soils; (vii) Alluvial soils; (viii) Alluvial, hydromorphic soils; (ix) Unclassified. See text, pages 45–49

various types of forest but, over large areas, this has been degraded by the action of man and his grazing animals.

(ii) *Brown and reddish-brown soils.* These are widely developed in the semi-arid areas of interior Anatolia and the south-east, together covering about 20% of the land surface. Despite the fact that there is a great deal of strongly sloping land in these areas, which restricts their agricultural potential, they make a major contribution to the arable land of Turkey and constitute the main areas of non-irrigated cereal production. Summer drought is a problem on these mainly calcareous soils which become a great deal more productive under irrigation. Where slopes are too steep for cultivation, there is widespread grazing.

(iii) *Chestnut soils.* These occur under climates somewhat wetter than those which produce the brown and reddish-brown soils but drier than those giving true chernozems, which do not in fact occur in Turkey. Generally derived from lime-rich parent materials, the chestnut soils are calcareous and, like the brown and reddish-brown types, are used for both dry farming of cereals and grazing. They occur only in rather small, disconnected areas, mainly in valleys and basins among the mountains of the east.

(iv) *Serozems* (*grey soils*) are semi-desert soils found only in the very driest parts of Turkey. They are confined to the southern part of the Konya basin and the Aras valley along the Soviet border. Serozems are highly calcareous and can generally be used for arable farming only if irrigated, when they can be highly productive.

(v) *Non-calcic brown soils with rendzinas and grumsols.* These three types occur in close association under climatic conditions intermediate between those of groups (i) and (ii). They are found in south-eastern Turkey, where only the non-calcic brown type is represented, and in a number of western areas, notably Thrace, where grumsols are dominant.

Non-calcic brown soils are a zonal type, developed mainly under a mediterranean climatic régime. They have some similarities to the red podsolic group but are less strongly leached and more alkaline in their lower horizons. In the south-east and along the Aegean, they are generally associated with rather rough, broken terrain and only small areas are cultivated, but in the lowlands of Thrace they provide good agricultural land.

Rendzinas and grumsols are azonal types found within the non-calcic brown zone. The former, which occur only in small, scattered areas, are highly calcareous, generally shallow soils developed from lime-rich parent materials. Grumsols, found mainly in lowland Thrace, also have a high calcium content but are deeper, heavier soils and of much greater value for agriculture.

These three types together cover only about 5 or 6% of the land surface.

(vi) *Terra rossas and red prairie soils.* Both occur within the mediterranean climatic zone and are dominant in the Çesme peninsula and on the terraces of the Antalya and Adana lowlands. Both are zonal types, the product of limestone weathering under the mediterranean régime. The prairie soils, developed under warmer, damper conditions, are slightly more leached than the terra rossas, but the distinction is a fine one.

(vii) *Alluvial soils.* Although they cover only about 5% of the country, these soils are usually intensively farmed and make an important contribution to the total arable land. Acre for acre the alluvial soils are the most productive as well as the most intensively used of all Turkish soils and the agricultural potential of the various regions is largely dependent upon their distribution. The largest continuous blocks occur along the valleys of the Aegean and Marmara regions, in the delta plains of the Seyhan, Ceyhan, Kızılırmak and Yeşilırmak and in the enclosed basins of central and eastern Anatolia.

TABLE III

MAJOR SOIL TYPES

		Area		
		000 ha	*000 acres*	%
(i)	Red and grey-brown podsolic soils with brown forest soils	28 899	71 409	38·4
(ii)	Brown and reddish-brown soils	15 643	38 654	19·5
(iii)	Chestnut soils	3 381	8 354	4·4
(iv)	Serozems (grey soils)	351	867	0·5
(v)	Non-calcic brown soils with rendzinas and grumsols	5 020	12 404	6·5
(vi)	Terra rossas and red prairie soils	1 834	4 532	2·4
(vii)	Alluvial soils	3 817	9 432	5·0
(viii)	Alluvial hydromorphic soils	2 443	6 037	3·2
(ix)	Unclassified	15 458	38 197	20·1

(viii) *Alluvial hydromorphic soils.* The basic feature of these soils is their poor drainage, which distinguishes them from the fertile alluvia of group (vii). Cultivation is at present very limited in extent but in many areas drainage works could raise the productivity of these soils to a high level. In some places, however, salinity is an added problem which has sometimes been made worse by unwise irrigation practices.

Alluvial hydromorphic soils are particularly widespread in the Konya and Tuz Gölü basins of central Anatolia.

(ix) *Unclassified.* About 20% of the land surface has been placed in this category, mainly in eastern regions where classification has so far been less thorough. The areas concerned are generally mountainous ones, developed for the most part on igneous and volcanic rocks. In these areas there is a great deal of bare rock and the soil cover is thin and discontinuous. In contrast to other mountain areas, there is little forest and the natural vegetation at best provides poor grazing. It should not be imagined, however, that these areas are completely devoid of cultivation: there are numerous small pockets of arable land in the valleys and basins.

Soil-management Groups

In view of the fact that Turkey is a predominantly agricultural country and thus the agricultural potential of the various regions is of particular significance, a second map is included here (Fig. 13) based on Harvey Oakes' soil-management groups. Oakes distinguishes fifteen of these on the basis of their suitability for arable farming, taking into account conditions of altitude, slope and drainage as well as the nature of the soils themselves. Particularly striking is the fact that approximately 80% of the total area is allocated to groups 11–15, classed as unsuitable for arable farming and left unshaded on Fig. 13. Small pockets of actual and potential arable land are included in these areas, but the great bulk of this land is suitable only for grazing or forestry.

Groups 1–10, covering about one-fifth of the territory, are the potentially cultivable lands, but these vary a great deal in productivity.

1. *Well-drained alluvial and youthful soils from alluvium.* These soils provide the most fertile arable land in Turkey and over large parts of the country they constitute the only land suitable for crop production. Disadvantages include the liability of these soils to flooding in many areas and the fact that they are often heavy and rather difficult to work without mechanical aids.

2. *Non-arable poorly drained and saline soils* occur for the most part in wetter alluvial areas. At the moment, such soils are little used but many of them could become highly productive if drained and carefully managed. Saline areas, however, would require more elaborate reclamation measures.

3. *Nearly level to gently sloping brown and reddish-brown soils of dry sub-humid and semi-arid areas.* These are most extensive in central Anatolia. They are probably the second most productive soils after the alluvial group and have a moderate degree of natural fertility. Their productivity is, however, restricted by moisture deficiency.

4. *Gently sloping, reddish-brown, medium-depth soils in moist sub-humid*

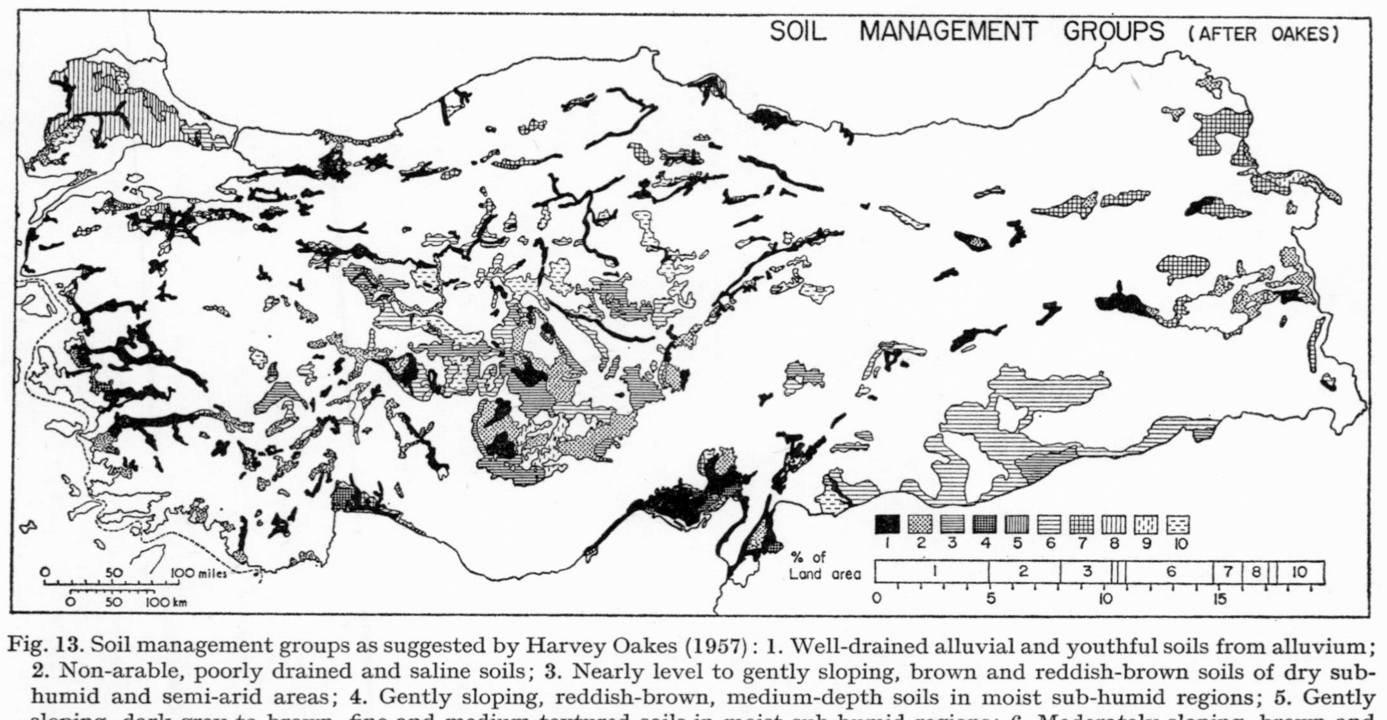

Fig. **13**. Soil management groups as suggested by Harvey Oakes (1957): **1**. Well-drained alluvial and youthful soils from alluvium; **2**. Non-arable, poorly drained and saline soils; **3**. Nearly level to gently sloping, brown and reddish-brown soils of dry sub-humid and semi-arid areas; **4**. Gently sloping, reddish-brown, medium-depth soils in moist sub-humid regions; **5**. Gently sloping, dark grey to brown, fine and medium-textured soils in moist sub-humid regions; **6**. Moderately sloping, brown and reddish-brown soils of medium depth, in sub-humid and semi-arid regions; **7**. Moderately-sloping, reddish-brown to dark grey soils of medium to shallow depth, in moist sub-humid regions; **8**. Moderately sloping, dark grey to brown, fine and medium-textured, deep soils of moist sub-humid regions; **9**. Grey soils of semi-arid and dry sub-humid regions; **10**. Strongly sloping, shallow soils; **11–15**. (Unshaded) soils not suited to arable farming *regions*, comprising terra rossas and red prairie soils, occur over limited areas of the Aegean and Mediterranean coastlands.

5. *Gently sloping, dark-grey to brown, fine and medium-textured soils in moist sub-humid regions.* Restricted almost entirely to small areas in Thrace, these are by Turkish standards good, high-yielding soils, though rather difficult to cultivate.

6. *Moderately sloping brown and reddish-brown soils of medium depth in sub-humid and semi-arid regions.* These soils are of similar type to those in group 3 but their productivity is reduced by the fact that they are shallower and occur on steeper slopes. As Fig. 13 shows, this group is most widespread in the south-east.

7. *Moderately sloping reddish-brown to dark grey soils of medium to shallow depth in moist sub-humid regions.* The soils are similar to those of group 4, but they are shallower, thinner and less retentive of moisture.

8. *Moderately sloping, dark grey to brown, fine- and medium-textured, deep soils of moist sub-humid regions.* Such soils are typical of much of lowland Thrace. Already extensively cultivated, they have a considerable potential for further development under better systems of soil management.

9. *Grey soils of semi-arid and dry, sub-humid regions.* Here, the major hindrance to cultivation is lack of moisture. These soils have a moderate inherent fertility, but can only realise their potential under irrigation.

10. *Strongly sloping, shallow soils* are widely distributed and offer only very limited possibilities for further development.

From this necessarily brief treatment of the soil-management groups, it emerges that the potentially cultivable land area is much smaller than might be supposed from the soil map (Fig. 12) alone. Only in the south-east, in the Konya basin and in Thrace is such land continuous over large areas: elsewhere it is confined to valleys and basins and broken into scattered blocks by negative areas of steep relief. Because practically all the land physically suited to cultivation has been taken up and any future increase in agricultural production must come from land already in use, the pattern shown in Fig. 13 is of particular significance. The map emphasises the relatively limited amount of land suitable for arable farming and shows those parts of the country on which the growing population must rely for its sustenance. While the average population density is only 41 per square km (107 per square mile) the density per square kilometre of potentially cultivable land is five times that figure.

This is a theme to which we shall return at a later stage. For the moment we must take note of the fact that, despite the large size of the country, Turkey's land resources are limited. Furthermore, over very large areas, soils are much poorer than their equivalents in other parts of the world.

TABLE IV

SOIL-MANAGEMENT GROUPS

		Area		
		000 ha	*000 acres*	%
1.	Well-drained, alluvial and youthful	3 187	9 432	5·0
2.	Poorly drained and saline	2 423	5 987	3·2
3.	Nearly level to gently sloping brown and reddish-brown	1 710	4 225	2·2
4.	Gently sloping, reddish-brown, medium depth	203	502	0·3
5.	Gently sloping, dark grey to brown fine and medium texture	200	494	0·3
6.	Moderately sloping brown and reddish-brown, medium depth	2 956	7 304	3·8
7.	Moderately sloping reddish-brown to brown, medium to shallow	1 003	2 478	1·3
8.	Moderately sloping, dark grey to brown, fine and medium texture	877	2 167	1·1
9.	Grey soils of dry regions	331	818	0·4
10.	Strongly sloping, shallow soils	1 546	3 820	2·0
11–15	Non-arable soils	15 066	37 228	80·4

Cultivation and grazing over many centuries have greatly reduced soil fertility and the majority of soils are deficient in organic matter and plant nutrient, while large areas are subject to serious soil erosion. All these problems are most marked in the drier parts of the country, particularly in the interior of Anatolia.

Vegetation

Patterns of vegetation in Turkey show close relationships with those of relief, climate and soils discussed in earlier sections. However, while laying due emphasis on these relationships, we must also note that, over wide areas, the natural vegetation has been much modified by the action of man, both directly through his cultivation techniques and indirectly through the agency of his grazing animals.

There is a basic twofold division of vegetation types. Steppe-grasslands occupy large areas of central Anatolia, the lowlands of Thrace, much of south-eastern Turkey and a number of valleys and basins among the eastern mountain ranges. Various types of predominantly forest vegetation are found on uplands and mountains and along the Aegean and Mediterranean coasts. A total of seven main types of natural vegetation have been distinguished (Fig. 14) each of which has a good deal of internal diversity.

1. *Pontic or Colchian Forest.* In the extreme north-east, along a narrow coastal strip which extends from the Soviet frontier as far west as Ordu, is a particularly rich type of forest vegetation, developed where rainfall is heavy, there is no summer drought and winters are mild. This zone, which extends upwards from the Black Sea coast to heights of 500–700 m (1500–2100 feet) is a continuation into Turkey of the type of forest more widely developed in the Colchis lowland (Kolkhida) of Soviet Georgia. The forest contains a great variety of species, among which the sweet chestnut, hornbeam, oriental spruce and alder are the most common. However, areas of high forest are now rather limited in extent and

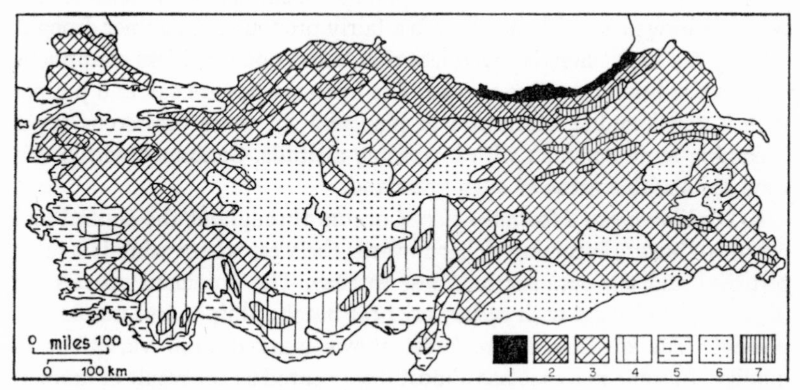

Fig. 14. Major vegetation types: 1. Pontic or Colchian forest; 2. Humid, deciduous forest; 3. Drier deciduous and mixed forest; 4. Mediterranean mountain forest; 5. Mediterranean lowland vegetation; 6. Steppe; 7. Alpine vegetation

the most striking characteristics of this area is the rich brushwood and bush layer which contains numerous, mainly evergreen species such as rhododendron, laurel, holly, myrtle, hazel and walnut, together with wild vines and other climbers.

2. *Humid Deciduous Forest.* Further inland in the east, over the whole of the Black Sea coastlands from Ordu to Sakarya and on the uplands of north-west Anatolia and Thrace is a zone of predominantly deciduous forest second in richness and variety only to the Colchian type. The main species are oriental spruce, beech, hornbeam, alder, oak, fir and yew, with oak and Scots pine in the drier parts. There is a rich shrub layer, particularly in the east, where rhododendron is widespread. Above about 1000 m (3300 feet) coniferous species, mainly fir and spruce, become dominant and around 2000 m (6500 feet) these give way to alpine grasslands. West of Sinop the forest becomes more open and less continuous. The variety of tree species remains, but the undergrowth is a good deal

less luxuriant. In this somewhat drier area there is a marked contrast between the well-watered, north-facing slopes and the drier southern flanks of the mountains, where a poorer, more open forest of oak, fir and juniper is characteristic. Although much of this region has been cleared for agriculture or degraded by lumbering and grazing, valuable reserves of timber remain in some parts, notably in Zonguldak, Bolu and Kastamonu provinces.

3. *Drier Deciduous and Mixed Forest.* In the north-west, north-centre and east of Turkey is a broad belt of territory in which climatic and vegetation conditions are intermediate between those of the northern forest on the one hand and the steppe and mediterranean zones on the other. Winters are cold and there is a fairly pronounced summer drought so that the forest here is much less rich, more open and less continuous than in the humid deciduous zone. The main species are oak and juniper with a considerable admixture of pine and fir, these coniferous types becoming more common with increasing altitude. Contained within this zone are sizeable areas of open grassland.

4. *Mediterranean Mountain Forest* occurs throughout the central and western Taurus, becoming richer towards the west where rainfall is more plentiful and the summer heat less intense. The dominant species are pines, firs and oaks with cedar, oriental beech, juniper and maple also present. The mediterranean forest shows marked local variations in quality. In some places it has almost disappeared as the result of lumbering or uncontrolled grazing, especially by goats, while in others it is virtually untouched and remains a valuable economic resource. In high, enclosed basins within this zone a park-like vegetation of dry grassland with scattered, drought-resistant trees and shrubs occurs, notably in the limestone areas of the western Taurus.

5. *Mediterranean Lowland Vegetation.* Along the south coast, the natural vegetation is of the maquis (Tk. *maki*) type with myrtle, wild olive, laurel, carob and only occasional oak, pine and cypress. A somewhat richer shrub vegetation, with small forests of oak and pine occurs in the lowlands along the Aegean and Marmara coasts. In some of the more poorly drained alluvial plains there are stretches of marsh vegetation, while in the driest areas, notably on limestone platforms, the *maki* degenerates into a thorny scrubland.

6. *Steppe.* The precise limits of the steppe and its relationship to particular climatic factors are matters still very much open to debate. In Turkey at least, steppe vegetation appears to coincide fairly closely with areas where de Martonne's aridity index is 20 or below (see Fig. 10(*b*) and p. 39) which in turn roughly correspond with those parts of central Anatolia which receive less than 400 mm (16 inches) annual precipitation.

In south-eastern Turkey, with its higher summer temperatures, steppe extends to the 500 mm (20 inches) isohyet. Another much-debated question in the case of Turkey is the extent to which the steppe is natural. Many writers hold that long-continued cultivation and grazing in Anatolia have extended the area of steppe at the expense of the surrounding dry forest (zone 3) and that truly natural steppe occurs only in the driest areas such as the Konya basin.

Over much of the year the steppelands have an extremely bare appearance. The grasses and other herbaceous shrubs grow rapidly in spring, the period of maximum rainfall, but are burnt off by the high temperatures of the summer months. Only in a few, better-watered areas is a grass cover retained throughout the summer. In any case, over large areas where the slopes are not too steep, the land is cultivated and the steppe grassland species are found only on untilled land, which is usually heavily grazed.

7. *Alpine Vegetation.* On the higher mountain ranges, above the limits of tree growth, alpine grasslands occur. Where accessible from the surrounding lower ground, these are used as summer pastures.

Part Two

HUMAN GEOGRAPHY

Chapter 4

HISTORICAL AND POLITICAL GEOGRAPHY

The history of the territory which now constitutes the Turkish Republic is intimately bound up with its position at the junction between south-east Europe and south-west Asia and its role as a bridgeland between the two continents. Turkey has, at different stages in her history, formed part of a number of highly distinctive cultural zones and has been included within empires originating to the west, east and south of her present boundaries. To the west lies Mediterranean Europe, dominated in the past by the classical civilisations of Greece and Rome. To the north-west are the Balkans, affected to only a limited degree by developments in the classical world but in modern times an area through which central European influences have impinged upon Turkey. To the east, Persia long formed the centre of a distinctive civilisation, while more recently the most significant influences from that direction, as from the north, have been those of the Russian empire and the Soviet Union. To the south lies the Arab world, once a major power centre, for a brief period the domain of western European powers, and now uncommitted in the contest between 'western' and 'eastern' blocs. Classical, Persian and Arabic civilisations have all had a great deal of influence upon each other, and Turkey, lying at their meeting place, has been strongly influenced by all three. In addition to these external influences there have appeared, on various occasions, cultural entities and political organisations centred in Turkey itself. At times these were hemmed in by surrounding, stronger powers. On other occasions they have stretched out to encompass large areas beyond Turkey's present boundaries.

As a result of all this, much of the history of Turkey is an integral part of the history of the neighbouring territories which have been alternately areas from which Turkey was dominated or over which Turkey held sway. Once again, contrasts between the Anatolian heartland and the peripheral areas are a major theme. Outside influences have been most effective in the fringe areas of Turkey, while essentially Turkish features have tended to originate and remain most vigorous in Anatolia. Perhaps paradoxically, when Turkish territory reached its greatest extent, at the apogee of the Ottoman empire, the political centre lay not in Anatolia but at Constantinople, to which Anatolia was subordinate in much the same way as the Balkans. It is significant that the capital was situated in a central position with respect to the empire as a whole, but was markedly eccentric in relation to Turkey proper. It could be argued that, as the Ottoman empire expanded it became increasingly divorced from its Anatolian–Turkish roots and that, when the empire collapsed, the retreat of the capital to Ankara marked a renewed emphasis on the Turkic origins of the Turkish state.

Economic and commercial matters have tended to strengthen the contrasts between heartland and periphery visible on so many occasions in Turkish history. By reason of their physical environment the coastal fringes have generally been the most productive parts and have been most closely linked by trade with the outside world. Anatolia, poorer, though at most times self-supporting, has tended to remain somewhat isolated, a world apart, though important trade routes have passed across it, linking the richer fringing areas, and trade along these routes has brought additional wealth, at least to the cities. Today, political power is firmly centred in Anatolia but economic wealth is still derived to a large degree, from the northern, western and southern coastal zones. This is not to say that Anatolia should be wholly discounted as a source of wealth. Its traditional function as a supplier of grain and livestock has enabled it to maintain a degree of self-sufficiency throughout its history.

A further general point which should be made at this stage is that the history of what is now Turkey is not solely concerned with the people now known as Turks. Groups which can be firmly identified as Turkic in origin did not reach Anatolia until the 11th century A.D., and it is generally assumed that the population of Asia Minor prior to that date was of wholly non-Turkic stock. To what extent this pre-Turkic population was replaced by Turkic settlers is uncertain, and there can be no doubt that the present population of Turkey is of very mixed ethnic origin. Despite the persistence of sizeable Kurdish and Arabic-speaking minorities (see page 88), the modern Turk is best defined as a person living in Turkey and speaking the Turkish language. Whether or not he is the descendant of Turkish settlers is altogether a separate matter, lying mainly within the purview of the physical anthropologist. Many would hold that, while the cultural and linguistic effects of the Turkic invasions were profound, they had very little effect on the racial composition of the population as a whole.

The history of Asia Minor falls fairly readily into two major periods on either side of the 11th century A.D. Prior to that date, the peninsula was inhabited by a variety of peoples and was generally under the control of empires centred outside Asia Minor, though parts of the area were at times their own masters. The 11th century marks the arrival of the Seljuk

(Selçuk) Turks, followed rapidly by the Ottomans (Osmanlis), and the period up to the First World War is occupied by the growth and subsequent decline of the Ottoman empire. The last fifty years have been the period of the Turkish Republic, during which a largely successful attempt has been made to break with the imperial past and to establish a new type of Turkish state.

It is not the purpose of this chapter to make a thorough examination of Turkish history. Much must be passed over in brief review and attention will be focused mainly on the processes by which the Turkish state assumed its present form and the factors which have played a part in giving modern Turkey a personality very different from those of her Middle Eastern neighbours.

Turkey before the Seljuks

Little need be said of the early history of Asia Minor, save that varied local cultures, involving pastoralism, agriculture and the use of metals, were established in Anatolia well before 2000 B.C. Around 1800 B.C. the Hittites entered Turkey from the steppelands of eastern Europe, probably via the Caucasus, and established their capital at Hattasus (modern Boğazköy) some 150 km (90 miles) east of Ankara. Originally pastoral nomads, the Hittites, like so many of the later nomadic invaders of Anatolia, adopted sedentary farming and developed towns and trade routes. By 1400 B.C., their empire (Fig. 15(*a*)) stretched from the Aegean, where it was in contact with the Minoan culture of Greece and Crete, to the Euphrates river and was extending southwards into Syria, where frontiers were established with Egypt and Babylonia in the 13th century B.C. Modern Turkish scholars have paid a great deal of attention to the Hittite culture and to the Hittite empire as the earliest ancestor of the present Turkish state, though the extent to which there is any real continuity is questionable. The Turkish language and the Moslem religion were first brought to Asia Minor by the Seljuks some 2500 years after the demise of the Hittite empire. It does seem probable that the pre-existing Anatolian population was neither exterminated nor wholly replaced by Turkic settlers and that the latter were a relatively small ruling group whose language and religion were adopted piecemeal by the indigenous majority. Thus, in one sense it could be said that elements of Hittite culture were carried on into the Seljuk and Ottoman periods and thence into modern Turkey. On the other hand, the Hittite culture had been overlain by centuries of Persian Greek, Roman and Byzantine culture long before the arrival of the Seljuks.

In the 13th century B.C. the Hittite empire was overthrown by invaders from the north-west who spoke an Indo-European language akin to

Persian and Sanskrit. This group, known to history as the Phrygians, probably entered Asia Minor across the Straits from Thrace and established their capital at Gordium, about 90 km (50 miles) south-west of Ankara. They remained the dominant power in Anatolia for six hundred years, extending their empire eastwards to the southern flank of the Caucasus where the modern Armenians speak a language descended from Phrygian. South of the Taurus, the limit of the Phrygian domain was set by the Babylonian and Assyrian empires (Fig. 15(*b*)).

It was during the same period that Greek influence began to make itself felt around the coasts of Turkey, an influence which, in the west at least, remained important right down to the 20th century A.D. From about 1200 B.C. onwards, successive groups of Greek colonists established numerous city-states along the littoral of Asia Minor. By 800 B.C. practically the whole coast from the Dardanelles to Rhodes had been colonised, and in ensuing centuries Greek settlements were founded throughout the length of the Marmara, Black Sea and Mediterranean coasts. Only in the west, however, where the relief was favourable to such a movement, did Greek colonists penetrate far inland, moving up the broad valleys of the Meander (Menderes) and other rivers into Western Anatolia. Many of the sites chosen by the Greeks, like Trapezunt (Trabzon), Byzantion (Istanbul) and Smyrna (İzmir), are still occupied, while others are marked only by ruins as at Perge, Termessos and Side. There was at this time a considerable trade between Anatolia and the Hellenic world, Phrygia being noted as a supplier of grain, woollen cloth and metals.

During the 7th century B.C. the Phrygian empire broke up. In the west it was replaced by the Lydian dynasty, which, with its capital at Sardis in the Gediz valley, succeeded in gaining control of the Greek colonies along the Aegean (Fig. 15(*c*)). The Lydian domain, however, stretched only as far east as the Kızılırmak. Beyond that river Anatolia became part of the empire of the Medes, while the south-eastern part of what is now Turkey was absorbed into the Babylonian empire. Thus, while the western part of Asia Minor remained closely attached to the European civilisations of the Aegean, the remainder of the country was controlled by empires centred in the Middle East and for many centuries Turkey was pulled in opposing directions by these two forces.

In the middle of the 6th century B.C. the Persians under Cyrus became a major power in the Middle East. Asia Minor was absorbed into the Persian empire which, at its maximum extent during the reign of Darius (5th century B.C.), stretched from Thrace to the Indus and from Cyrenaica to the Jaxartes (Amu Darya). This was the first of a series of great empires which, in pre-classical and classical times, brought virtually the

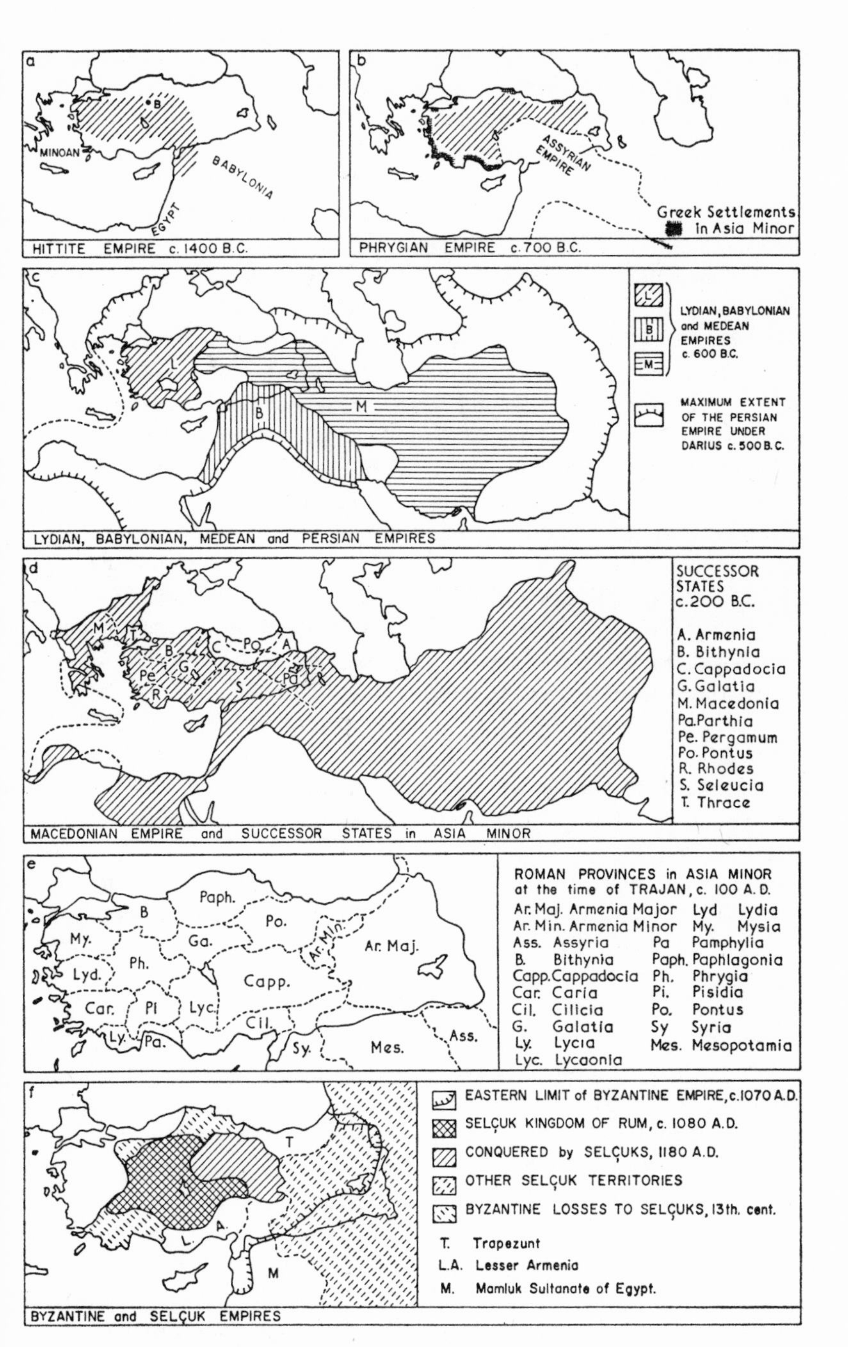

Fig. 15. Ancient empires of the Middle East and Asia Minor

whole civilised world under a single authority, imposed a centralised administration and developed an integrated system of routes, fortresses and trading posts throughout the Middle East.

Persian rule lasted for approximately two hundred years until, in the 4th century B.C., eastern domination of the Middle East was replaced by its inclusion within an empire centred to the west of the Aegean. This was the Macedonian empire of Alexander the Great who, with the whole of Greece under his control, invaded Asia Minor in 334 B.C. and in the space of a single lifetime took command of the entire Persian realm (Fig. 15(*d*)). An outstanding feature of this period was the growth in importance of urban life. Old cities were enlarged and new ones founded to become centres of Hellenic culture, trade and political control. City life was, of course, by no means a wholly Greek innovation but it reached its apogee in the Middle East during Greek and Roman times. In rural areas the impact of classical civilisation was less strong and life went on much as before save that there was a general intensification of agricultural activity and trade.

On the death of Alexander in 323 B.C. his empire fell apart into a number of successor states ruled at first by various of his generals but later by local potentates. Within the boundaries of modern Turkey the successor states included, in the west Pergamum and Rhodes, in the north Pontus and Bithynia. The south-east became part of the Seleucid domain, centred in Mesopotamia, while in the north-east Armenian and Parthian kingdoms were established. In central Anatolia a somewhat different development took place when celtic tribes from the Danube basin moved across Thrace and the Straits to establish themselves in that area, where they became known as the Galatians. Thus after a period of some three hundred years of unity, first under Persian and then under Macedonian control, the Middle East was again split into numerous smaller political entities.

Unity was once again imposed by an outside power during the period of the Roman empire. By the beginning of the 2nd century B.C. Rome had become the dominant power in the western Mediterranean following the collapse of Carthage, her only serious rival. The extension of Roman influence into Asia Minor began as the result of appeals from Pergamum and Rhodes for assistance against the Seleucid (or Syrian) empire and with this end in view the Romans entered western Anatolia about 180 B.C. From 150 B.C. onwards parts of the Middle East under Roman control were organised into Provinces and became part of the Roman empire (Fig. 15(*e*)). The eastern limits of the empire fluctuated considerably during the ensuing four hundred years. At its maximum extent in the time of Trajan (A.D. 98–116) it reached the Caspian and the Persian Gulf, but for most of the period the frontier lay along the Euphrates and the western edge of the Syrian desert. In Roman times Turkey supplied metals, grain, timber, wine and oil to other parts of the empire and agriculture flourished. In addition, the function of Asia Minor as a route-way between Asia and Europe continued. There were extensive trading contacts between Rome and the empires of Parthia, India and China along routes which skirted the dry centre of Anatolia, the more northerly of these running through Ancyra (Ankara) and the more southerly through Tarsus and Iconium (Konya) to reach the Aegean coast.

At the end of the 3rd century A.D. the Roman empire was divided for administrative purposes into 'praefectures', a division which led eventually to the more fundamental separation into western and eastern empires. The latter was centred, from A.D. 330 on the 'new Rome' at Constantinople or Byzantium and the two parts were finally severed in A.D. 395. The eastern Roman empire or as it soon became known, the Byzantine empire, covered Asia Minor west of the Euphrates and linked that area politically with Balkan Europe. This combination, centred on the Straits, provides a preview of the shape assumed by the Ottoman empire a thousand years later. From its foundation, the Byzantine empire was engaged in almost continuous conflict with the Sassanid dynasty, which had taken control of Parthia in A.D. 224, and this prolonged struggle weakened both parties so that they became relatively easy prey to the new force which emerged from the remote and hitherto insignificant Arabian peninsula.

This new force was that of Islam which swept northwards from Arabia in the 7th century to embrace large areas of the Middle East and North Africa. The greater part of Asia Minor, however, never succumbed to the Arab onslaught: only Cilicia and Armenia came under direct Arab rule, and that only for a relatively short period. For more than four hundred years the frontier between the Byzantine Christian world and the Moslem Middle East lay across eastern Turkey, and Anatolia was a frontier zone between these rival powers. Thus the economic decline of Anatolia, begun when it was a zone of conflict between the Byzantines and Sassanids, continued. Not until the arrival of the Turks themselves and their replacement of the Arabs as the dominant force in the spread of Islam did the peninsula of Asia Minor finally become part of the Moslem world.

The Seljuk and Ottoman Periods

The 11th century saw a major turning-point in the history of Asia Minor, marked by the arrival in Anatolia of the first recognisable Turkic-speaking groups; the first inhabitants of Turkey who may legitimately be referred to as Turks. The Turkic tribes of what is now Soviet Central

Asia and was for so long known as Turkestan were converted to Islam in the 8th century. They soon asserted their independence from their Arab overlords and, during the 10th and 11th centuries under the Seljuk dynasty, replaced the Arabs as rulers of much of the Moslem world. By the end of the 11th century the Seljuk Turks were firmly established in Anatolia, and in 1107 Konya (Iconium) became capital of the 'Kingdom of Rum', that is of the 'Roman' or 'Infidel' part of the Seljuk empire carved from the Byzantine domain (Fig. 15(*f*)). By the beginning of the 13th century the Seljuks controlled the whole of Asia Minor with the exception of the Aegean–Marmara area, Trebizond on the Black Sea coast and 'Lesser Armenia' (Cilicia), which remained Christian. As already stated, the Seljuk Turks brought the Turkish language and the Moslem religion to Anatolia, but these nomadic invaders were themselves probably few in numbers. Their rule in Anatolia was imposed upon a numerically superior indigenous population which eventually adopted the speech and religion of its conquerors. In this process of cultural cross-fertilisation, however, the majority of Turks abandoned nomadism and adopted aspects of Arabic, Persian and even Byzantine cultures, a process which gave rise to the unique amalgam of cultural traits which to this day distinguishes the Turk from the other peoples of the Middle East yet at the same time ensures that he has much in common with them.

As the Seljuks were reaching the height of their power, another Turkic group appeared on the scene. Under its leader Osman or Othman, whence Osmanli or Ottoman, this group settled within the Seljuk domain and, in 1299, was granted territory and independence in north-western Anatolia. By their capture of Bursa in 1326 the Ottoman Turks consolidated a base in the Marmara region from which grew the vast Ottoman empire (Fig. 16(*a*)). The history of this empire spans some six hundred years of which the first three centuries were a period of almost continuous expansion and the last three one of steady decline.

The growth of the Ottoman empire took place in two main directions, south and south-eastwards into the Moslem Middle East and north-westwards into the Balkans. By the former movement, Ottoman control reached as far as the Arabian peninsula, the Persian Gulf, the Caspian and the Caucasus and eventually extended along the north coast of Africa as far as Algiers. Balkan Europe was the scene of a protracted struggle between Christian and Moslem, culminating in the unsuccessful Turkish assault on Vienna in 1529, an event which marked the end of Turkish expansion towards central Europe. Equally significant was the failure of the Turks to capture Malta in 1565, their defeat on this occasion putting an end to their ambitions as a maritime power in the central and western Mediterranean. However, the 16th century was not entirely

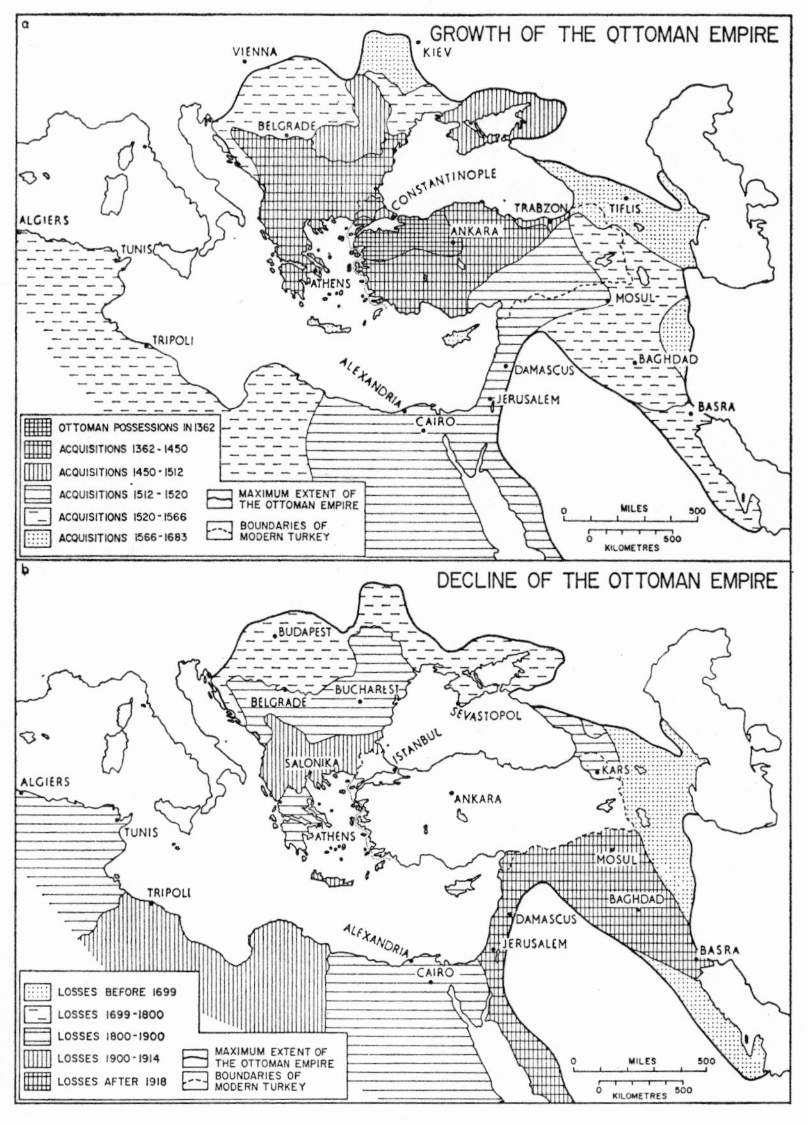

Fig. 16. The rise and fall of the Ottoman empire

devoid of success for the Turks who annexed large areas around the northern shores of the Black Sea at a time when the Tatar empire was in decline and Russian power had not yet extended so far south. The high water mark of Ottoman expansion may be placed in the year 1683, when a second attempt to capture Vienna failed, and the ensuing 250 years were a period of almost continuous decline which ended only with the establishment of the Republic in 1923.

The power and extent of the Ottoman empire at its height is expressed in the titles of the emperor Suleyman I, the Magnificent, who ruled from 1520 to 1566:

> Sultan of the Sultans of the East and West, fortunate lord of the domains of the Romans, Persians and Arabs, Hero of Creation, Champion of the Earth and Time, Padishah and Sultan of the Mediterranean and the Black Sea, of the extolled Kaaba, of Medina the illustrious and Jerusalem the noble, of the throne of Egypt and the province of Yemen, of Aden and San'a, of Baghdad and Basra, of Lahsa and Ctesiphon, of the lands of Algiers and Azerbaijan, of the region of the Kipchaks and the lands of the Tatars, of Kurdistan and Luristan and all Roumelia, of Anatolia and Karaman, of Wallachia and Moldavia, Hungary and many kingdoms and lands besides, the Sultan Suleyman Khan, son of Sultan Selim Khan.

Of the whole Middle Eastern world, only Persia remained outside the Ottoman empire, and it was in fact Persia which was the first to offer a challenge to Ottoman dominance. Much more serious, however, was the challenge from the growth of new imperial powers in Europe, including Russia on the northern and north-eastern frontiers, Austria in the north-west and others which, though not in direct contact with the Ottoman realm, were anxious to see its expansion checked as it was in Vienna in 1529 and Malta in 1565 by forces drawn from all over Europe.

The Ottoman empire was one of great diversity in the nature of its territories and its peoples and was never wholly unified or united. Nor was it all highly centralised in its organisation, the degree of control from İstanbul diminishing rapidly towards the more outlying provinces. Throughout most of its life, the organisation of the empire involved a large measure of local autonomy for its individual provinces and a good deal of tolerance towards its non-Moslem minorities. The latter, too, had a certain autonomy under the *millet* system whereby the leader of each community was responsible for its submission to central authority but the community or *millet* carried on its traditional way of life relatively undisturbed. These factors permitted the empire to linger on, without major internal disruption, long after its initial impetus was spent and it was only in the final stages of its decay that such uncharacteristic excesses as the massacre of the Armenians in the 1890s occurred and the word Turk became anathema to the peoples of Europe. The relatively enlightened policy of the Ottoman rulers towards their non-Turkish subjects had the major disadvantage that the empire as a whole had no popular unifying factor of the sort which strengthened nationalism in 18th- and 19th-century Europe. Thus, when nationalism spread to the Ottoman empire, it first affected the minority peoples who became increasingly discontented with Turkish rule which, in response, grew more and more repressive. Turkish nationalism, which eventually became the driving force of the Republic, became prominent only at the beginning of the 20th century.

As time passed, the Ottoman empire became progressively less powerful in the military sense and lagged behind its rivals in the economic field as well. The Turks were, by origin, pastoral nomads, and although they settled to agriculture and urban life, they lacked any tradition of industry or trade. These activities were in the hands of minority groups like the Armenians, Greeks and Jews and in the 19th century were increasingly controlled by foreign companies and individuals. With the centre of power at Istanbul, Anatolia, the 'most Turkish' part of the empire, became a primitive provincial backwater, its peasant population despised by the more sophisticated and to some extent europeanised inhabitants of the capital and the western seaboard. Indeed, the very word 'Turk' was rarely used by the Ottoman ruling class, save with reference to the uncultured Anatolian peasant. Thus, when Turkish nationalism eventually developed it took the form not only of opposition to foreign domination but of opposition to the traditional ruling class as well.

The stages by which the empire fell prey to the territorial ambitions of its rivals and, in the later stages, to the nationalistic movements along its non-Turkish peoples are illustrated in Fig. 16(*b*). The earliest losses of territory were along the eastern frontier, where areas in dispute with Persia were finally abandoned and a boundary established in roughly its present position early in the 17th century. In the north-west, the Hapsburg empire had attained the level of a major power and in 1699 the Ottomans lost Transylvania to Austria, Podolia to Poland and the Dalmatian coast to Venice which had for so long checked Turkish expansion on the Adriatic. By the end of the 18th century, all the lands to the north of the Black Sea had been lost to Russia and it was clear that the latter had become a major threat to the continued existence of the Ottoman empire. A major element in Russian policy at this time was her desire to obtain control of an outlet to the Mediterranean and to this end she repeatedly attempted to extend her influence south-westwards to the Straits. As a result, on two occasions in the 19th century, Russia was engaged in a major conflict with Turkey. On the first occasion, that of the Crimean War, the Ottomans were assisted by Britain and France, who viewed Russian ambitions with alarm, but the war of 1877–8 saw Turkey unsupported, and the Treaty of Berlin, dictated by a consortium of the European powers, resulted in large losses of territory. Montenegro and Serbia became fully independent and the state of Rumania was formed from the provinces of Moldavia and Wallachia. Greece, which with the aid of Britain, France and Russia, had asserted its independence in 1830, gained further territory in Thessaly, while Roumelia became the nucleus of a new Bulgarian state which proclaimed full independence in 1908. Meanwhile, in the Caucasus, the Russian advance beyond the main ranges, which had occupied Georgia in 1801 and detached Azerbaijan and Armenia in 1828, continued and the area around Kars and Ardhan was annexed in 1878. In the same year Cyprus, with its mixed Greek and Turkish population, became a British possession. The 19th century also saw the retreat of the Ottomans from North Africa. Algiers, Tunis and Tripoli achieved a degree of autonomy which was close to complete independence. The first two were annexed by France, but Tripolitania, together with Cyrenaica, remained nominally part of the Ottoman empire until 1912, when they were taken over by Italy. Egypt was occupied by Britain in 1882. A final episode was that of the Balkan Wars of 1912–13 in which Greece, Bulgaria, Serbia and Montenegro fought Turkey, forcing peace treaties in which the latter lost all her European possessions save eastern Thrace. Thus, on the eve of the First World War, the Ottoman empire was reduced to Turkey proper and the Arab lands of the Levant, Mesopotamia and the coast of the Arabian peninsula.

The First World War and its Aftermath

The alliance of the Ottoman empire with the Central Powers during the war of 1914–18 brought Turkey into conflict with both Russia and the western allies and had disastrous results. Much of eastern Anatolia fell to Russia whose advance had, by 1916, reached a line from Trabzon through Erzincan to Bitlis, and large areas were devastated. The British attempt to seize the Dardanelles in the Gallipoli campaign of 1916 was thwarted, but British armies, with the help of Arab nationalists, advanced up the Levant coast to Aleppo and through Mesopotamia to Mosul. The Russian collapse in 1917 was followed by a rapid Turkish re-advance to the east and there was even an attempt to establish independent republics under Turkish influence in the Caucasus but these plans were thwarted first by western intervention and later by a Soviet reoccupation of all the territories of the former Russian empire. The Turco-Soviet boundary was finally fixed by an agreement signed between the two countries in 1921, under which the Kars–Ardahan area was returned to Turkey.

When Turkey surrendered to the western powers in 1918 she had already lost all her Arab possessions, and in 1920 these were placed under League of Nations mandates operated by Britain and France. The victors, however, were intent on dismembering Turkey itself: the Straits were to be placed under international control, large areas in the west and south

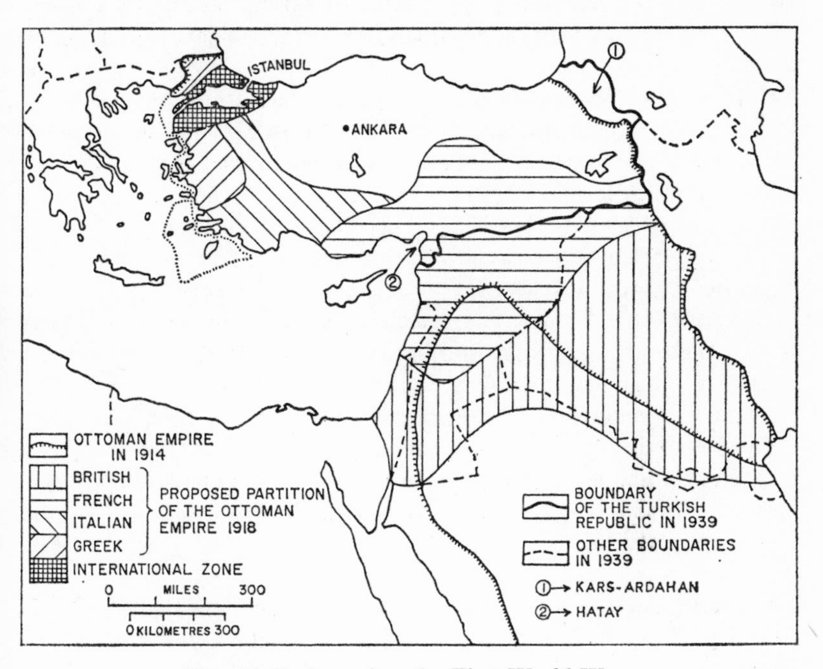

Fig. 17. Turkey after the First World War

were to be occupied by Greece, Italy and France, and the Turkish state was to be reduced to an area embracing only central and eastern Anatolia and the Black Sea coast (Fig. 17). Opposition to these terms and to the acquiescence of the Ottoman rulers were major factors in the rise of a new Turkish nationalism, directed from Ankara by Mustafa Kemal Pasha, later known as Atatürk (Father of the Turks). In the face of the nationalists, the French and Italians, who had occupied their zones in 1919, soon withdrew, but the Greeks, backed by the local Greek-speaking population, were more determined and a bitter struggle between Greece and Turkey lasted from 1919 to 1922. This ended in a victory for a revitalised Turkish army and people and, by the Treaty of Lausanne, signed in 1923, the boundaries of Turkey were established for the most part along their present lines. The Straits were demilitarised, but in 1936 were, with international agreement on the rules governing their use, placed under full Turkish control. A further major provision of the Treaty of Lausanne was the exchange of populations between Greece and Turkey, a move intended to put an end to rival territorial claims. The large Greek-speaking element of western Turkey was 'repatriated' to Greece while Turkish-speakers from Greek Thrace and other Balkan areas returned to Turkey. Today, of a Greek-speaking population of several hundred thousand, only about 65 000 remain in Turkey, the great majority of them in Istanbul.

Only one significant adjustment has been made to the boundaries of Turkey since the establishment of the Republic in 1923 and this concerns the province of Hatay, the area around İskenderun and Antakya (Alexandretta and Antioch). In 1920 Hatay came under French control as part of the Syrian mandate, but Turkey objected and in 1936 the area was given independent status as the Sanjak of Alexandretta, renamed the Republic of Hatay in 1938. In 1939, Hatay was absorbed into Turkey by agreement with France. The desire to obtain one of the few good ports on the Mediterranean coast no doubt had much to do with Turkey's interest in the area, but the fact that her claim to it was made primarily on linguistic grounds is of particular significance.

The Republic of Turkey, proclaimed in 1923 and confirmed by the Treaty of Lausanne, was from the outset intended to be a nation–state with the Turkish language as its main unifying force although, in the words of the Constitution:

> The word Turk, as a political term, shall be understood to include all citizens of the Turkish Republic without distinction of or reference to race or religion.

This was, in part, a policy decision of the new republican leaders, but it was also an inevitable result of Turkey's new situation. With the loss of her Arab territories, the expulsion of the majority of the Greeks and the flight of the Armenians from the eastern provinces, the new Turkey was more homogeneous ethnically than any of the earlier states of Asia Minor. Over the past forty-five years this homogeneity has increased as members of minority groups have been assimilated into the Turkish majority. Thus, according to the census of 1960, nine out of every ten among the population claimed Turkish as their mother tongue and only the Kurds may be said to constitute a sizeable linguistic minority (see chapter 5, p. 88). In the years following the First World War various attempts were made to establish an independent Kurdistan embracing Kurdish-speaking areas of Turkey, Syria, Iraq, Iran and the Transcaucasus, and when these failed there were numerous revolts against the governments of those countries. Such revolts have continued down to the present—the most recent took place in Iraq between 1961 and 1966—but in Turkey the Kurds have remained quiescent since the 1930s and no longer appear to present any real danger to the stability of the Turkish state.

The Republic is even more homogeneous in religion than in language, only about 1% of the population professing a religion other than Islam. The position of religion in the state has remained a controversial matter ever since the establishment of the Republic. In the 1920s, despite strenuous opposition from the faithful, Islam was 'disestablished', but it has remained a highly influential force. Although an increasing number of the more sophisticated town-dwellers are Moslem only in name, the great bulk of the rural population remains faithful. Political opposition to Atatürk and his successors has often had the support of religious leaders, and the belief that the Menderes government was excessively influenced by the religious authorities was one of the several reasons for its overthrow by the army in 1960.

The desire to deprive religion of its political power was but one of the many revolutionary ideas on which the Republic was founded. Another general aim has been the 'westernisation' of the country and the development of a modern society and economy more akin to those of western Europe. This aim has been expressed not only in such matters as internal economic and political organisation but also in such details as the abolition of the fez and the adoption of a Roman script in place of Arabic characters. It is also to be seen in Turkey's approach to international affairs which has frequently been very different from those of other Middle Eastern countries. The new Turkey has renounced the imperialist ambitions of the old, and the alternative philosophy of Pan-Turkism or Pan-Turanianism, which aspires to unite all Turkish-speaking peoples, has found little favour. After a period of political isolation in the inter-war years and during the Second World War, when she remained neutral, Turkey has for the past twenty years been closely aligned with the western powers. Twenty thousand Turks served with the United Nations in the Korean War, and in 1952 Turkey was admitted to membership of the North Atlantic Treaty Organisation. She was a signatory of the Baghdad Pact of 1955, replaced since 1960 by the Central Treaty Organisation, comprising Turkey, Iran, Pakistan, the United Kingdom and the United States. She is also a member of O.E.C.D. and the Council of Europe. The policy of alignment with the west came about partly as a result of Turkey's general desire for recognition as a modern state akin to those of western Europe and partly as a result of her traditional suspicion of Russia, an attitude heightened in the first post-war decade by Soviet demands for a greater say in the control of the Straits. As the Arab states have moved further away from Europe, their relations with Turkey have become more distant and the Turks have shown no interest in Pan-Islamic movements or attempts to achieve Middle Eastern unity. Turkey's recognition of and friendly relations with Israel have done little to endear her to her Arab neighbours.

During the 1960s, although Turkish foreign policy has undergone no profound change, there have been discernible shifts of emphasis. Turkey's alliances with the west and her suspicions of the Soviet Union remain, but relations with the latter, if not positively friendly, have at least been 'normalised'. Goodwill visits have been exchanged by the leaders of the two countries and trade and technical co-operation are on the increase. At the same time, some elements in Turkey have begun to question the value of the western alliance. While this has undoubtedly brought great benefits in the form of economic, technical and military assistance, the political benefits have not always been as great as was expected. This disenchantment with the west stems in particular from the Cyprus question, which has exacerbated the long-standing hostility between Greece and Turkey and in 1967 brought the two countries to the brink of war. In this conflict, many Turks have felt that their European allies have, almost instinctively, favoured the Christian Greeks.

Thus the present problems and policies of the Turkish Republic, like those of the past, plainly reflect the country's geographical and cultural situation, set between Europe and Asia, involved in both and belonging wholly to neither.

Internal Political Geography (see also Fig. 3)

It is useful at this stage to introduce a brief note on the administrative divisions of the Turkish Republic since these form the basis of so many of the tables and diagrams in this book. The country is divided, first of all, into Provinces, known in Turkey as *Vilayet* or *İl* (plural *Vilayetler*, *İller*). The preference in official documents is for *İl*, but Vilayet is still widely used. These are large units, ranging in size from 3920 square km (1490 square miles) in the case of Rize to 47 721 square km (18 420 square miles) in Konya, with population varying from 67 766 (Hakkâri) to 1 882 000 (İstanbul). With few exceptions—Ağrı (capital: Karaköse), Hakkâri (Çölemerik), Hatay (Antakya), İcel (Mersin), Kocaeli (İzmit), Sakarya (Adapazarı) and Tunceli (Kalan)—provinces are named after their administrative centres. The number of provinces changes from time to time: at present there are sixty-seven. Provinces are grouped into Regions (*Bölge, Bölgeler*) in a variety of ways for statistical purposes.

Each province is divided into districts, known as *Kaza* or *İlce* (plural *Kazalar, İlceler*) of which there are now more than six hundred. In thinly settled areas, an *İlce* may be as large as a small *İl*, but most are between 500 and 2000 square km (200–770 square miles) in extent. The majority of *İlceler* contain populations of less than 50 000 and several have fewer than 10 000 inhabitants. İstanbul and Ankara, however, each contain a number of small *İlceler* and these have populations of 100 000 or more.

İlceler are in turn divided into sub-districts (*Bucak, Bucaklar* or *Nahiye, Nahiyeler*) which number more than six thousand. The smallest administrative division is the *Köy Muhtarlik* (literally Village Headmanship) which consists of a village or, in some cases, a number of scattered settlements administered by a Muhtar. There are at present approximately 35 000 *Köy Muhtaliklar* in Turkey. The boundaries of sub-districts and smaller divisions are for the most part undefined and do not appear on published maps. Consequently it has been necessary for data in this book to be mapped on an *İl* or *İlce* basis.

Finally, it should be mentioned that a number of larger cities have *Belediye* (Municipality) authorities. In the cases of İstanbul, Ankara and İzmir, these cover a number of *İlceler*.

Chapter 5

POPULATION

The Present Distribution of the Population

According to the census of 1965 the population of Turkey in that year was 31 381 421, an increase of 3 636 601, or 13·1% over the total of 27 754 820 recorded five years earlier in 1960. Thus, with an annual growth rate of some 2·5%, the Turks are among the more rapidly increasing of the world's peoples. At present, however, the average density is quite low, standing in 1965 at 40 per square km (104 per square mile). The distribution of the Turkish population is markedly uneven, with large sections of the country showing a density below the national average and more restricted areas recording figures above that level. A useful prelude to more detailed consideration of the present pattern is provided by Table V which shows the distribution of the population among the eight major statistical regions.

TABLE V

POPULATION DISTRIBUTION BY MAJOR REGIONS, 1965

Region*	*Area (000 square km)*	*Population (000)*	*Density (per square km)*	*% of area*	*% of population*
European Turkey	24	2 656	110·7	3·1	8·5
Marmara and Aegean	89	5 480	61·6	11·4	17·5
Black Sea	82	4 961	60·5	10·5	15·7
Mediterranean	59	2 407	40·8	7·6	7·7
Western Anatolia	77	2 570	33·4	9·9	8·2
Central Anatolia	237	7 884	33·3	30·4	25·1
Eastern Anatolia	172	4 074	23·7	22·0	13·0
South-east	40	1 360	34·0	5·1	4·3
Total	780	31 392	40·2	100·0	100·0

* For the boundaries for these regions see Fig. 3.

European Turkey, together with the Black Sea, Marmara and Aegean coastlands, stand out as a zone of pronounced population concentration where 42% of the country's inhabitants occupy a quarter of its total area. There is a marked contrast between this zone and the interior of Turkey. The three Anatolian regions, western, central and eastern, together account for 62% of the area but contain only 46% of the popula-

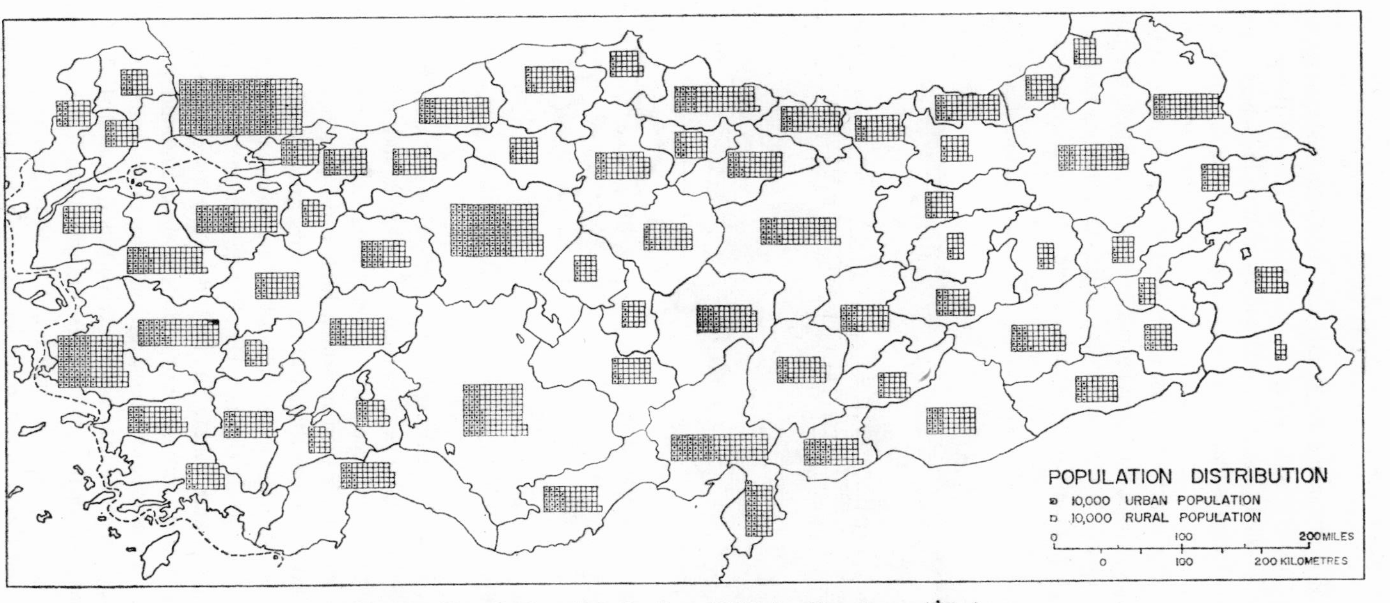

Fig. 18. Population distribution, 1965, by Provinces (*İller*)

tion. The Mediterranean coastlands and the south-eastern region strike a more even balance, with 13% of the area and 12% of the people

A more detailed picture is obtained from Fig. 18, where the distribution of population is mapped on the basis of provinces, and from Fig. 19 showing the density by districts. The latter is drawn on the basis of the smallest administrative unit for which details of both area and population are available, the use of provinces for density mapping having proved unsuitable owing to their large size, and is designed in such a way that areas where population density is above the national average can be

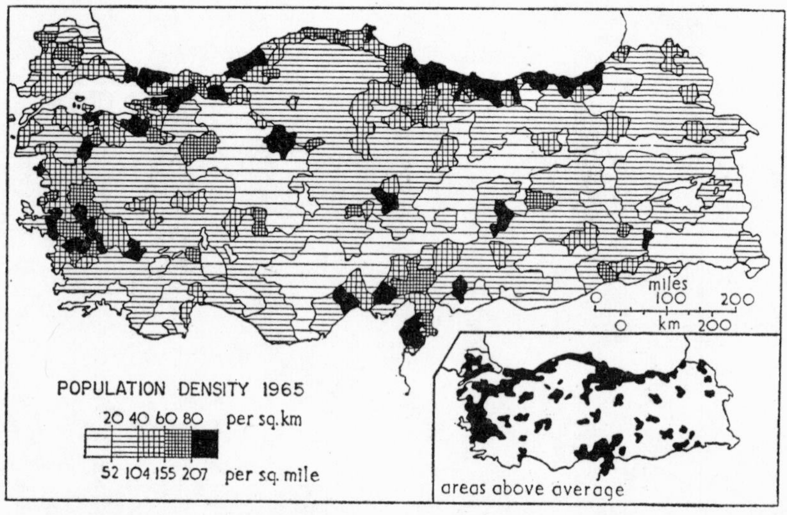

Fig. 19. Population density, 1965, by Districts (*İlceler*)

easily picked out. The arrangement of such areas is markedly peripheral. The Black Sea coastal zone from Rize to Samsun includes important areas of commercial tea, tobacco and hazel-nut production and is a highly productive agricultural region in which high rural densities are common, rising in places to more than 100 per square km (250 per square mile). High rural densities also extend inland where the valleys of the Kızılırmak and Yeşilırmak break through the Pontic ranges in the provinces of Çorum, Amasya and Tokat. The high density zone is narrow along the coast of Kastamonu province but widens again in Zonguldak, which contains Turkey's main source of coal and her major iron- and steel-producing areas. Another high density zone is to be found around the Sea of Marmara, particularly on its eastern and southern shores. The belt of territory from İstanbul eastwards through İzmit to Adapazarı and thence southwestwards past Bursa to the lower Simav valley is one in which, in addition to the attraction of İstanbul itself, important industrial developments are now taking place. The predominance of gentle, lowland relief in this area also encourages high rural densities and agriculture is stimulated by access to sizeable urban markets. In European Turkey, too, high densities are widespread, particularly in the Ergene lowlands. A dense rural population, together with numerous towns, are to be found throughout the Aegean region. High densities are most marked around the port and industrial centre of İzmir, but also extend inland along the broad, fertile valleys of the Gediz, Küçük Menderes and Büyük Menderes rivers. Quite separate from the areas mentioned above is the zone around the head of the Gulf of İskenderun, which covers much of the provinces of İçel, Adana and Hatay. The whole region is one of high agricultural productivity and there has been a certain amount of industrial development in recent years.

Over most of the remainder of the country densities are well below average, falling to less than 15 per square km (40 per square mile) over large parts of Anatolia. Here climate, as it affects the productivity of farming, is a major influence and population density tends to decline with diminishing annual precipitation. In eastern Anatolia rugged relief, which restricts the amount of land availability for agriculture, is the main factor, though the harsh winters are an added deterrent to dense settlement. The provinces of Van and Hakkâri with densities of 10 and 7 per square km (26 and 18 per square mile) respectively, are the most sparsely populated in the whole country. It is also noteworthy that much of the Mediterranean coastal zone, particularly in Antalya province, is one of below-average density. In part, this situation reflects the presence of a good deal of mountainous terrain, but it is also indicative of a lack of development in a region where the agricultural potential is quite high but which suffers a considerable degree of isolation from the remainder of the country.

Throughout the thinly settled interior, pockets of high density mark the position of the larger towns, usually the provincial capitals. A clear example is that of Ankara, the national capital, which is bounded on its southern side by one of the most thinly peopled parts of Central Anatolia.

Urban Population and Towns

Turkey is a country in which, although growing much more rapidly than the rural population, the urban element is still relatively small. In 1965 the urban population, as defined for census purposes, stood at 10 805 817 (34·4%) as compared with 8 858 347 (31·9%) in 1960. Thus in five years there was an increase of some 22% in the size of the urban element as compared with a rise of about 9% in the rural population, indicating that urbanisation is proceeding at a moderate rate. The census data, however, somewhat exaggerate the importance of the truly urban element. For census purposes, urban population is defined as that living in the administrative centres of provinces and districts. In many such places agricultural workers form a large proportion of the population, and in district centres they are often in the majority. Furthermore, although they do provide the bulk of what little non-agricultural employment exists in predominantly rural areas, district centres are often very small (Table VI) and have few of the functions normally associated with an urban settlement.

TABLE VI

POPULATION OF PROVINCE AND DISTRICT CENTRES, 1965

Size	*No.*	*Population (000)*	*% of urban pop.*	*% of total pop.*
Over 250 000	4	3 350	31·0	10·7
100–250 000	10	1 358	12·6	4·3
50–100 000	16	1 117	10·3	3·6
20–50 000	69	2 028	18·8	6·5
10–20 000	79	1 013	9·4	3·2
Below 10 000	443	1 940	17·8	6·1
Total	621	10 806	100·0	34·4

Note: The total number of centres (621) is smaller than the number of districts (637) because İzmir, Ankara and İstanbul, counted here as single centres, contain two, four and thirteen districts respectively.

Towns in Turkey are for the most part small. Only 18·6% of the population lives in cities with more than 50 000 inhabitants and more than half these are found in the four main centres with over 250 000. The number living in all centres above 10 000 is only 28·3% of the total population. Within the generally low level of urbanisation there are considerable regional contrasts, though no sizeable areas of Turkey could be described as highly urbanised. Provinces in which the urban element is significantly above the national average (Fig. 20) are confined to two zones, one embracing parts of the Marmara and Aegean regions and extending inland through Eskişehir to Ankara, the other around the Gulf of İskenderun. The urban proportion is particularly low along the densely settled Black Sea coastlands as well as in the thinly populated eastern parts of the interior.

Fig. 21 shows the distribution of 178 towns with more than 10 000 inhabitants and indicates, as a crude measure of remoteness, those areas which are more than 50 km (30 miles) from even the smallest of these centres. Such areas are most extensive in the east but also cover sizeable parts of central Anatolia and sections of the Mediterranean and Black Sea coasts. The largest city of all is İstanbul (1 743 000) which, as Turkey's chief port and commercial centre, continues to grow rapidly, despite the difficulties of its site (see page 154). Ankara (906 000), the national capital, İzmir (412 000), the second port, and Adana (290 000) are the only other cities with more than a quarter of a million inhabitants. The last-named, focus of the densely populated Seyhan–Ceyhan plains, lies in an area noteworthy for the number of sizeable towns which it contains. These include the ports of Mersin (87 000) and İskenderun (69 000) and the commercial centres of Tarsus (58 000) and Antakya (58 000). All have a long history going back to classical times The ten cities with

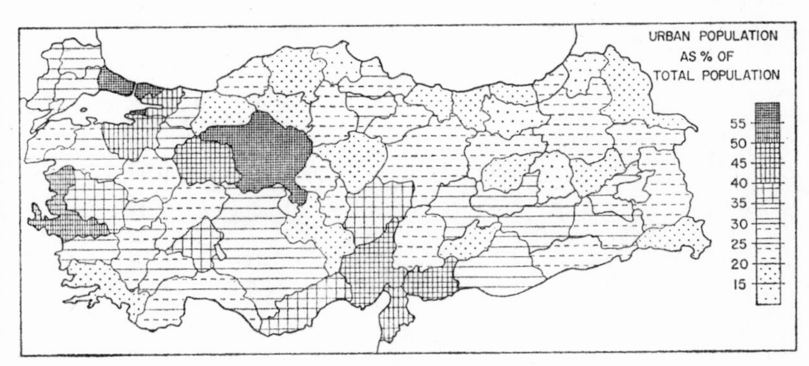

Fig. 20. Urban population as a percentage of total population, 1965, by Provinces (*İller*)

populations of between 100 000 and 250 000 are the commercial and administrative centres of their provinces and in most cases act as regional foci for much wider areas. While the majority are in the more densely populated parts of the country, a few, like Erzurum and Diyarbakır, are situated in regions where the general population density is low. Next in order of size after Adana are Bursa (212 000), Turkey's leading textile centre and regional focus for the lands to the south of the Sea of Marmara, and Eskişehir (174 000), a city of mixed industrial structure and organising centre for the grainlands of north-western Anatolia. Gaziantep (160 000), Konya (158 000), Kayseri (127 000), Sivas (108 000), Samsun (107 000), Erzurum (105 000), Malatya (104 000) and Diyarbakır (103 000), although they have some industries, are primarily regional centres of marketing, transport and administration. Much the same may be said of the sixteen towns with populations between 50 000 and 100 000, fourteen of which are provincial capitals. These include such places as Elâzığ (79 000) in eastern Anatolia, Urfa (73 000) in the south-east,

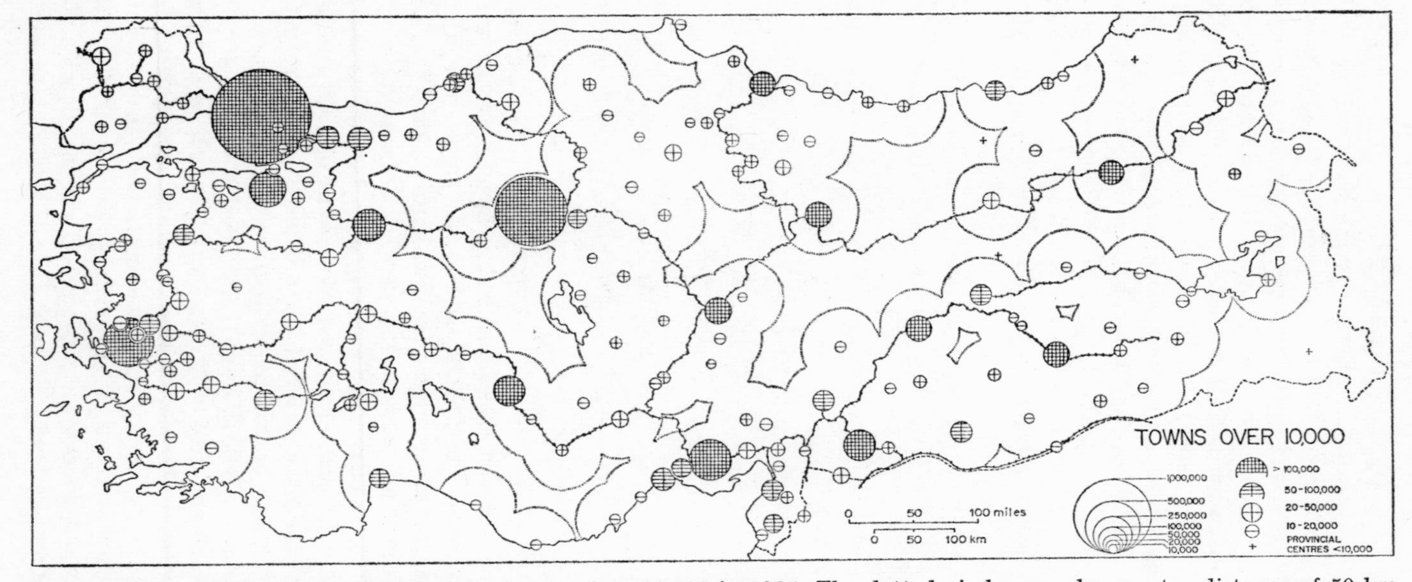

Fig. 21. Urban centres with a population of more than 10 000 in 1965. The dotted circles are drawn at a distance of 50 km (31 miles) from these centres

Trabzon (66 000) on the Black Sea and Antalya (72 000) on the Mediterranean. Only in a very few cases can a town be said to owe its present size mainly to the growth of industry. İzmit (90 000), Kırıkkale (58 000), Zonguldak (55 000) and Karabük (46 000) are among the few examples. The thirty cities with more than 50 000 inhabitants, which in the Turkish context can fairly be described as the main urban centres, are remarkably evenly spaced. Over the greater part of the country they are separated by distances of between 150 and 200 km (95–125 miles). Only around the Sea of Marmara, on the Aegean coast and by the Gulf of İskenderun is there any appreciable 'clustering' of these larger urban centres. Many provinces, particularly in central and eastern Anatolia, have only one town of any size. In the province of Erzurum, for example, the chief town has two-thirds of the urban population, the remainder being distributed among thirteen district centres, the largest of which has 9000 and the smallest only 800 inhabitants.

TABLE VII

POPULATION DISTRIBUTION BY SIZE OF SETTLEMENT, 1965

Size	*No.*	*Population*	
		000	*%*
Over 10 000	200	9 343	29·8
5–10 000	206	1 433	4·6
2–5 000	948	2 669	8·5
1–2 000	3 430	4 509	14·3
500–1 000	10 447	7 238	23·1
Below 500	21 028	6 199	19·7
Total	36 259	31 391	100·0

Over Turkey as a whole, the great bulk of the population live in villages, more than half of them in settlements with fewer than 1000 inhabitants (Table VII). In 1965 villages numbered over 36 000, of which 21 000 had a population of less than 500, and the average size of a settlement in Turkey, including all towns as well as rural types, was only 866. Even these data do not give a full picture of the extent to which the Turkish population lives in small rural settlements, for the 'village' referred to above and in Table VII is in fact the *Köy Muhtarlık*, which may itself consist of a number of quite separate building clusters several miles apart.

Population Growth

Apart from a few very unreliable estimates, little or no information is available on the population of Turkey before the establishment of the

Republic. The first census was held in 1927, but this was incomplete and reasonably accurate figures exist only for the period since 1935, during which there have been censuses at regular five-year intervals. The results of these censuses are set out in Table VIII.

No certain reason can be advanced for the apparent decline in the rate of population growth indicated by the results of the first four censuses. The very rapid increase suggested for the period 1927–35 may have been due in part to the immigration of Turks from outlying areas of the Ottoman empire and in part to a reduction in the death rate; it may

TABLE VIII

POPULATION GROWTH, 1927–65

		Average annual increase	
Year	*Population*	*No.*	%
1927	13 648 270	—	—
1935	16 158 018	313 718	2·13
1940	17 820 950	332 586	1·74
1945	18 790 174	260 362	1·06
1950	20 947 188	431 403	2·29
1955	24 064 763	623 515	2·96
1960	27 754 820	862 714	2·89
1965	31 391 400	899 858	2·49

equally well be a reflection of errors in the 1927 census. The relatively slow rate of growth between 1940 and 1945 is probably a product of abnormally high mortality and a sharply reduced birth rate during the war years since, although Turkey was not directly engaged in hostilities, this was a period of considerable economic difficulty. Whatever the uncertainties concerning these earlier periods, however, there can be no doubt that the first post-war decade saw a marked acceleration in the rate of population growth, resulting from a recovery in the birth rate and a sharp decline in mortality. Official estimates of the death rate show a downward trend from an average of 20 per 1000 between 1940 and 1945 to 12 per 1000 for 1955–60, while the birth rate showed a marginal increase from 40 to 42. Since 1960, fertility appears to have declined somewhat and the rate of growth has slackened off to just below 2·5% per annum. The numerical increase in population between 1960 and 1965, however, was greater than ever before, averaging almost 900 000 each year. Practically all the rapid post-war growth of the Turkish population may be attributed to an excess of births over deaths. Immigration has played its part in particular years, as for example in 1950–1, when 154 000 Turks were repatriated from Bulgaria, but it is of little or no long-term significance. Temporary emigration of Turkish workers to jobs in the Common Market countries, mainly Germany has become important in recent years and about 200 000 males are employed abroad at any one time. Population projections made in connexion with the Five-Year Plan (1963–7) suggest that, by 1985, the population of Turkey will have risen to at least 51 and possibly as high as 59 million. The latter figure is more than twice the 1960 total and these estimates indicate that Turkey will shortly be faced by, if she is not already experiencing, serious pressure of population on resources. It is significant that the authorities have recently come out in favour of a family planning programme.

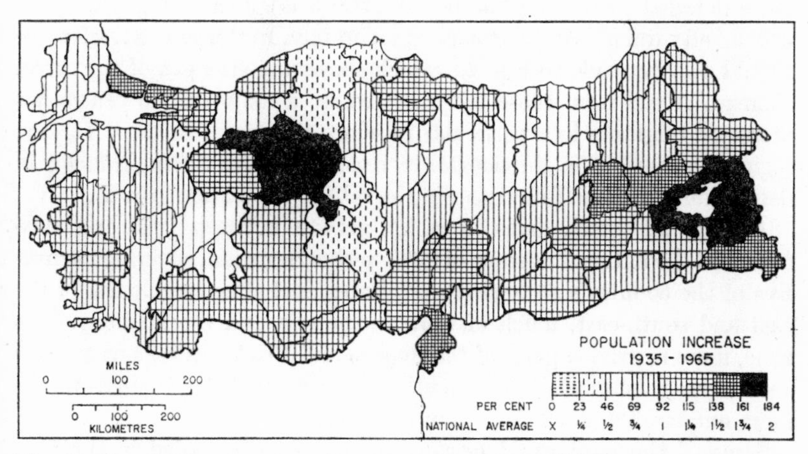

Fig. 22. Population growth, 1935–65, by Provinces (*İller*). Areas where the rate of growth was above the national average are enclosed by a thicker line

In view of the unsatisfactory nature of the 1927 data, the map of population growth (Fig. 22) has been prepared for the period 1935–65. In common with others in this chapter, the map has been compiled in such a way as to permit comparison between the situation in Turkey as a whole and that in individual provinces. Over the thirty-year period, the population of Turkey has increased by approximately 92%. The contributions made by natural increase and migration respectively in particular areas cannot be assessed with any degree of accuracy since vital statistics at the provincial level are not available, nor is detailed information on movement from one part of the country to another. Place-of-birth data in the 1965 census suggest that the volume of movement between provinces is quite modest: only 15% of the population, some 5 million people in all, were recorded as living outside the province in which they were born.

However, a relatively small number of provinces have attracted the bulk of these migrants and thus owe a considerable part of their population growth to immigration. Of the 5 million people recorded as living outside the province in which they were born, half lived in the provinces of Ankara, İstanbul and İzmir which had 38, 59 and 35% of their respective populations in this category. It should also be noted that, while a few major cities attract migrants from a wide area, a large volume of movement from rural to urban areas takes place within the boundaries of each province and thus goes unrecorded in the place-of-birth data. Because urban growth is an important element in population change, a more detailed picture for the period 1960–5 is given in Fig. 23, where urban and rural increase are mapped separately. In this context, reference should also be made to Fig. 20, which shows the strength of the urban element. Apart from those few cases where a major urban centre has attracted migrants to a particular province from large areas of Turkey, regional variations in the natural increase rate have the main factor in determining regional differences in the rate of population growth.

As Fig. 22 shows, areas in which growth between 1935 and 1965 exceeded the national average of 92% were widespread, covering twenty-five of the country's sixty-seven provinces, including large parts of the east and south-east, much of central Anatolia and the Mediterranean zone, more restricted parts of the Aegean and Black Sea regions and the area around İstanbul. Consequently, attention will be focused on the more outstanding deviations from the mean.

Some of the most rapid rates of growth were recorded in the five, predominantly rural, eastern provinces of Ağrı, Bitlis, Muş, Van and Hakkâri, which together increased their population by more than 120% in thirty years. This region, though still sparsely populated, has been one of rapid growth ever since the early 1930s. Widespread devastation and the flight of a large part of the population during and immediately after the First World War were followed by the return of many of its former inhabitants. Natural increase in this region has been well above the national average owing to particularly high fertility. Rapid growth in the provinces of Ankara (208%), İstanbul (160%), Kocaeli and Sakarya (121%) and İzmir (107%) is largely the product of immigration towards rapidly growing towns in the more highly urbanised parts of the country. This is indicated by the fact that, of the population in İstanbul province, no less than 59% were born elsewhere, the corresponding figures for Ankara and İzmir being 38 and 35% respectively. Another zone of rapid growth includes Adana (135%), Maraş (132%) and Hatay (153%), a region of prosperous agriculture and some industrial development which has attracted immigrants from less favoured areas.

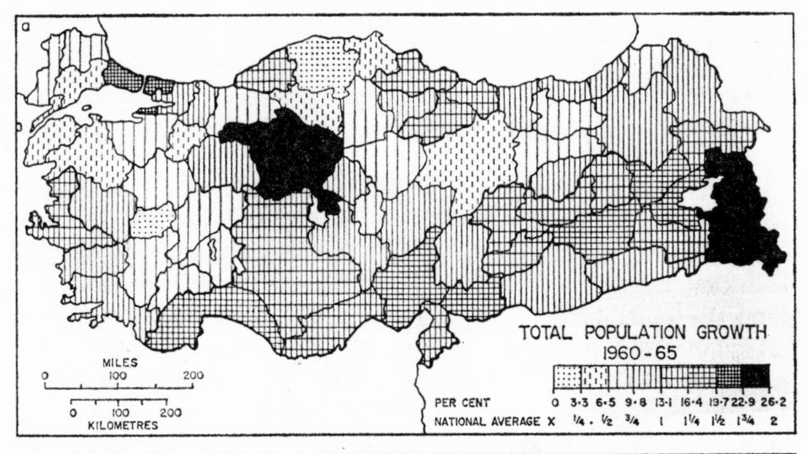

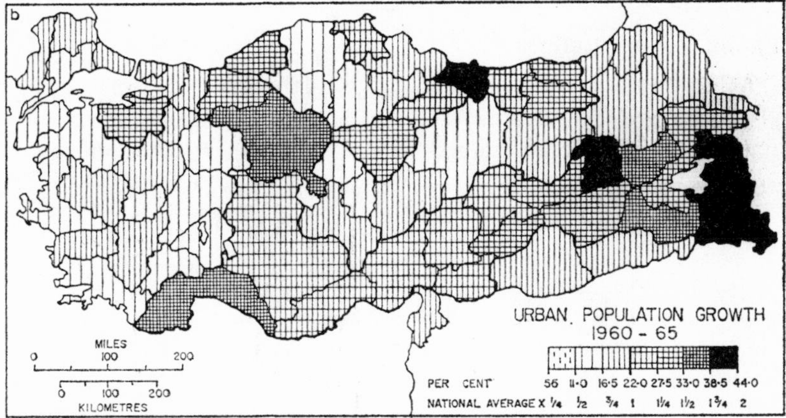

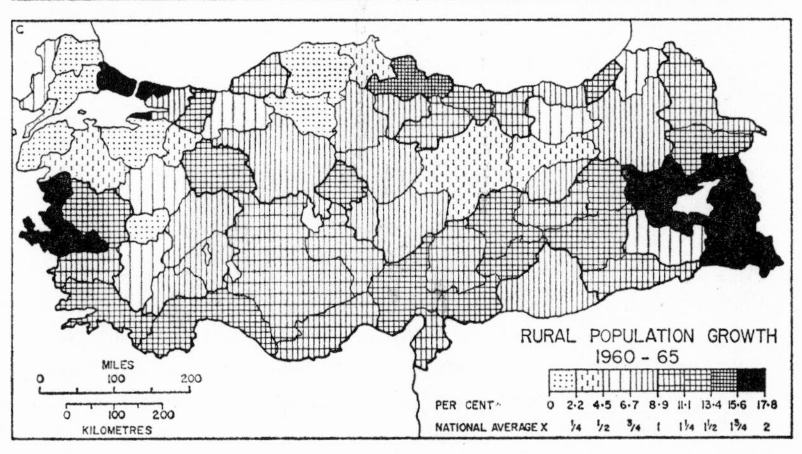

Fig. 23. Growth of (*a*) total population, (*b*) urban population and (*c*) rural population, 1960–5, by Provinces (*İller*)

G

By way of contrast, much of the Black Sea and Aegean coastal zones, despite high agricultural productivity, have not shown particularly rapid growth over the period as a whole. These are areas of high rural density from which there would appear to be a considerable flow of emigrants. Exceptions are the provinces of Samsun (124%), where land reclamation has taken place in the Kızılırmak delta, and Zonguldak (102%) with its coal and steel. The remaining parts of the country, where growth has been close to or below the national average, are predominantly agricultural, the poorer districts being characterised by particularly slow growth rates, owing to a steady flow of emigration to the towns and more prosperous rural areas. Birth rates are probably well below those of more remote eastern areas, while mortality is probably above the national average, giving a natural increase rate below that for Turkey as a whole.

Language and Religion

As already indicated, the Turkish population is by no means completely homogeneous in language, though minority linguistic groups continue to diminish in importance (Table IX) if not in actual numbers.

TABLE IX

POPULATION BY MOTHER TONGUE, 1935–65

	1935		*1945*		*1965*	
	000	%	*000*	%	*000*	%
Turkish	13 899	86·0	16 598	88·3	28 289	90·1
Kurdish	1 480	9·3	1 477	7·9	2 219	7·1
Arabic	154	1·0	247	1·3	365	1·2
Greek	109	0·7	89	0·5	48	0·2
Circassian	92	0·6	67	0·4	58	0·2
Armenian	58	0·4	56	0·3	33	0·1
Georgian	57	0·4	40	0·2	34	0·1
Yiddish	43	0·3	51	0·3	10	—
Laz	63	0·4	47	0·2	26	0·1
Others	138	1·1	118	0·6	309	1·0
Total	16 157	100·0	18 790	100·0	31 391	100·0

90% now claim Turkish as their mother tongue and 98% claim the ability to speak that language and the only sizeable minorities are those speaking Kurdish (2·2 million) and Arabic (0·3 million). Kurds are present in substantial numbers throughout eastern Anatolia and the south-east (Fig. 24) forming a majority in the eight provinces of Ağrı, Bitlis, Diyarbakır, Hakkârı, Mardin, Muş, Siirt and Van, and the largest single group in Urfa. Arabic speakers are found mainly in Hatay, where they constitute 36% of the population, and in Adana, Mardin, Siirt and Urfa.

Greeks, whose numbers continue to diminish, are now almost entirely confined to İstanbul. They no longer form a numerically significant group and barely outnumber the Circassians, who are widely dispersed over eastern Anatolia. Armenians, who in the 19th century formed a majority in some eastern districts, have virtually disappeared, and the 33 000 remaining are found mainly in İstanbul. Georgians, in contrast, are more scattered, with their largest concentration in the frontier province of Artvin. They are also to be found in Sakarya, Kocaeli and Bursa. Other groups shown in the table are the Jews of İstanbul and the Laz of the north-east.

Religious minorities are even smaller than linguistic ones. 99% of the

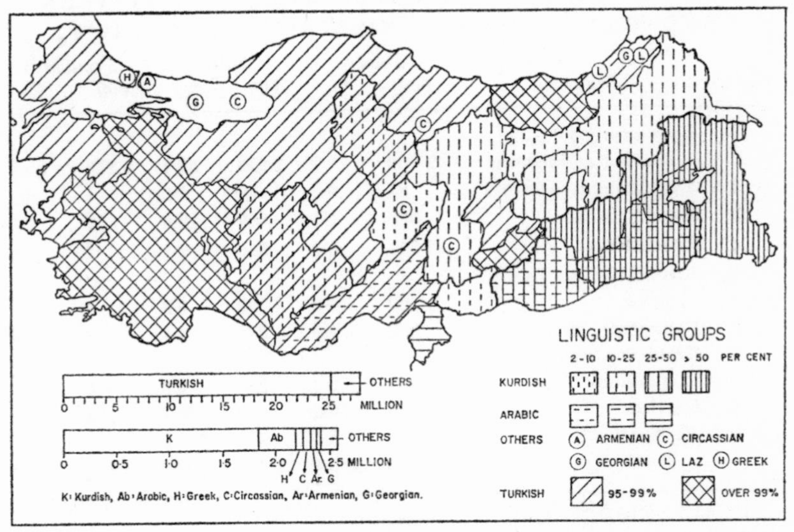

Fig. 24. Distribution of the main linguistic groups. A thick line encloses those provinces of the south-east in which Turkish-speakers are in a minority

population profess adherence to Islam. There are 38 000 Jews and 206 000 Christians. Of the latter, 74 000 adhere to the Greek Orthodox church, 70 000 are Gregorians, 25 000 Roman Catholics and 17 000 Protestants.

Occupational Structure

Table X shows the economically active population aged fifteen years and over classified by major industrial groups. The overwhelming preponderance of agriculture as a means of livelihood is immediately apparent from these figures. Of those employed in Group 1 activities, only about 40 000 are engaged in hunting, forestry and fishing, leaving 71·5% of the labour force in agriculture alone. Agricultural employment shows an almost equal division between the sexes, and agriculture is the leading occupation for women to an even greater degree than it is for men. Female employment outside agriculture is very limited indeed, only 301 000 women being employed in other occupations as compared with some 3·8 million men. Regional variations in the proportion employed in agriculture are relatively slight (Fig. 25) only the three provinces of İstanbul, Ankara and İzmir showing figures substantially below the national average. Even so, Ankara and İzmir each have over 45% of their

TABLE X

ECONOMICALLY ACTIVE POPULATION, AGED FIFTEEN AND OVER, BY MAJOR INDUSTRIAL GROUPS, 1965

Group	*Industry*	*Total*		*Males*		*Females*	
		000	%	*000*	%	*000*	%
1	Agriculture, forestry hunting and fishing	9 750	71·9	4 914	58·4	4 836	94·1
2	Mining and quarrying	87	0·6	86	1·0	1	n
3	Manufacturing	960	7·1	883	10·5	77	1·5
4	Construction	351	2·6	349	4·1	2	n
5	Electricity, gas and water	29	0·2	29	0·3	n	n
6	Commerce, banking, etc.	392	2·9	372	4·4	20	0·4
7	Transport, storage and communications	287	2·1	281	3·3	6	0·1
8	Services	835	6·2	732	8·7	103	2·0
9	Unclassified*	868	6·4	777	9·2	91	1·8
	Total	13 558	100·0	8 420	100·0	5 137	100·0

* Includes military personnel. n = negligible.

workers in farming, leaving İstanbul as the only province where farmers are in a really small minority (11%). If these three provinces are excluded, the figure for agricultural employment over the remainder of the country rises to 80%, proportions for individual provinces ranging from 64% in Eskişehir to 93% in Sinop. Regions with particularly high figures include most of the Black Sea coastlands and eastern Anatolia. The lowest figures away from the three main centres are recorded along the Marmara and Aegean coasts and in western Anatolia.

Of the 30% of all workers who are not employed in agriculture, 6% are unclassified, leaving only 24%, 2 940 000 workers to be distributed among the seven other industrial groups. The most important of these is manufacturing, though it occupies only 7·1% of the labour force, but if public utilities, commerce, transport and service activities (groups 5–8) are put together, they amount to 11·4%. Mining and quarrying are very poorly represented, being less important even than construction work. In all non-agricultural activities combined, male workers outnumber female by more than ten to one, an indication of the very restricted range of employment opportunities available to women in present-day Turkey.

Mining and quarrying employ 86 000 workers, of whom about half are found in Zonguldak province, the main coal-mining area, but even here they represent only 14% of the labour force. The remainder are dispersed

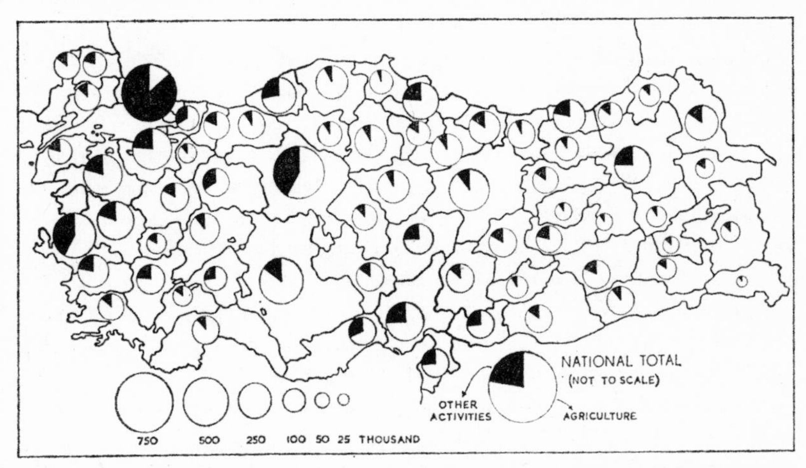

Fig. 25. The economically active population, 1965, by Provinces (*İller*). The size of the circles is proportional to the numbers employed in each Province. The black sector indicates those engaged in non-agricultural activities

in small numbers over a dozen or so provinces, reflecting the scattered nature of Turkey's mineral resources. In the majority of provinces, employment in this sphere is virtually non-existent.

Manufacturing industry employs 960 000, including 77 000 women, and even this small total marks an increase of 240 000 in the last ten years. The most important branch is textiles and clothing (30%) followed by metallurgy and engineering (23%) and food, drink and tobacco (17%). Appreciable numbers are employed in manufacturing in most provinces, but the bulk of the labour force is concentrated in a few. İstanbul alone has about 255 000 manufacturing workers, followed at a considerable distance by İzmir (84 000) and Ankara (59 000). These are provinces with a mixed industrial structure and no particular specialisation. Bursa (40 000) and Denizli (12 000) contain the country's main textile factories, while Adana (32 000), Kayseri (15 000) and Konya (25 000) provinces have a variety of products. The eight provinces named contain two-fifths of the manufacturing labour force: another fifth are to be found in the remaining provinces of the Marmara, Aegean and western Anatolia regions. Elsewhere a few provinces such as Zonguldak (metallurgy), Gaziantep (textiles) and Samsun (tobacco) have significant numbers. In contrast, the whole of eastern Anatolia, which is the home of some 3 million people, has only 35 000 workers in manufacturing industry.

The tertiary sector of industry as a whole (groups 5–8) employs 1 743 000 workers, just over 11% of the national labour force. A striking feature is that only about one in thirteen of the workers in this sector is a woman. While 16·1% of all male workers are included, only 1·8% of the females fall into this category. The distribution of workers in the tertiary sector shows similarities to that of manufacturing. The three provinces of Ankara (172 000), İstanbul (315 000) and İzmir (101 000) contain more than two-fifths of the workers. Another fifth are found in the Marmara and Aegean regions and in western Anatolia, and a further tenth in Adana, İçel, Hatay and Gaziantep. The remaining 10% are thinly spread over the rest of the country.

The total impression gained from the data on occupational structure is one of strong contrast between areas in which agriculture is predominant to an extremely high degree and those where other activities, though still subordinate as sources of employment, are sufficiently well developed to give a more mixed economy and occupational structure. The latter situation is most clearly to be seen in a zone running from İstanbul and İzmir inland through Eskişehir to Ankara. It also occurs, in a less marked form, in the area around the Gulf of İskenderun.

Part Three

ECONOMIC GEOGRAPHY

INTRODUCTION

The previous chapter drew attention to the major role of agriculture as a source of employment and its position as the dominant mode of life among the Turkish people, at least 75% of whom depend upon farming for their livelihood and pass their days in rural surroundings. The contribution of agriculture to the national income, however, is a good deal less impressive than its status as a source of employment, a fact which indicates the relatively low level of productivity achieved in most farming areas. According to official estimates, agriculture was responsible, in 1967, for 34·9% of the national income. This marks a striking fall in the relative importance of farming as a source of wealth, for in 1948 the proportion of the national income derived from agriculture was 52%. Although these two figures may not be strictly comparable, there can be no doubt that other forms of economic activity are contributing a progressively larger share of the national income and that the productivity of industrial and other workers is very much higher than that of workers on the land. Furthermore, the contrast between the two categories is becoming more and more marked, for the reduction in the significance of agriculture as a source of employment has been much less rapid than the decline in its contribution to the national income. In any case, published data on national income tend to underestimate the importance of farming to the nation. It is improbable that full account is taken of the large volume of foodstuffs consumed on the farms which produce them; furthermore, a considerable proportion of manufacturing industry involves the processing of agricultural products.

Agriculture is strikingly dominant in Turkish foreign trade. In 1967 at least 80% of the country's exports were in the form of agricultural produce, with cotton (25%) and tobacco (23%) in the lead. Other important items are raisins, figs, hazel-nuts, olive oil, hides and skins. The income from these sources is, of course, influenced by fluctuations in world commodity prices and may also be affected by the size of the Turkish crop in a particular year. This latter factor is particularly well illustrated in the case of cereals, the output of which is particularly subject to climatically induced variations (see p. 117).

The extractive and manufacturing industries make a modest but growing contribution to the national economy, accounting for some 18% of the national income and nearly 20% of the exports. Although there is a sizeable import of industrial raw materials, this is exceeded by exports, among which minerals, especially the ores of chrome and copper, are the major item. Turkey's mineral resources cover a wide range, including coal, chrome, copper, iron, sulphur, manganese, mercury, bauxite and others, but many of the deposits are small and difficult to work so that a large number of them are worth exploiting only at times when world prices are high. The extent of the deposits and the size of reserves are by no means fully known and new sources continue to be discovered as geological exploration proceeds. In several cases, known resources remain undeveloped owing to inaccessibility or to shortages of capital, suitable labour or power. As regards power, Turkey is fortunate in possessing coal, which is virtually absent from the remainder of the Middle East, in quantities sufficient for her present, rather limited industrial needs. On the other hand, oil has so far been discovered only in modest quantities and petroleum products account for 12% of imports. There is a large hydro-electric potential and current plans envisage a number of major developments in this sphere.

In summary it can be said that, although a successful start has been made in the industrialisation of the country, Turkey remains in the 'developing' rather than the 'developed' category, and is likely to remain so for some time to come. *Per capita* income, though well above that of most Middle Eastern states and rising at about 4% per annum, is still low by European standards. A large part of the rural population remains near subsistence level and, despite technical innovations, the character of life for the majority is changing but slowly. Turkey thus continues as a primary producer, heavily dependent upon agriculture as a source of income and the mainstay of the export trade, with minerals as an important supplement. In consequence she relies largely on imports for her requirements of manufactured goods, and particularly for capital equipment. In 1967 machinery and transport equipment accounted for 42% of imports, other manufactures for a further 21% and raw materials and foodstuffs for most of the remainder. During the 1930s and the Second World War, when internal consumption was even lower than at present and Turkey's exports were much in demand, she achieved a large surplus in foreign trade, but this was replaced in 1947 by a deficit which has continued ever since. In 1967 imports exceeded exports by $162 million. A slow rate of economic growth, due mainly to lack of capital, a failure to attract foreign investment on a really large scale, heavy reliance on foreign loans and aid and a chronic balance of payments deficit have all been features of the Turkish economy in the post-war years. Plans to overcome this situation are now being vigorously pursued and these include, as major elements, investment in agriculture designed in part to boost exports, the further development of industry to reduce imports, improvement of the infrastructure, particularly transport and power supplies and the encouragement of tourism as a source of foreign currency. The Turkish economy is a mixed one, part operated by the state and part in private hands. Under these circumstances it has not always been possible to direct private investment in the most desirable direction, nor has state enterprise always been wholly wise. The achievements of the 1963–7 period were somewhat less than had been hoped, the Gross National Product increasing by an average of 6·5% per annum instead of the anticipated 7·0%. In particular, the industrial sector of the economy failed to grow as rapidly as had been hoped. Nevertheless, considerable progress was made, agricultural production rising by 13·2% and industrial output by 40·4% over the five-year period, average annual gains of 3·3 and 8·9% respectively.

The Second Five-Year Plan, covering the period 1968–72, was published early in 1969. Like its predecessor, the Plan aims at a 7% annual growth rate. Within this overall figure, industry is to expand at 11·1% and agriculture at 4·2% per annum, thus continuing the diversification of the economy which has been characteristic of the past decade.

Chapter 6

AGRICULTURE, FORESTRY AND FISHERIES

Environmental influences

The traditional dominance of agriculture in the economy of Turkey and the life of its people has continued over many centuries despite the fact that environmental conditions over much of the country are by no means wholly favourable. Here again we may note the contrast between the interior and the periphery. Coastal areas benefit from the relatively southerly latitude in which the country is situated. In these areas, apart from the possibility of occasional frost, temperature and length of growing season present no problems to the farmer and permit the cultivation of a wide range of crops including a number of sub-tropical, and in the most favoured parts even tropical varieties. Bananas, for example, are grown commercially in eastern parts of Antalya province and tea plantations have been established on the north-east coast. The Mediterranean and, to a slightly lesser degree, the Aegean coast, are, it is true, affected by the summer drought of the Mediterranean climate régime, but the presence inland of high mountain ranges where much of the winter precipitation is stored in the form of snow and released during the summer months, gives ideal conditions for the development of irrigated agriculture, the potential for which has only been partially developed. The Black Sea coast is perhaps the most favoured of all regions climatically, having mild winters, hot summers and an adequate supply of moisture throughout the year, but it is topographically rather difficult, with only small areas of flat or gently sloping land. In the interior, the situation is quite different and the advantage of latitudes are offset by high altitude and continentality. Conditions may be considered as similar, in a more intensive form, to those of the Iberian interior or as a somewhat less extreme form of those encountered in Iran. The western half of the interior contains large expanses of flat or gently sloping land and soils which are at least moderately fertile in their natural state. This, however, is one of the driest parts of Turkey, both in terms of actual rainfall and those of moisture availability, which is much reduced by the high summer temperatures. Over considerable areas, particularly along the northern and southern fringes of this zone, proximity to well-watered mountains permits irrigation, but towards the centre of Anatolia this becomes increasingly difficult, particularly as the larger rivers tend to be quite sharply incised. In any case, the range of crops which can be grown, even with the aid of irrigation, is restricted by the length of the growing season and by the low winter temperatures, both of which exclude many of the high-value crops characteristic of the coastlands. More easterly parts of the interior have further disadvantages. Although the lack of moisture in the summer months is less severe, it still presents problems in several areas and the winter cold is more intense. Most important of all, land suitable for cultivation is limited by the prevalence of high mountain terrain with flat or gently sloping land restricted to relatively small, enclosed basins. Finally the south-eastern part of the country combines large areas of land topographically suited to agriculture with a summer drought even more intense than that of the Mediterranean coast and less easily remedied by irrigation owing to the distance of much of the area from suitable sources of water. Turkey's agriculture is thus faced with many problems inherent in the physical geography of her various regions. In addition there are a number of economic and social problems at least as intractable as the physical ones.

Land Use

Basic data on land utilisation and the changes which have occurred over the past fifteen years are set out in Table XI.

From these figures it would appear that 83·2% of the land surface of Turkey is used in one way or another as cropland, grazing or forest, but such a statement tends to exaggerate the extent to which the country's land resources are in fact utilised. Of the 10·6 million ha (26·2 million acres) classed as forest, for example, only about one-third is categorised by the State Forestry Directorate as 'productive forest': most of the remainder is bush and scrub, the degraded remnants of the natural vegetation. The 28 million ha (69 million acres) of grazing land include large areas of very poor vegetation, virtually indistinguishable from waste-land. About one-third of the total area is under cultivation, 2·3 million ha (5·6 million acres) in orchards and vegetable gardens and 23·8 million ha (58·8 million acres) under field crops. Of the latter, rather more than one-third is classed as fallow. Thus in 1965 there was approximately 0·83 ha (2·05 acres) of cultivated land, including fallow, per head of the population. These figures are indicative of the low level of intensity of most forms of agriculture in Turkey, among which extensive grain growing and stock farming are the dominant activities.

The period since 1950 has witnessed a number of highly significant changes in land use (Fig. 26) which are discussed in the concluding section of this chapter. For the moment our attention will be focused on regional variations as revealed by the 1965 figures. There are marked regional differences in the proportion of land under cultivation and in the areas devoted to individual crops. In the statistical appendix to this chapter (p. 126) details are given for the nine standard agricultural regions used in Ministry of Agriculture publications and a number of aspects are illustrated in Fig. 27. The proportion of sown land (Fig. 27(*c*)) exceeds the

TABLE XI

LAND USE, 1950–65

	Total area	*Cropland*				*Orchards and gardens*	
		Sown		*Fallow*			
	000 ha	*000 ha*	%	*000 ha*	%	*000 ha*	%
1950	78 000	9 868	12·7	4 674	6·0	1 466	1·9
1955	78 000	14 205	18·2	6 793	8·7	1 810	2·3
1960	78 000	15 305	19·6	7 959	10·2	2 060	2·6
1965	78 000	15 294	19·6	8 547	11·0	2 305	3·0
% change	—	+55·0	—	+82·9	—	+57·0	—

	Grazing land		*Forest*		*Waste*	
	000 ha	%	*000 ha*	%	*000 ha*	%
1950	37 806	48·5	10 418	13·4	13 466	17·3
1955	31 009	40·0	10 418	13·4	13 463	17·3
1960	28 658	36·7	10 584	13·6	13 132	16·8
1965	28 232	36·2	10 584	13·6	13 096	16·8
% change	−25·3	—	+1·6	—	−2·7	—

national average over much of central Anatolia, where the area under crops reaches 30% in Ankara province, 35% in Konya and 45% in Nevşehir. These levels are surpassed only in Thrace (Edirne 43%, Tekirdağ 50%) and in the Seyhan–Ceyhan lowlands (Adana 43%). The proportion of cropland is particularly low in the extreme east, where the provinces of Bitlis, Bingöl and Hakkâri record only 3·6, 1·6 and 0·5% respectively. Other parts of the country in which relief restricts the availability of cropland include the Black Sea and Mediterranean coasts (Artvin 3·6%, Rize 4·6%, Antalya 11·6%), but in both these areas tree-crops, not included in the sown area, are important. Fig. 27(*b*) shows regional contrasts in the major uses of the sown area and the great predominance of cereals is immediately apparent. Only in the four coastal

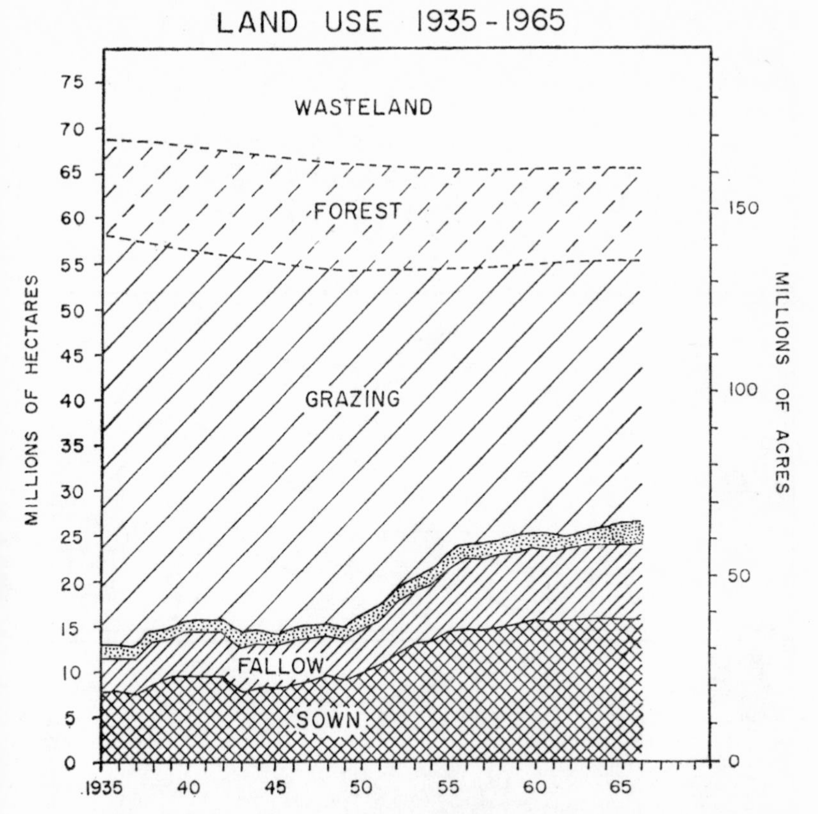

Fig. 26. Changes in land use, 1935–66. Note the rapid increase in the sown area between 1950 and 1955 and its relative stability since the latter date. The dotted section of the graph indicates the area under orchards and vegetable gardens

regions—Black Sea, Marmara, Aegean and Mediterranean—do cereals occupy less than 90% of the sown area.

Crops (Figs. 28–30)

Cereals occupy almost 85% of the total cropland and more than 90% over large parts of the interior (Fig. 27). In the provinces of Van and Ağrı, to quote extreme cases, 97 and 99% respectively of the sown area are devoted to grain. So great is the predominance of cereals that any area with less than 70% of its cropland devoted to them must be considered an important producer of other crops: such areas are wholly confined to coastal provinces. Of all the cereals, wheat is the most important, occupying nearly 60% of the grainland and over 50% of the whole sown

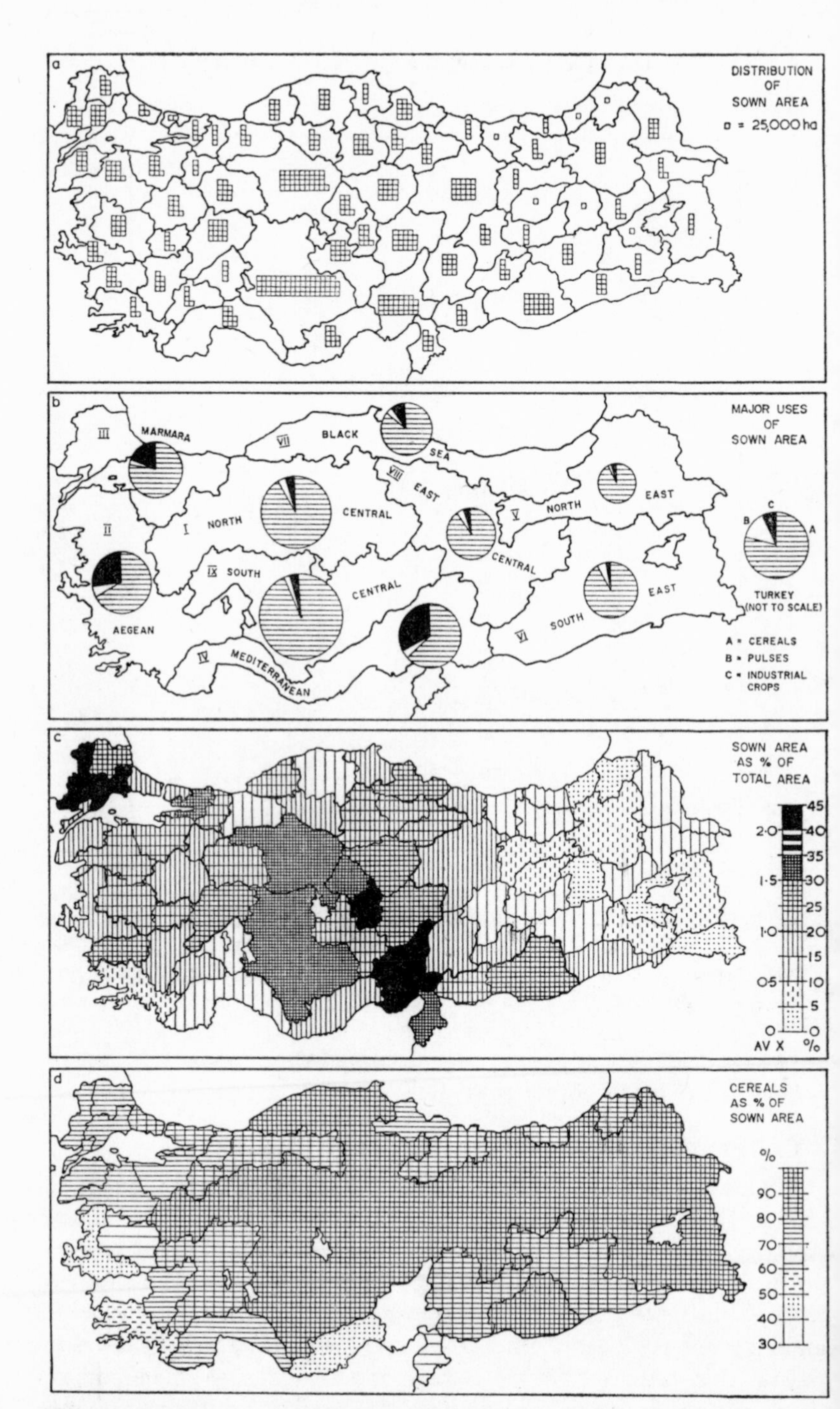

Fig. 27. The extent and uses of the sown area, 1965. Maps (*a*), (*c*) and (*d*) are drawn on the basis of Provinces (*İller*). Map (*b*) makes use of the regions used in Ministry of Agriculture statistics

area. In all nine regions, wheat is the most important single crop in terms of land use, but it accounts for less than 30% of the sown area in the Black Sea and Aegean regions, where industrial crops and tree crops are particularly important. As regards production (Fig. 28(*a*)) the most significant

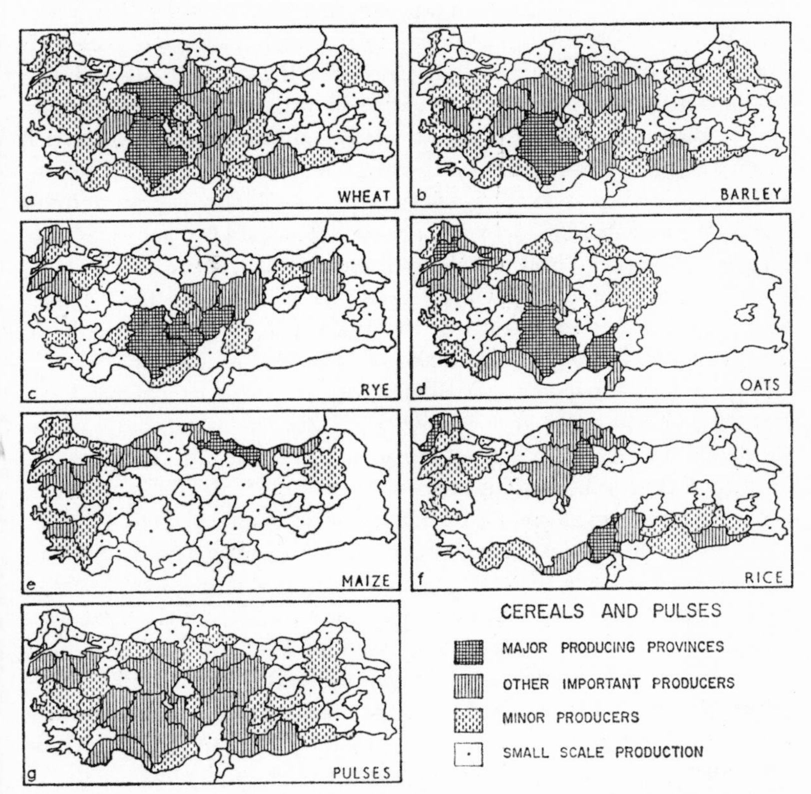

Fig. 28. Production of (*a*) wheat, (*b*) barley, (*c*) rye, (*d*) oats, (*e*) maize, (*f*) rice and (*g*) pulses. Each Province is assessed on the basis of its share of total Turkish production in 1965; major producers: over 10%; other important producers: 5–10%; minor producers: 1–5%; small-scale producers: less than 1%

area is central Anatolia, where the north-central, south-central and east-central regions together produce more than half the total crop.

Barley (Fig. 28(*b*)) occupies about one-fifth of the sown area and the bulk of production again comes from the three central regions. Its importance to local agriculture, however, is greatest in the north-east and Aegean regions, where it occupies more than a quarter of the land devoted to cereals. The other cereals, which include oats, rye, maize and small areas of rice and millet, are more restricted in their distribution and together take up only 15% of the sown area. Oats (Fig. 28(*d*)) are produced mainly around the Sea of Marmara, in central Anatolia and in Adana province and are conspicuously absent from the eastern third of the country. Rye (Fig. 28(*c*)) is important in southern and eastern parts of central Anatolia, in Erzurum province and in the less fertile parts of Thrace, but is virtually unknown in the south-east. Maize (Fig. 28(*e*)) is a speciality of the warm, wet Black Sea coastal zone, and although it is also grown on a significant scale in the Marmara and Aegean regions, 45% of the crop comes from the area between Sinop and Rize. Millet is grown mainly in the hot, dry south-east, one-third of the output coming from Urfa province. Rice (Fig. 28(*f*)), which in Turkey is grown almost entirely on irrigated land, covers only 50 000 ha (124 000 acres). 26% of the production comes from the Mediterranean region, where Adana (11%) is the most important province. A further 34% comes from a zone extending north from Ankara to the Black Sea, 10% from the lower Meriç valley in Edirne province and 12% from the south-east.

Despite a recent increase in the area under pulses or legumes, (Fig. 28(*g*)), these still cover only 550 000 ha (1 359 000 acres), 3·6% of the sown area. A number of different crops are included in this category, the most important being various types of bean and vetch, of which the former are a significant element in human as well as in animal diets. There are very few areas in which pulses are not grown to some extent, but they are most significant in the Marmara and south-eastern regions.

The crops so far described, particularly the cereals, are the most basic elements of the Turkish agricultural system. They are fundamental to the provision of a satisfactory food supply for the population and, together with grazing lands, grainlands are the most characteristic element of the rural landscape throughout the greater part of the country. Grain and grazing lands attain their greatest degree of dominance in the interior, and peripheral zones are distinguished, not by any absence of cereals, which are the main crops in these areas as well, but by the presence of other crops, which lend a greater diversity to the agricultural landscape.

Industrial crops (Fig. 29) which, in the Turkish statistics, include such food items as the onion and potato, as well as those more commonly associated with this term, occupy some 10·3% of the cultivated area. Three-quarters of the land under industrial crops is found in the Aegean, Marmara and Mediterranean regions and another 7% along the Black Sea coast. The group includes a number of items which are fairly widespread and others which are strongly localised. In the first category are potatoes and sugar-beet, both of which are grown over large areas of Anatolia. Sugar-beet production (Fig. 29(*b*)) is the more concentrated of the two, 50% of the crop being derived from the six provinces of Afyon, Amasya, Eskişehir, Konya, Sakarya and Tokat, each of which now has its large processing works. The area under sugar-beet has much increased in recent years and production multiplied fourfold between 1950 and 1965. Sunflower (Fig. 29(*c*)), a crop commonly grown in association with cereals in the Balkans, is concentrated in the north-western part of Turkey. 90% of the crop comes from the Marmara region and the adjacent provinces

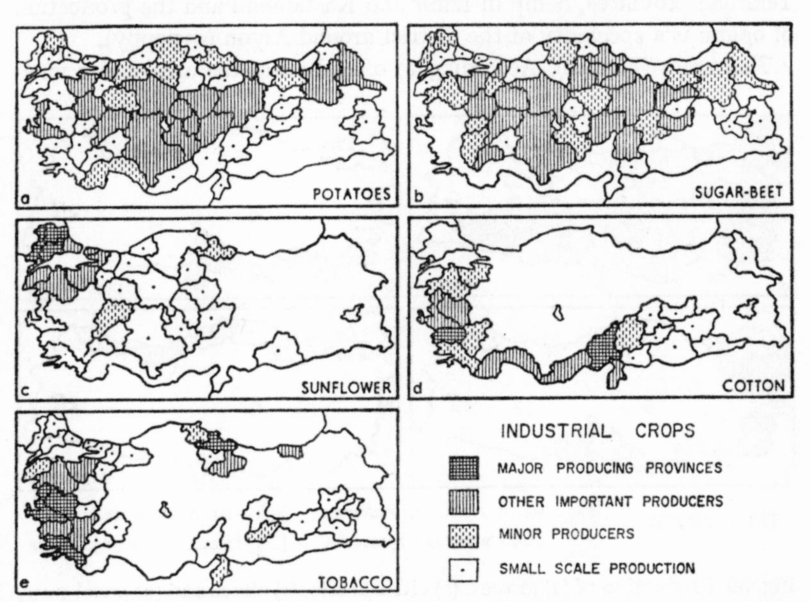

Fig. 29. Production of (*a*) potatoes, (*b*) sugar-beet, (*c*) sunflower, (*d*) cotton and (*e*) tobacco. (For details, see caption to Fig. 28)

of Balıkesir and Çanakkale. Cotton (Fig. 29(*d*)) is strongly localised in the Aegean and Mediterranean regions, particularly in Aydın and Adana provinces, which together account for nearly 50% of the output. The area devoted to cotton more than doubled in the 1950s, rising from 300 000 to 650 000 ha (740 000–1 606 000 acres). This rapid increase was not wholly beneficial. In some parts of the country much of the best land available was turned over to cotton, relegating food crops to the poorer land. At the same time, injudicious irrigation methods, together with the practice of growing cotton on the same land for several successive years led in places to soil deterioration and falling yields. On the other hand, cotton has played an increasing part in the Turkish export trade and now accounts for more than a quarter of all agricultural exports by value. Finally among the major industrial crops, special significance attaches to tobacco (Fig. 29(*e*)) which, although it occupies only 1·5% of the sown area, accounts for nearly 25% of agricultural exports. About a quarter of the crop comes from İzmir province and 73% from the Aegean region as a whole. A further 10% is derived from Bursa, Balıkesir and Çanakkale, and 9% from Samsun, on the Black Sea coast. Production elsewhere is on a very limited scale. Mention should also be made of a number of other industrial crops of local importance. Flax is grown mainly in Kocaeli and Tekirdağ provinces, hemp in İzmir and Kastamonu and the production of opium is a speciality of the district around Afyon (=poppy).

Tree crops (Fig. 30). According to official data, the area under vine-

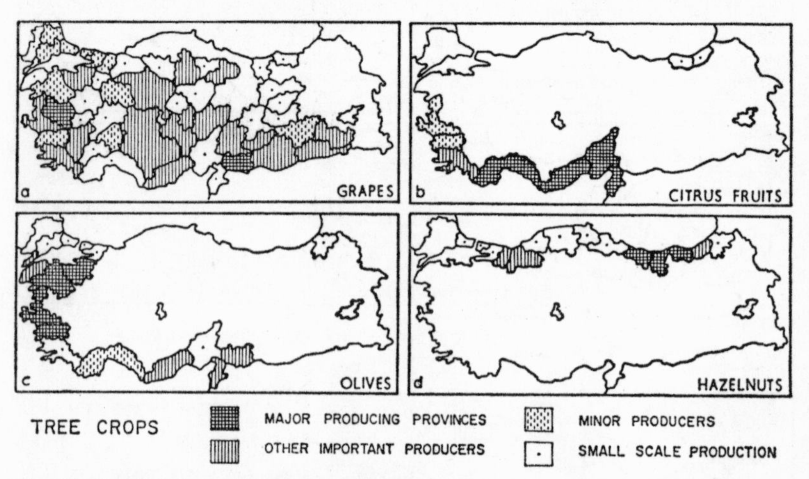

Fig. 30. Production of (*a*) grapes, (*b*) citrus fruits, (*c*) olives and (*d*) hazel-nuts. (For details see caption to Fig. 28)

yards, orchards, vegetable gardens and olive groves amounted in 1965 to 2·3 million ha (5·7 million acres) a total equivalent to about 15% of the sown area. These figures are, at best, rough estimates of the area devoted to tree crops since many trees grow, not in orchards, but scattered about the arable land and detailed data always refer to number of trees rather than hectares. On the basis of volume of production, tree crops rank in the following order: grapes, non-citrus fruits, citrus, olives, pistachio, walnut, almond and other nuts, hazel-nuts. In terms of their value to the export trade, the order is grapes (raisins), olive oil, figs, citrus fruits.

Vines (Fig. 30(*a*)) which occupy a notional 800 000 ha (1 977 000 acres) are grown not only in the south-eastern, Mediterranean and Aegean regions but also over much of central and western Anatolia where their ability to withstand frost makes them one of the few high-value crops which can survive. Thus, although the leading producers are Gaziantep

(15%) and Manisa (12%), a further 10% comes from Ankara and Konya. In contrast, vines are almost absent from the Black Sea coastlands. Hazel-nuts (Fig. 30(*d*)), the export of which is exceeded in value only by cotton and tobacco, are perhaps the most highly localised of Turkish agricultural products. Very few indeed are grown outside the provinces fronting on the Black Sea and 80% of the crop comes from Giresun, Ordu and Trabzon. Olives and citrus fruits are rigidly confined by climatic factors to the Mediterranean and Aegean regions. 80% of all olives (Fig. 30(*c*)) are produced along these coasts and olive oil is now a significant export item. Citrus fruits (Fig. 30(*b*)) are more a speciality of the Mediterranean, 90% coming from Antalya, İçel, Adana and Hatay. Figs are a speciality of Aydın province, despite their traditional name of Smyrna (İzmir) figs, a reference to the port of shipment rather than to the area of production. There is a considerable potential for further expansion of tree-crop production, particularly of citrus fruits in the Mediterranean region. If the quality of the crop could be improved and marketing sufficiently well organised, Turkey might be able to compete with other major exporters.

An interesting, though minor recent addition to the range of crops grown in Turkey is tea. Numerous attempts were made, in the late 19th century and in the early part of the 20th, to establish tea plantations along the Black Sea coast, but as late as 1949 tea gardens covered only about 2000 ha (5000 acres). Rapid expansion occurred in the 1950s and 16 000 ha (40 000 acres) are now devoted to this crop, mainly in the provinces of Rize and Artvin.

LIVESTOCK (Fig. 31)

In 1965, there were about 13 million cattle, of which 4 million were dairy cattle, 20 million goats, including 5·5 million of the Angora variety, and 33 million sheep. The numbers of cattle and sheep were in fact very close to those in the United Kingdom, but the latter produced at least five times as much meat and milk as Turkey. Low yields are as characteristic of Turkish livestock farming as they are of crop production. Over the past twenty years there has been a steady increase in the numbers of sheep and cattle, while the goat population has declined. In addition to these three main types of livestock there are a large number of other animals, including 1·2 million water buffaloes (used as draft animals and milk producers), 1·2 million horses, 2·2 million mules and donkeys and 45 000 camels. The Moslem tradition ensures that there are very few pigs: only 18 000 in 1965.

Sheep (Fig. 31(*a*)) are most numerous in the extreme east of Turkey, in the southern part of central Anatolia and in Thrace and the Marmara

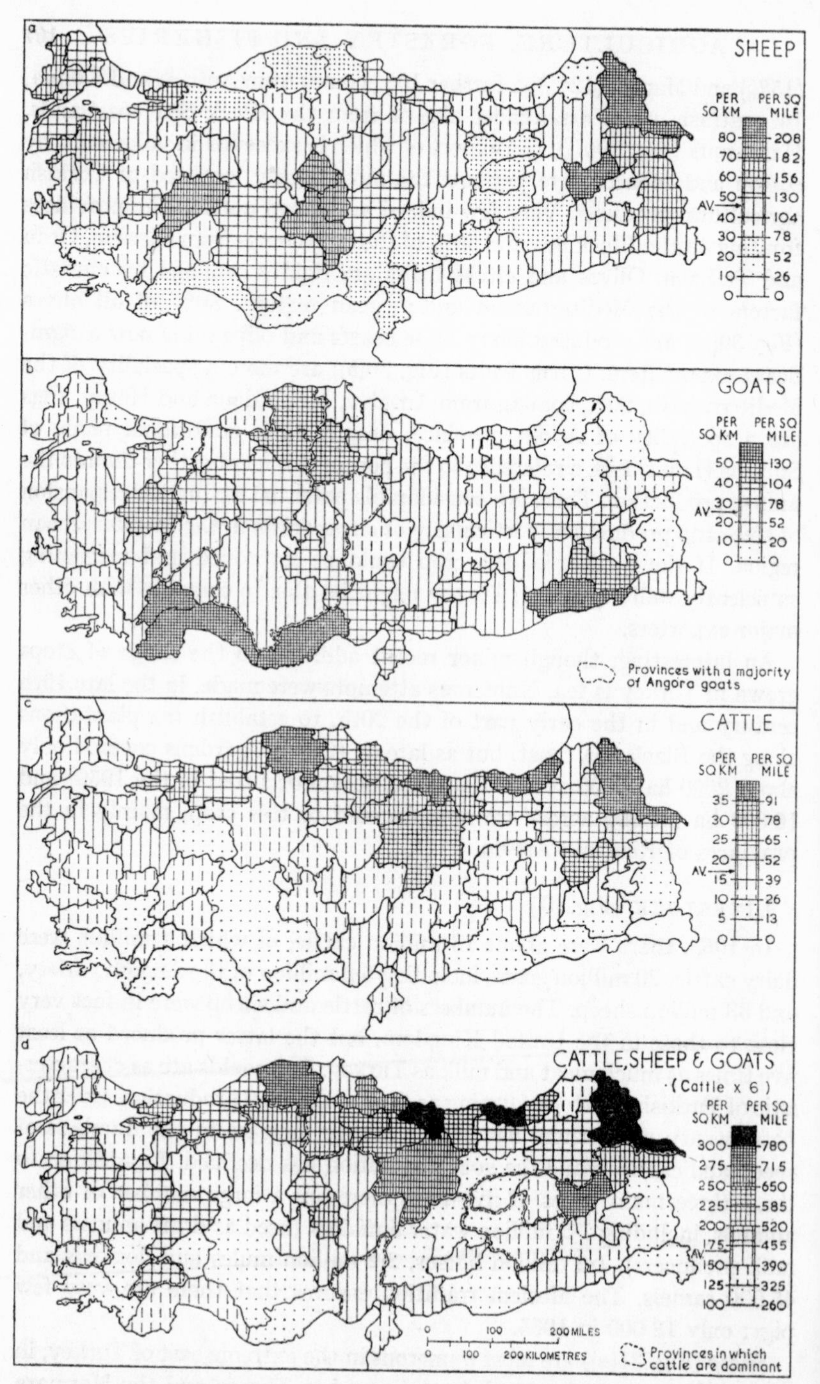

Fig. 31. Densities of (*a*) sheep, (*b*) goats, (*c*) cattle and (*d*) sheep, goats and cattle combined. In the preparation of map (*d*), one head of cattle has been counted as equivalent to six sheep or goats. The national average density is indicated on the key to each map

region. Along with goats, sheep are the main users of low-grade pastures in the semi-arid interior and in mountainous areas. They are multi-purpose animals, kept for their meat, milk and wool. These products are for the most part consumed within Turkey, but there is a small export of wool and skins.

Goats (Fig. 31(*b*)) outnumber sheep over much of the Mediterranean region, where the provinces of Antalya and İçel have particularly high densities. They are also numerous over much of the south-east and in central Anatolia. Goats make a considerable contribution to the meat and milk supply. Of special value is the Angora goat, found mainly in central Anatolia: mohair is a significant item in the export trade. Attempts have been made in recent years to discourage the raising of goats and their number is now on the decline. While these animals are the only livestock which can make use of the poorest and most steeply sloping pastures, they have also been instrumental in degrading large areas of forest by their uncontrolled grazing.

Cattle (Fig. 31(*c*)). Although cattle are found in significant numbers in all the provinces of Turkey, there is a marked concentration in the northern parts of the country, where natural pastures are more lush and fodder crops more widely grown. The rearing of cattle in preference to sheep or goats has been much encouraged by the Ministry of Agriculture in recent years and cattle provide an increasing proportion of the meat and milk supply. Over large areas, however, the quality of the animals is poor and yields are low. This is due largely to the traditional use of cattle as draft animals and the heavy reliance, particularly in the more remote and backward parts of the country, on poor natural pastures and fallow land. With increasing mechanisation, efforts have been made in many districts to improve the quality of cattle, but progress is slow: many are still used for draft purposes and fed on fallow or rough grazing.

An attempt has been made in Fig. 31(*d*)) to indicate the relative importance of livestock in the various provinces, using the rough yardstick that one head of cattle is equivalent to six sheep or goats. On this basis, the three central Anatolian regions have 38% of all livestock, the Black Sea and north-east 26%, the Marmara, Aegean and Mediterranean regions 24% and the south-east 12%. The highest livestock densities are recorded in the north and north-east. The provinces of Ordu and Kars, for example, have densities four or five times as great as those of Konya in the dry interior, İçel on the Mediterranean coast or Van and Hakkârı in the mountainous east.

A characteristic feature of Turkish agriculture is the lack of integration between arable and livestock farming. Even cattle receive only a limited part of their diet from fodder crops, and sheep and goats practically none. Grazing land and arable land are almost completely separate from each other, overlapping only where livestock are grazed on fallow, which in most districts provides very little sustenance. In earlier times the population of Turkey contained a large nomadic element, which with its flocks of sheep and goats wandered at will over much of the interior. During the past forty years, however, the nomads have been largely settled, in the sense that they now have permanent settlements, and the tented encampment is becoming a rarity. In any case, expansion of the cultivated area, particularly during the past two decades, has considerably reduced the available area of grazing land. In becoming settled, the former nomads have in many cases become cultivators as well as stock-rearers. However, it is still the general practice for the two functions to be kept separate in the village organisation. While the cultivator may also own livestock, the latter are usually tended by full-time herdsmen who have no land of their own and get their living by caring for the animals of the more prosperous farmers. While true nomadism had declined, transhumance remains a characteristic feature of Turkish livestock farming and regular movements between winter and summer pastures occurs in many parts of the country. In the east, this generally involves fairly short journeys between valley and mountain, but along the Mediterranean and, to a lesser extent, along the Black Sea coast, summer pastures are found not only in the Taurus and Pontic ranges but also around the edges of the central Anatolian plains. It is now common for people engaged in transhumance to have twin summer and winter villages many miles apart. Along the Mediterranean coast, for example, many villages are nearly deserted in the summer months when their inhabitants move, with their livestock, to basins in the surrounding mountains. There they not only pasture their animals but also grow cereals and other crops, living in villages, which in their turn, are deserted from autumn to spring.

The great majority of Turkish farms are now owner-occupied. More than 70% of all farming families work their own land and the majority of the remainder have some form of shared ownership. Farms are generally of modest size, 30% being less than 20 ha (50 acres), and a further 30% between 20 and 50 ha (50–125 acres). Only 6% of all farms exceed 200 ha (500 acres). In recent years, under the encouragement of various government agencies, there has been a considerable degree of co-operation both in the purchase and utilisation of mechanised equipment and in the sale of farm produce.

Agricultural Regions

In earlier sections of this chapter, regional contrasts have been illustrated by reference to the standard agricultural regions used for statistical purposes in official publications. Since agricultural data are collected on a provincial basis, they can only be assembled for groups of provinces; consequently the boundaries of these statistical regions must follow provincial boundaries. Fig. 32 divides Turkey into agricultural regions on the basis of farming practice and thus gives a more realistic picture of actual conditions in different parts of the country. The scheme of agricultural regions used here is a modified form of that suggested in 1952 by Erinç and Tunçdilek,* and involves the following units:

	Region		*Sub-region*
1	Interior Anatolia	A	Central Anatolia
		B	Kayseri–Niğde
		C	Malatya–Elâzığ
		D	Erzincan
		E	Northern transitional
		F	Lake District
		G	Afyonkarahisar
		H	North-western transitional
2	Eastern Anatolia	A	Kars–Erzurum
		B	Aras Valley
		C	Van–Tunceli
3	Black Sea	A	Rize
		B	Giresun–Ordu
		C	Samsun
		D	Kastamonu–Kocaeli
		E	Istranca
		F	Düzce–Adapazarı
4	Interior Thrace		
5	Marmara		
6	Aegean		
7	Mediterranean	A	Muğla–Mersin
		B	Seyhan–Ceyhan
		C	Hatay–Gaziantep
8	South-east		

* Erinç, S., and Tunçdilek, N., 'The Agricultural Regions of Turkey', *Geographical Review*, Vol. XLII, No. 2, 1952, pp. 179–203.

1. Interior Anatolia

This, by far the largest of the regions, consists of a central semi-arid core, around which are a number of marginal sub-regions, most of them distinguished by their more favourable climatic conditions. Central Anatolia (1A) is characterised by very low rainfall and by soils whose poverty is partly natural and partly the result of human misuse extending back to prehistoric times. Writing in 1952, Erinç and Tunçdilek could say that 'an average of only 10% is cultivated', but the figure is now nearer

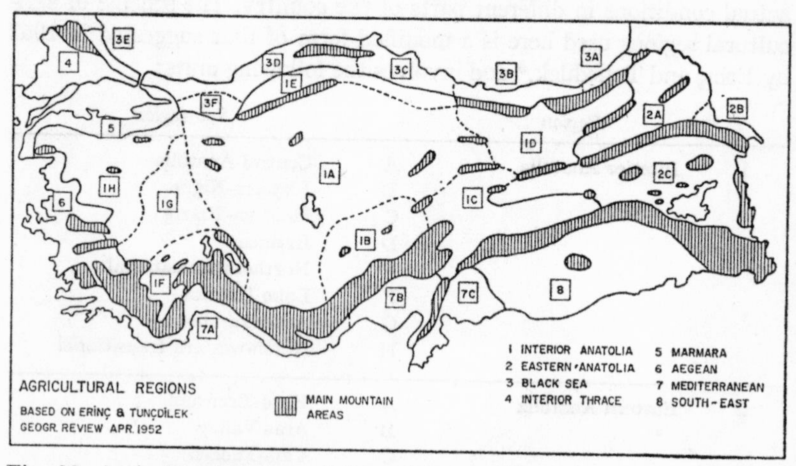

Fig. 32. Agricultural regions. Adapted from Erinç, S. and Tunçdilek, N., 'The Agricultural Regions of Turkey', *Geographical Review* (Vol. 42, 1952, p. 183), copyrighted by the American Geographical Society of New York

25% as a result of the expansion of the cultivated area carried out in the 1950s. The amount of land under cereals has more than doubled over large areas. Grain is dominant to a degree exceptional even for Turkey and in many districts wheat and barley are virtually the only crops grown. Rye and oats occur on a small scale and vines are present in the more favoured parts. Sugar beet is of increasing importance. This region is in many ways the agricultural heartland of Turkey, supplying, for example, some 50% of the country's wheat. However, the climate over much of the region is marginal for wheat production, cultivation is on an extensive basis and yields are low. Annual variations in total rainfall result in fluctuations in the volume of the harvest. In particularly good years enough grain is produced to provide Turkey with an exportable surplus. More commonly, production is only sufficient to supply local and national needs, and in poor years production falls below subsistence level and import is necessary. In areas where irrigation is carried on, as in the southern part of Konya province (see p. 193) a more consistent harvest is assured and the farmers are more prosperous. Over large parts of the region, however, living standards are low. Stock-rearing, particularly of sheep and Angora goats, is a major activity but this, too, can be adversely affected by drought.

In most of the bordering sub-regions, climatic conditions are more favourable for agriculture, though in some cases the relief factor limits the amount of land available for cultivation. In the Kayseri–Niğde sub-region (1B), volcanic soils from Erciyas and Hasan Dağı give more fertile soils and, although cereals remain dominant, yields are higher and fruit and vines are quite widely grown. The Malatya–Elâzığ sub-region (1C) with its very hot, dry summers, produces cotton, rice and tobacco from irrigated land. In contrast, the Erzincan sub-region (1D) is one where climatic conditions are even more severe than in central Anatolia and relief is much more accidented. Consequently the land available for crops is very limited, and vegetables, notably potatoes, are the only major product apart from grain. In the northern transitional zone (1E), the climate is appreciably warmer and less dry than in central Anatolia and the deep-set river valleys provide sheltered sites for cropland, though steep slopes limit its extent. In addition to wheat, which remains the dominant crop, this area produces maize, some rice, fruit, tobacco, hemp and sugar-beet. Westwards from central Anatolia are three regions transitional between the interior and the Aegean. The productivity of the Lake District (1F) is limited by its karstic topography, but in its sheltered, fertile basins fruit and vines are grown as well as cereals. In the Afyon sub-region (1G) poppy cultivation for opium is a local speciality and the grazing of sheep and goats is of more than average significance. Stock densities of sheep are among the highest in the country. The north-western transitional zone (1H) has considerable areas of maize, sugar-beet and tobacco.

2. Eastern Anatolia

In this region, altitude and relief are both adverse factors. There are three main landscape units: mountain ranges, high plateaus and deep-set valleys, but even the last are 1000–1500 m (3000–5000 feet) above sea level. Consequently, the climate is severe throughout the region and soil erosion from steep slopes is an additional hazard. Once again, cereals are dominant, but in some of the depressions, where erosion debris accumulates and where irrigation can be applied, there is a fairly wide range of crops. In the Kars–Erzurum sub-region (2A), cereals and vegetables are about the only crops which the climate allows. However, the soils on the high plateaux of this sub-region are often derived from basaltic rocks and support relatively rich pastures so that sheep and cattle are raised in large numbers. There is a large-scale movement of animals and animal products from this region to markets in other parts of Turkey. In the extreme east, the Aras Valley (2B) lies below 1000 m (3300 feet), and is in complete contrast to the rest of the region. The valley has a very low rainfall but is extensively irrigated and produces vines, rice, fruit and cotton. The Van–Tunceli sub-region is the poorest agricultural region of Turkey apart from the mountainous areas indicated on Fig. 32. Cropland is very limited in extent and stock-rearing is the dominant activity throughout most of the region. In depressions around Lake Van, however, where irrigation is practised, fruit and vegetables are grown as well as grain.

3. Black Sea Coastlands

This moist, warm region is among the most densely populated, and intensively cultivated parts of Turkey, despite the difficulties resulting from steep slopes and soil erosion. Maize is the most important crop throughout the region, which is subdivided according to the nature of the secondary products. The Rize sub-region (3A) is the wettest part. It contains practically all the country's tea plantations, citrus and other fruits are grown, but the most valuable crop is tobacco. In the Giresun–Ordu sub-region (3B), on the other hand, the most important commercial product is the hazel-nut and tobacco occurs only on a small scale. The Samsun sub-region (3C) is the driest part of the Black Sea coastlands. It is also an area of gentle relief and nearly 30% of the land is under crops. Wheat and barley are important, as well as maize, but the region is most famous for its tobacco which is considered to be of higher quality than that grown in the Aegean region. In the zone between Sinop and İstanbul (sub-region 3D), possibilities for cultivation are more restricted and few crops other than cereals are grown. The same applies to the area on the northern side of the Istranca ranges in Thrace (3E), where population densities are particularly low. The Düzce–Adapazarı sub-region (3F), however, has extensive lowlands with fertile soils and grows tobacco, fruit, vegetables, sunflower and sugar-beet as well as wheat, barley and maize.

4. Interior Thrace

This region bears similarities to interior Anatolia in terms of climate and natural vegetation, but the soils are generally more fertile, relief is gentle and, because of the lower altitude, the growing season is longer. In addition, rural population densities are much higher than in central Anatolia and the region has a greater proportion of cultivated land than any other part of Turkey. In the province of Tekirdağ, for example, 50% of the land is under crops. Winter temperatures restrict the crop range, however, and cereals, particularly wheat, oats and maize, are dominant, though to a lesser degree than in Anatolia. Sugar-beet and sunflower have become important in modern times and their use in rotation with cereals has greatly increased the productivity of the region. There is a long tradition of viticulture, but production has never fully recovered from the phylloxera epidemic of the 19th century. Rice is grown in the Meriç valley and hemp is important in Tekirdağ.

5. Marmara

The Marmara region is transitional in climate between the Black Sea and Aegean zones and temperature and rainfall vary greatly with exposure. There are a number of extensive lowlands and both rural population densities and the proportion of cultivated land are high. Agriculture has to some extent been stimulated by the needs of İstanbul and other urban markets. There is a wide variety of crops. Wheat, barley and maize occupy large areas, but tobacco, sunflower, vegetables, fruit and vines are all important and olives are grown in sheltered districts. Cattle and sheep are numerous and their quality is higher than in other parts of the country, largely because of the greater attention paid to fodder crops.

6. Aegean

Cereal crops are less important in the Aegean region than in any other. Field crops as a whole occupy only about 25% of the total area and only 40% of this is under cereals. Industrial crops occupy 25% of the sown area. Of particular importance are cotton, grown mainly in the Büyük Menderes valley, and to a lesser extent in the valley of the Gediz, and tobacco, which occurs widely on the lower hill slopes. The region accounts for about a quarter of the national production of these commodities. Tree crops are also of great importance. Some 60% of Turkey's olives are produced in the region and olive groves are particularly important in the north around Edremit and Ayvalık. Vines, often grown on hill-slope terraces, are widespread and the region is famous for its raisins and sultanas. Another local speciality is the fig. Over most of the area, however, winter temperatures are at times too low for successful cultivation of citrus fruits and these are found in only a few districts. All in all, agriculture in the Aegean region is more varied, more productive, more highly commercialised and export-oriented than in any other part of the country.

7. Mediterranean

This region falls into three parts. In the provinces of Muğla, Anatalya and much of İçel (sub-region 7A), the extent of cultivable land is limited by the presence of high mountain ranges and crops occupy only about 12% of the area of these three provinces. Farmland occurs in a series of disconnected basins and coastal plains of which the Antalya plain is by far the largest. Some of these are quite intensively cultivated but the general level of productivity is rather low and agricultural development has been slow, largely because of the area's isolation from the rest of the country. The areas devoted to, for example, citrus fruits or olives could be much increased. In contrast, the Seyhan–Ceyhan sub-region (7B), which is roughly coincident with the southern half of Adana province, contains wide alluvial plans and cultivation is continuous over large areas. This is a highly productive district, with relatively advanced farming methods and a high degree of mechanisation. Eastwards, beyond the Amanos ranges, the Hatay–Gaziantep sub-region (7C) is transitional between the true Mediterranean and the south-east.

In the western part of the Mediterranean region (sub-region 7A), cereals are dominant, but a wide variety of other crops is grown, including cotton, flax, sesame, vines, fruit, rice and even, around Alanya, bananas. The area is important for citrus fruits and produces about 60% of the small Turkish crop. The Seyhan–Ceyhan plains (7B), particularly the southern part, are unique in Turkey. A higher degree of mechanisation, modern crop rotations and heavy use of fertilisers are distinctive features. All the standard Mediterranean crops are grown, but the region is most noteworthy for its cotton, production of which has greatly increased in the post-war period. 30% of the sown area of Adana province is under cotton; the province contains 40% of Turkey's cotton land and contributes 30% of the crop. In Hatay and Gaziantep (sub-region 7C), citrus fruits are grown only on a small scale, but vines, olives and groundnuts are all widespread. The pistachio nut is a local speciality.

8. South-East

The south-eastern region consists mainly of a series of plateaux, dissected by the Euphrates and Tigris river systems. The climate is extreme, with very hot summers, frequent winter frosts and low annual rainfall. Where irrigation is possible, rice, vegetables, fruit and vines are grown in addition to the ubiquitous cereals, but the bulk of the cropland is under extensive, low-yielding grain production. Livestock, mainly sheep and goats are important throughout the region, though livestock densities are generally low.

Recent Trend and Developments

During the last twenty years, a number of important changes have occurred in Turkish agriculture, mainly as a response to rapid population growth. As we have already seen (p. 84) the post-war period has seen a demographic upsurge in Turkey which now has well over 800 000 new mouths to feed each year. To maintain these rapidly growing numbers, even at the rather low level of subsistence common to the bulk of the population, requires an equally rapid expansion of agricultural production. There were, in the late 1940s, two possible ways in which this could

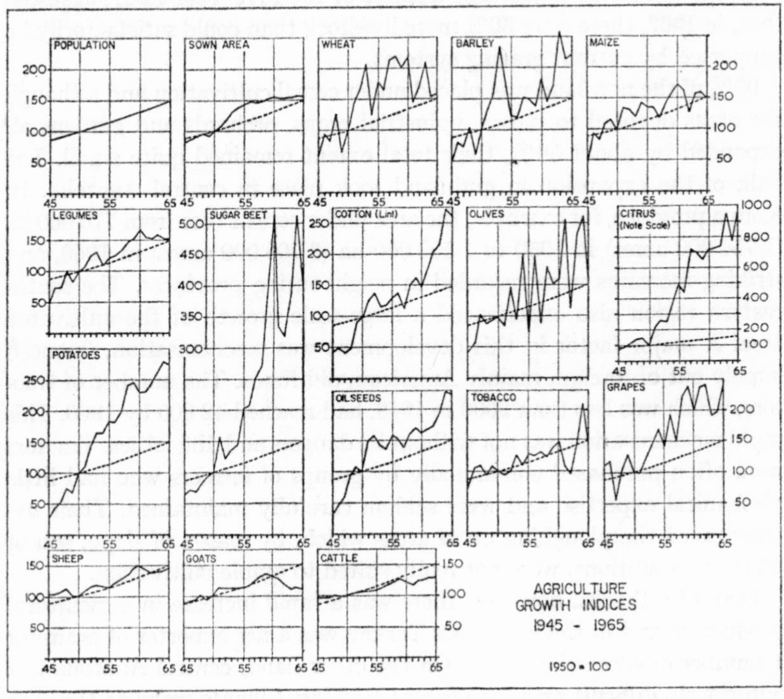

Fig. 33. Changes in population, sown area, crop production and livestock numbers, 1945–65. The curve of population growth is repeated on each of the other graphs

be achieved: by an increase in output from land already under cultivation or by an expansion in the size of the cultivated area. During the 1950s, while the first alternative—intensification—was undertaken on a limited scale in some areas, such as the Seyhan–Ceyhan plains, the main emphasis was on areal expansion as a means of obtaining additional food. The results can be seen in Fig. 33, which illustrates major changes in land use and agricultural production. Between 1950 and 1960, while the population rose by 32%, the amount of arable land and the sown area both increased by some 55%, and cereal production, though fluctuating from year to year, more than kept pace with population increase. An expansion of 8·8 million ha (21·7 million acres) in the size of the cultivated area was achieved and the amount of cropland *per capita* actually rose from 0·7 to 0·85 ha. This expansion was achieved entirely at the expense of grazing land, the area of which fell by 9·1 million ha (22·5 million acres) or 24% in the same decade. Since the numbers of livestock continued to increase, albeit somewhat slowly, the perennial problem of overgrazing on poor pastures was made worse. The authors of the Five-Year Plan suggested that, in 1962, there were 30% more livestock than could satisfactorily be supported by current grazing systems.

90% of the new land was placed under cereal cultivation and although the areas devoted to pulses, industrial crops, orchards and gardens all expanded by about 50%, their total extent remained quite small. The bulk of the expansion in grainland took place in central Anatolia. In Konya province, for example, the area under cereals rose from 710 000 ha (1 754 000 acres) in 1950 to 1 500 000 ha (3 700 000 acres) in 1960, and striking increases were recorded in neighbouring provinces. The south-eastern region also experienced a large-scale growth of the cultivated area. A major factor in this development was mechanisation, financed largely out of foreign, mainly American, aid funds. The number of tractors, which was less than 2000 in 1948, had reached 42 000 by 1960. This rapid mechanisation was not without its dangers and difficulties. Tractors were often purchased communally by groups of farmers who had little mechanical expertise and were seldom carefully maintained. Their use encouraged the ploughing up of areas which, by reason of slope, soil or drainage conditions, were not really suited to arable cultivation.

Despite setbacks, however, there was a rapid increase in agricultural production and in the late 1950s Turkey was a net exporter of grain for a number of successive years. On the other hand, central Anatolia is a notoriously difficult area for peasant farming. Climate restricts the crop range and imposes the dominance of wheat and barley, yet at the same time does not permit an assured harvest. Rainfall over much of the region is marginal for cereal growing, which must inevitably be on an extensive, low-yielding basis. Furthermore, total precipitation varies considerably from year to year with resultant fluctuations in the size of the grain harvest, as Fig. 33 demonstrates. The traditional farming system over much of Anatolia involves a simple alternation of grain and fallow with virtually no other crop of any importance, and this would appear to apply as much to the new land opened up in the 1950s as to that cultivated in earlier years. During the 1950s the proportion of the cropland which was under fallow in any particular year remained unchanged at 30–35%.

It is obvious that the process of opening up new land to support a growing population can only be a short-term remedy to population pressure and must, by its very nature, eventually cease. In the case of Turkey, this turning point seems to have been reached about 1960. Between 1960 and 1965, population increased by a further 13%, but the cultivated area remained much the same and by 1965 the amount of cultivated land *per capita* had returned almost to the 1950 level. In short, Turkey would appear to have exhausted the possibilities of agricultural expansion by the opening up of new lands and must in future concentrate her attention on the process of intensification, that is on increasing yields from land already in use. Given that cereals are likely to remain the basis of arable farming and a major element in the Turkish diet for a long time to come, together with the need to reduce to a minimum the expenditure of scarce foreign currency on grain imports, a major element in any programme of intensification must be an improvement in grain yields. After the short period in the late 1950s when Turkey was a net exporter of grain, she again became, in the early 1960s, a net importer. Between 1960 and 1965 grain imports exceeded exports by an average of 650 000 tons a year. It is somewhat difficult to be precise on the subject of any changes in grain yields which may have occurred in recent years, particularly in view of the violent fluctuations in total output. Official data suggest that, during the expansion of the 1950s, yields also increased by 10 or 20% probably because of initial high yields from newly cultivated land. Since 1960, however, they appear to have remained stationary at the low level of 1200 kg per ha (approx 9·6 cwt per acre). In Anatolia improvement on this performance will not be easy. One possibility is the replacement of fallow by a leguminous fodder crop which would, at one and the same time, help to maintain soil fertility and provide additional sustenance for livestock. As Fig. 33 shows, there was a marked increase in the production of legumes in the 1950s, but this also ceased after 1960 and the proportion of the sown land devoted to such crops has remained at the very low level of 3·6%. Experiments on a number of State Farms in Anatolia have shown that such a development is possible but great difficulty has been experienced in convincing the farmers of its desirability. Traditional farming systems paid little attention to fodder crops and many peasants are unwilling to accept that it is worth while expending effort on growing them. On the other hand, a great deal of success has been achieved in expanding the production of crops which, although not primarily grown as fodders, do provide a valuable source of animal food, simply because their cultivation gives an extra cash income to the farmer. A prime example is the case of sugar-beet, production of which is now four or five times the 1950 level so that, in several parts of the country, sugar-beet residues are a major item in animal diets.

Another means of increasing yields is by a greater use of fertilisers. Centuries of cultivation have greatly reduced the fertility of many Turkish soils which are now in urgent need of improvement. The traditional separation between livestock and arable farming, together with the widespread practice of using animal dung as fuel, has resulted in little or no application of organic matter to the arable land, while over large parts of the country artificial fertilisers have been virtually unknown or, where known, have been misapplied. Current development plans envisage a large-scale increase in the production and consumption of mineral fertilisers which must be accompanied by schemes to instruct the peasants in their correct use.

The process of intensification can also be discussed with respect to livestock farming which at the moment is under-developed in the sense that much higher production could be achieved from available resources. The number of animals is large but their quality is generally low, a situation due in part to the neglect of scientific breeding but mainly to poor feeding practice. Since 1950 the number of livestock has continued to increase, but during the 1960s this increase has slowed down and the number of goats has actually declined. In 1965 the number of livestock per head of the human population was in fact smaller than in 1950. This is not necessarily an adverse trend, provided that the quality of animals is improved so that each yields more meat, milk or wool. Indeed, the policy formulated in the first Five-Year Plan (1963–7) envisaged the stabilisation of livestock numbers, accompanied by improvements in breeding and feeding practices.

As part of a long-term policy for the improvement of agriculture, major alterations in the balance of land use are highly desirable and are suggested in the Five-Year Plan. Large areas of land now used for low-yielding cereal production should be taken out of cultivation and returned to grazing as yields from the better grainland are increased. At the same time, much of the present pastureland should be retired from grazing and turned over to forest. This would increase the availability of timber for domestic fuel, thus permitting the use of more animal dung as manure. On the reduced pasture area, the number of livestock should be rigidly controlled to prevent overgrazing and animals should be excluded from the forest reserves. It has even been suggested that the common goat, which in the past has been responsible for the despoliation of large areas of woodland, should eventually disappear.

Another aspect of the intensification of agriculture is the development of irrigation, which in Turkey takes two forms. State projects involve the construction of barrages and the provision of permanent canal systems, while in private projects, which are generally small, water is led to the fields by the farmer from a nearby spring, stream or well. The latter type is by far the more widespread and, although accurate data are not available, it was estimated in 1965 to cover more than 1·1 million ha (2·7 million acres) out of a total irrigated area of 1·3 million ha (3·2 million acres) leaving less than 200 000 ha (500 000 acres) irrigated by state projects. Only 4·3% of the cultivated area was irrigated in 1965. The area to which irrigation could be satisfactorily applied is put at 5 million ha (12·4 million acres), nearly four times the present total. The distribution of areas irrigated by the State Water Authority (*Devlet Su İşleri*) is shown in Fig. 34 and details of the more important schemes are given in Table XII.

TABLE XII

MAJOR STATE IRRIGATION SCHEMES, 1965

Area	*No. of works*	*Land irrigated** *Hectares*	%
Konya (south)	2	31 102	19·3
Seyhan plan	2	30 923	19·2
Büyük Menderes	2	21 348	13·2
Gediz	3	17 022	10·6
Aras	1	15 600	9·7
Malatya basin	3	7 137	4·4
Antalya plain	4	6 726	4·2
Others	31	31 344	19·2
Total	48	161 202	100·0

* Figures indicate the actual area to which water was supplied in 1965.

The majority of these schemes occur either in areas where the total annual precipitation is very small, as in the southern part of central Anatolia, the Aras valley and the Malatya basin, or where there is very marked summer drought, as in the Gediz and Büyük Menderes valleys and the basins of Antalya and Adana.

On irrigated land as a whole, the most important crop is cotton, which occupies 22% of such land, followed by wheat (18%), fruits (17%) and vegetables (16%). Small areas of maize, rice and fodder crops are also grown under irrigation. The mention of wheat as a major element in irrigated farming again draws our attention to the vast moisture-deficit areas of central Anatolia. The large irrigation schemes in Konya province are devoted mainly to wheat and it has been found that, in areas of this sort, irrigation can raise yields by 75–100%. While this is a smaller increment than that achieved by the irrigation of fruit, vegetables, fodders and industrial crops, it nevertheless indicates that irrigation of dry-farmed grainlands would do much to increase and stabilise the volume of cereal production. Unfortunately, large parts of the region are far removed from

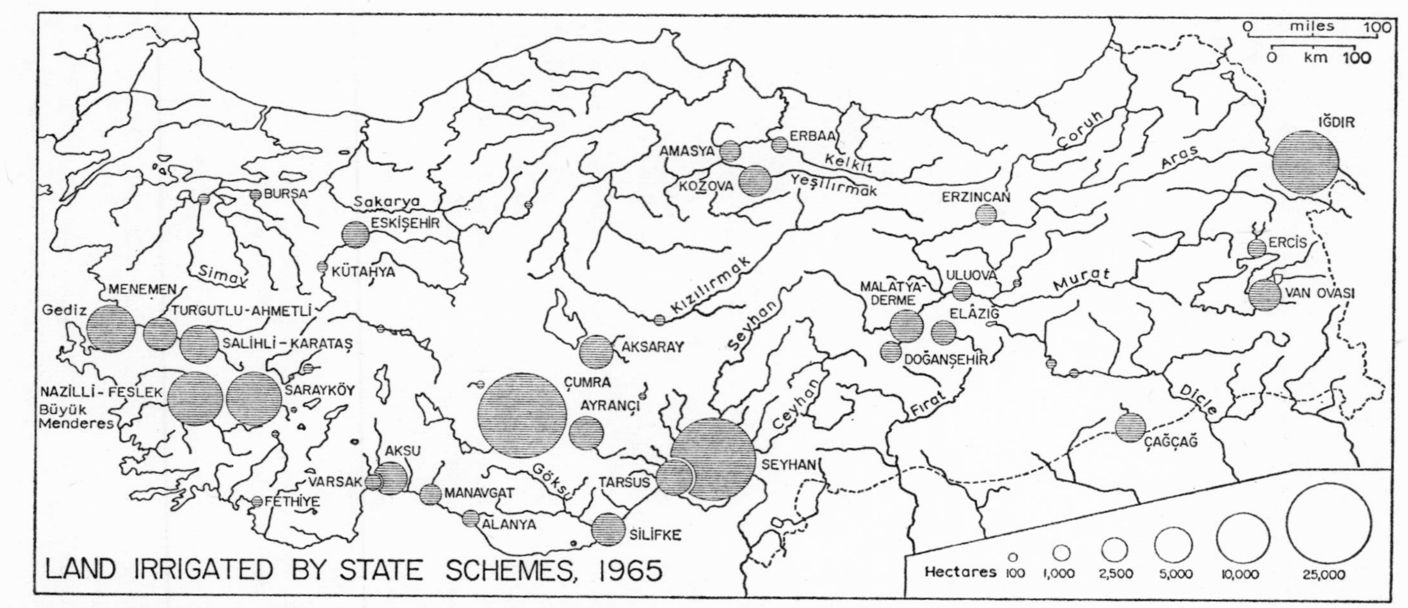

Fig. 34. State irrigation schemes, 1965. The size of the circles is proportional to the area of land actually supplied with irrigation water in 1965

easily exploited sources of water. As Fig. 34 shows, the irrigation schemes now in operation lie along the southern edge of the Konya basin, where rivers descend from the Taurus. Plans are now in hand to extend the irrigated area northwards, but these will involve expenditure on a much larger scale than before.

Great attention has been paid to irrigation during the period of the first Five-Year Plan (1963–7) which aimed at increasing the irrigated area by some 500 000 ha (1 235 000 acres). 50% of all investment in agriculture was to be devoted to this purpose. Preliminary data suggest that this ambitious target has not in fact been achieved, though considerable progress has been made.

Conclusion

In conclusion, we may note the following as the main objectives of Turkish agricultural policy:

(*a*) Expansion of the cultivated area is to be discouraged and the poorer parts of the land now under crops are to be turned over to grazing.

(*b*) The total grazing area and the numbers of livestock are to be stabilised at approximately their present level and some of the poorer land now used for grazing is to be placed under forest.

(*c*) Intensification of production from existing arable land and livestock is to be the prime method of increasing agricultural output.

(*d*) Crop yields are to be raised by the use of better rotations, particularly grain/fodder rotations in place of the traditional grain/fallow system, by increased irrigation and by heavier application of animal and chemical fertilisers.

(*e*) The output of livestock products is to be increased by the use of improved methods of breeding and feeding and by better veterinary services.

(*f*) Organisational reforms are to include the consolidation of fragmented holdings, the break-up and redistribution of the remaining large estates, the establishment of more producers co-operatives among the farmers and the provision of better credit and marketing facilities.

(*g*) While grain, meat, milk and vegetables are to be produced mainly for the internal market, agriculture will continue to make a major contribution to the export trade, supplying skins, hides, wool, mohair, cotton, tobacco, olive oil, hazel-nuts, grapes, figs and citrus fruits.

Provided a steady development along these lines takes place, there is no reason why Turkey should not support her growing population at a rising standard of living. Her agricultural resources, if properly utilised, are sufficient to enable her to avoid the problems of overpopulation which afflict some of her less fortunate Middle Eastern neighbours.

Forestry

13·6% of the land surface of Turkey, a total area of 10·6 million ha (26 million acres), is classed as forest, but of this nominal area, little more than one-third (3·8 million ha/9·4 million acres) is described by the State Forestry Directorate (*Devlet Orman Müdürlüğü*) as 'productive'; the remaining 6·8 million ha (16·8 million acres) are 'degraded'. As Fig. 35 shows, forest land is found mainly in mountainous districts, particularly those of the Black Sea, Aegean and Mediterranean regions, and is virtually absent from much of central, eastern and south-eastern Anatolia. Coniferous and hardwood forests occur in roughly equal proportions, with the former dominant in the southern half of the country and the latter in the northern.

As already indicated, the area of good forest has much declined in modern times as a result of uncontrolled cutting for fuel and building materials and the indiscriminate grazing of livestock. Over large areas these processes have completely removed the forest cover or reduced it to low scrub causing, among other things, accelerated soil erosion. Despite strenuous efforts by the authorities to prevent these abuses, they continue, albeit on a reduced scale. As a result, although Turkish consumption of timber products is small by the standards of more highly developed countries, the demand can no longer be met from internal resources and there is a sizeable importation of timber, pulp, paper and associated products.

Commercial lumbering activities, which employ fewer than 20 000 workers, are almost entirely confined to the north-western part of the country, where a number of state-owned sawmills have been set up, mainly in Bolu and Zonguldak provinces. A good deal of timber goes as pit props to the Zonguldak coal-mines, while pulp mills, relying in part on imported timber, have been established along the Marmara coast at İzmit, Gemlik and Bandırma. A speciality of the Aegean region is the Valonia oak, grown mainly on the hills to the north of the Gediz. This tree is a valuable source of tannin, and valonia extract is a minor export.

There is ample scope for the extension and improvement of the forests of Turkey as part of a general programme for the rationalisation of land use. Current government policies in this field involve the conservation of the remaining areas of good forest, the establishment of new productive forests, particularly around towns, where demand is heavy and supplies non-existent, and the restoration of degraded areas. In forestry, as in other forms of land use, careful development could make the country self-sufficient.

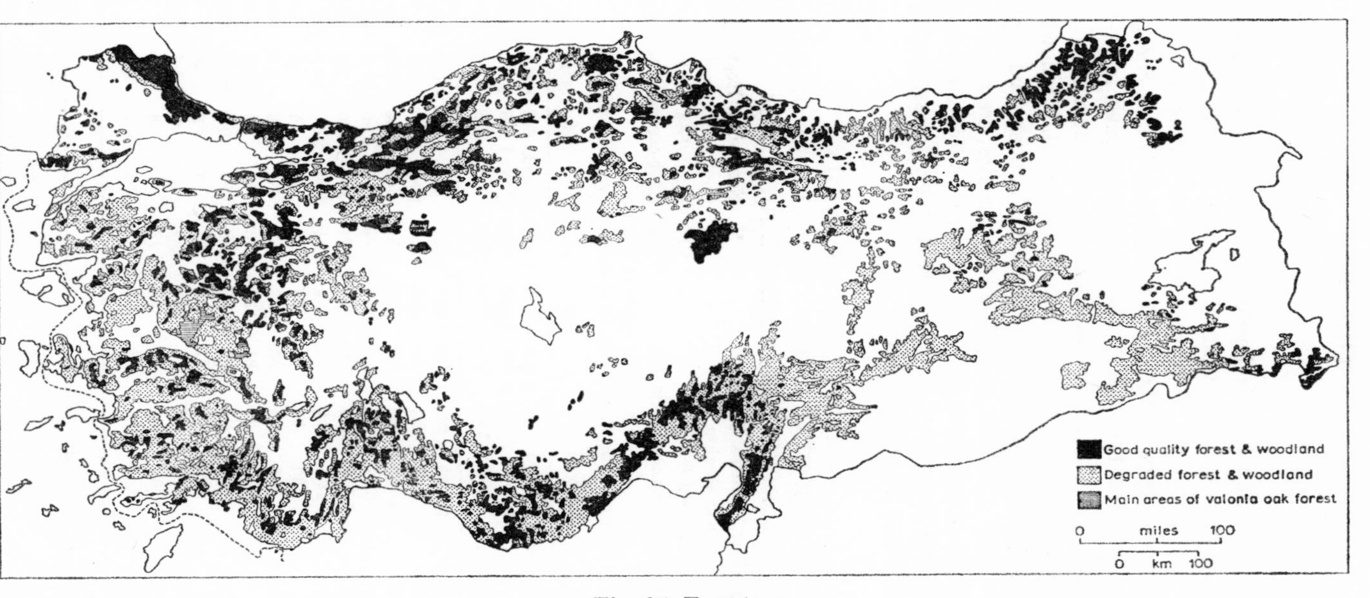

Fig. 35. Forests

Fisheries

The fishing industry is little developed and employs only about 10 000 people. Boats are small and venture no great distance from the shore. Landings fluctuate greatly from year to year: in 1967 they totalled 194 000 tons. About two-thirds of the catch is landed at Black Sea ports, primarily at Ordu, and the bulk of the remainder comes in at Marmara ports, mainly İstanbul. The most important species are anchovies, landed mainly at Ordu, and tunny and mackerel at İstanbul. It follows that fish make only a very minor contribution to the Turkish food supply and, apart from small quantities of fresh-water varieties, are not eaten at all over large parts of the country. While there are possibilities for expansion, these are rather limited and fisheries are unlikely to assume any major significance in the Turkish economy.

STATISTICAL APPENDIX

DATA FOR NINE STANDARD REGIONS OF THE MINISTRY OF AGRICULTURE, 1965

I North-central Region
II Aegean Region
III Marmara Region
IV Mediterranean Region
V North-east Region
VI South-east Region
VII Black Sea Region
VIII East-central Region
IX South-central Region

For the boundaries of these regions, see Fig. 27

Land use	TURKEY	I	II	III	IV	V	VI	VII	VIII	IX
Total area (000 ha)	78 142	11 899	9 938	4 426	8 157	7 408	11 340	6 894	8 068	9 970
Sown area (000 ha)	15 294	2 915	1 737	1 339	1 693	636	1 335	1 171	1 330	3 136
% of total area	19·6	24·5	17·5	30·3	20·8	8·6	11·8	17·0	16·5	31·5
Cereals (000 ha)	12 960	2 686	1 170	1 045	1 077	591	1 228	1 014	1 196	2 953
% of sown area	84·7	92·1	67·4	78·0	63·6	92·9	92·0	86·6	90·0	94·2
Wheat (000 ha)	7 900	1 889	566	547	684	350	894	363	816	1 790
% of sown area	51·7	64·8	32·6	40·9	40·4	55·0	67·0	31·0	68·2	57·1
Barley (000 ha)	2 770	559	320	126	238	164	280	150	294	640
% of sown area	18·1	19·2	18·4	9·4	14·1	25·8	21·0	12·8	22·1	20·4
Rye (000 ha)	730	69	75	64	29	45	7	32	46	362
% of sown area	4·8	2·4	4·3	4·8	1·7	7·1	0·5	2·7	3·5	11·5
Maize (000 ha)	650	40	81	134	13	17	9	337	14	5
% of sown area	4·3	1·4	4·7	10·0	0·8	2·7	0·7	28·8	1·1	0·2
Oats (000 ha)	400	49	71	112	55	n	n	20	9	84
% of sown area	2·6	1·6	4·1	8·4	3·2	n	n	1·7	0·7	2·7
Rice (000 ha)	50	9	3	10	12	1	6	8	1	0
% of sown area	0·3	0·3	0·2	0·7	0·7	0·2	0·4	0·6	n	0
Pulses (000 ha)	552	102	101	28	67	14	70	48	57	65
% of sown area	3·6	3·5	4·8	2·0	4·0	2·2	5·2	4·1	4·3	2·1

Land use	TURKEY	I	II	III	IV	V	VI	VII	VIII	IX
Industrial crops (000 ha)	1 582	99	423	233	419	28	21	105	69	84
% of sown area	10·3	3·4	24·4	17·4	30·7	4·4	1·6	9·0	5·2	2·7
Tobacco (000 ha)	222	7	142	13	3	n	1	42	13	n
% of sown area	1·5	0·2	8·2	1·0	0·2	n	0·1	3·6	1·0	n
Potatoes (000 ha)	145	33	12	14	7	10	1	31	7	29
% of sown area	1·0	1·1	0·7	1·1	0·4	1·6	0·1	2·7	0·5	0·9
Sugar beet (000 ha)	158	33	11	26	6	10	1	12	27	31
% of sown area	1·0	1·1	0·6	1·9	0·4	1·6	0·1	1·0	2·0	2·0
Sunflower (000 ha)	160	3	15	133	n	n	n	4	n	4
% of sown area	1·1	0·1	0·9	10·0	n	n	n	0·3	n	0·1
Cotton (000 ha)	685	3	193	6	455	5	10	0	13	n
% of sown area	4·5	0·1	11·1	0·5	26·9	0·8	0·7	0	1·0	n

Livestock	TURKEY	I	II	III	IV	V	VI	VII	VIII	IX
Sheep (000)	33 382	5 037	3 853	2 193	1 722	4 092	5 127	2 127	3 069	6 076
%	100·0	15·1	11·5	6·6	5·2	12·3	15·4	6·6	9·2	18·2
Goats	15 305	1 234	2 571	770	3 346	740	2 660	780	2 154	1 048
%	100·0	8·1	16·8	5·0	21·9	4·8	17·4	5·1	14·1	6·8
Angora goats (000)	5 500	2 928	37	n	1	n	519	636	33	1 346
%	100·0	53·2	0·7	n	n	n	9·4	11·6	0·6	24·5
Cattle	13 203	1 815	1 262	714	957	2 060	1 308	2 289	1 712	1 086
%	100·0	13·7	9·6	5·4	7·2	15·6	9·9	17·3	13·0	8·2
Buffalo (000)	1 216	207	88	160	39	122	120	268	142	69
%	100·0	17·0	7·2	13·2	3·2	10·0	9·9	22·0	11·7	5·7
Horses (000)	1 199	199	209	94	108	90	86	117	95	200
%	100·0	16·6	17·4	7·8	9·0	7·5	7·2	9·8	7·9	16·7
Mules (000)	225	33	29	7	31	6	39	43	25	13
%	100·0	14·7	12·9	3·1	13·8	2·7	17·3	19·1	11·1	5·8
Donkeys (000)	1 971	391	402	83	198	42	172	122	227	334
%	100·0	19·8	20·4	4·2	10·0	2·1	8·7	6·2	11·5	16·9
Camels (000)	46	1	13	1	23	n	6	0	1	1
%	100·0	2·2	28·3	2·2	50·0	n	13·0	0	2·2	2·2

Production	TURKEY	I	II	III	IV	V	VI	VII	VIII	IX
Cereals (000 tons)	14 670	3 020	1 493	1 411	1 332	596	1 101	1 232	1 247	3 237
%	100·0	20·6	10·2	9·6	9·1	4·1	7·5	8·4	8·5	22·1
Wheat (000 tons)	8 500	2 038	685	759	821	331	748	405	801	1 913
%	100·0	24·0	8·1	8·9	9·7	3·9	8·8	4·8	9·4	22·5
Barley (000 tons)	3 300	675	441	192	278	183	281	171	348	731
%	100·0	20·5	13·4	5·8	8·4	5·5	8·5	5·2	10·5	22·2
Rye (000 tons)	775	73	78	66	29	42	6	29	46	406
%	100·0	9·4	10·1	8·5	3·7	5·4	0·8	3·7	5·9	52·4
Oats (000 tons)	540	58	93	147	101	n	n	23	12	105
%	100·0	10·7	17·2	27·2	18·7	n	n	4·3	2·2	19·4
Maize (000 tons)	945	65	129	165	28	26	12	492	22	8
%	100·0	6·9	13·7	17·5	3·0	2·8	1·3	52·1	2·3	8·5
Rice (000 tons)	130	29	8	24	35	1	14	17	2	0
%	100·0	22·3	6·2	18·5	26·9	0·8	10·8	13·1	1·5	0

Production	TURKEY	I	II	III	IV	V	VI	VII	VIII	IX
Pulses (000 tons)	589	104	105	29	82	14	66	45	70	75
%	100·0	17·7	17·8	4·9	13·9	2·4	11·2	7·6	11·9	12·7
Tobacco (000 tons)	123	2	84	9	2	n	2	15	8	n
%	100·0	1·6	68·3	7·3	1·6	n	1·6	12·2	6·5	n
Potatoes (000 tons)	1 680	3·7	170	175	76	139	15	254	75	458
%	100·0	18·9	10·1	10·4	4·5	8·3	0·9	15·1	4·4	27·3
Sugar-beet (000 tons)	3 421	733	214	495	99	193	16	265	781	626
%	100·0	21·4	6·2	14·5	2·9	5·6	0·5	7·7	22·8	18·3
Cotton lint (000 tons)	325	1	118	4	196	1	3	0	3	n
%	100·0	0·3	36·3	1·2	61·3	0·3	0·9	0	0·9	n
Cotton seed (000 tons)	527	1	191	6	318	2	4	0	5	n
%	100·0	0·2	36·2	1·1	60·3	0·4	0·8	0	0·9	n
Sunflower	160	4	20	127	n	n	n	4	n	5
%	100·0	2·5	12·5	79·4	n	n	n	2·5	n	3·1
Grapes (000 tons)	3 350	322	801	255	800	9	416	17	250	480
%	100·0	9·6	23·9	7·6	23·9	0·3	12·4	0·5	7·5	14·3
Citrus fruits (000 tons)	425	0	30	n	390	n	n	5	0	0
%	100·0	0	7·1	n	91·8	n	n	1·2	0	0
Other fruits (000 tons)	1 206	140	293	113	90	52	26	154	113	224
%	100·0	11·6	24·3	9·4	7·5	4·3	2·2	12·8	9·4	18·6
Hazel-nuts (000 tons)	62	4	n	4	n	n	n	53	n	n
%	100·0	6·5	n	6·5	n	n	n	85·5	n	n
Other nuts (000 tons)	109	12	16	13	19	3	11	17	12	6
%	100·0	11·0	14·7	11·9	17·4	2·8	10·1	15·6	11·0	5·5
Olives (000 tons)	394	0	252	81	58	1	2	n	0	0
%	100·0	0	63·9	20·6	14·7	0·3	0·5	n	0	0

Chapter 7

INDUSTRY

Fuel and Power

TABLE XIII

PRODUCTION OF FUEL AND POWER

	1950	1969
Hard coal (000 metric tons)	4360	7721
Lignite (000 metric tons)	1212	8538
Oil (000 metric tons)	18	3624
Electricity (000,000 kWh)	790	7830
(of which, hydro-electricity)	(35)	(3192)

Apart from Iran, where production is small and scattered, Turkey is the only Middle Eastern country with significant coal reserves and a scale of output sufficient to supply all its needs. The main field, and the only one worked at present, lies between Ereğli and Zonguldak on the Black Sea coast, where the seams occur in rocks of Carboniferous age and include some valuable coking types. This field was first worked more than a century ago, but as recently as 1940, when ownership was transferred from foreign companies to the Turkish state, annual output was little more than 1 million tons. In 1969 pit-head production exceeded 7 million tons of which 4·6 million tons were classed as 'saleable'. Reserves are estimated at more than 1000 million tons, so that present output could be maintained for well over 100 years. The bulk of the coal produced is consumed by the railways, the metallurgical industry and in electricity generation. Domestic consumption remains very small, largely because of the high transport costs involved in moving coal over land to other parts of the country. The field is well placed for shipment by sea so that coal is used as a domestic fuel in İstanbul and at other Marmara and Black Sea ports, but only coal for industrial use is moved any distance by land. Lignite occurs very widely in Turkey and is produced on a small scale from many scattered locations. The most valuable deposits are in Thrace and in Kütahya province. The latter are worked on a large scale at Tunçbilek and are consumed mainly in the generation of electric power.

While Turkey is relatively fortunate as regards supplies of solid fuel, she is not among the oil-rich countries of the Middle East. Over the past twenty years intensive prospecting has been carried on and numerous strikes have been made, mainly in the south-east of the country, but the majority of these have not been considered an economic proposition. The only field from which significant production has been maintained is that in the Ramandağ district of Siirt province, which was discovered in 1940. Output remained extremely small until the 1950s, since when it has been expanded to about 3·6 million tons a year. There is a refinery at Batman, close to the wells, but its capacity has been outstripped by rising production and about two-thirds of the Ramandağ oil travels by pipeline to İskenderun, whence it is shipped to a much larger refinery at Mersin. The latter also refines a large proportion of the crude oil imported into Turkey from other Middle Eastern countries. A third refinery has recently been completed at İzmit on the Marmara coast and a fourth is to be built at İzmir. Turkey's present consumption of petroleum products is in the region of 6 million tons a year and it is probable that this level of demand, at least, could be met from internal sources, which at the moment supply only about one-half of the required amount. The main problem is the way in which reserves are widely scattered in small fields in remote areas. Development costs and transport costs make it cheaper to import.

The production of electricity, though much increased in recent decades, is still very low. The output of 7830 million kWh in 1969 represented a supply of only 235 kWh *per capita*, about one-twentieth of that available in industrial western Europe. As recently as 1950, only a few large towns had public electricity supplies. Today, supplies are available in all the provincial capitals and in four or five hundred smaller settlements but reach only minute fraction of the country's 35 000 villages. Grid systems exist in north-western Anatolia and in the Aegean region, but elsewhere single power stations supply a town and its immediate neighbourhood. The establishment of an integrated system of power stations and transmission lines (Fig. 36) covering the whole country has a high priority in current development plans. During the past fifteen years ten major generating stations have been built as well as a large number of smaller ones. Thermal plant are most common in the west and north-west, the largest being those at İstanbul, Anbarlı and the lignite-fired station at Tunçbilek. In addition, a large oil-fired plant at Mersin came into operation in 1965. Expansion of thermal-generating capacity will continue, supported largely by a growing output of lignite and low-grade bituminous coal, but attention is to be concentrated particularly on the building of new hydro-electric plant. Turkey has a large hydro-electric potential, which has been estimated at 53 million kWh per annum of which little more than 2% has so far been developed. Considerable progress has already been made: whereas in 1950 hydro-electric plant accounted for only 4·5% of the electricity supply, by 1969 the proportion

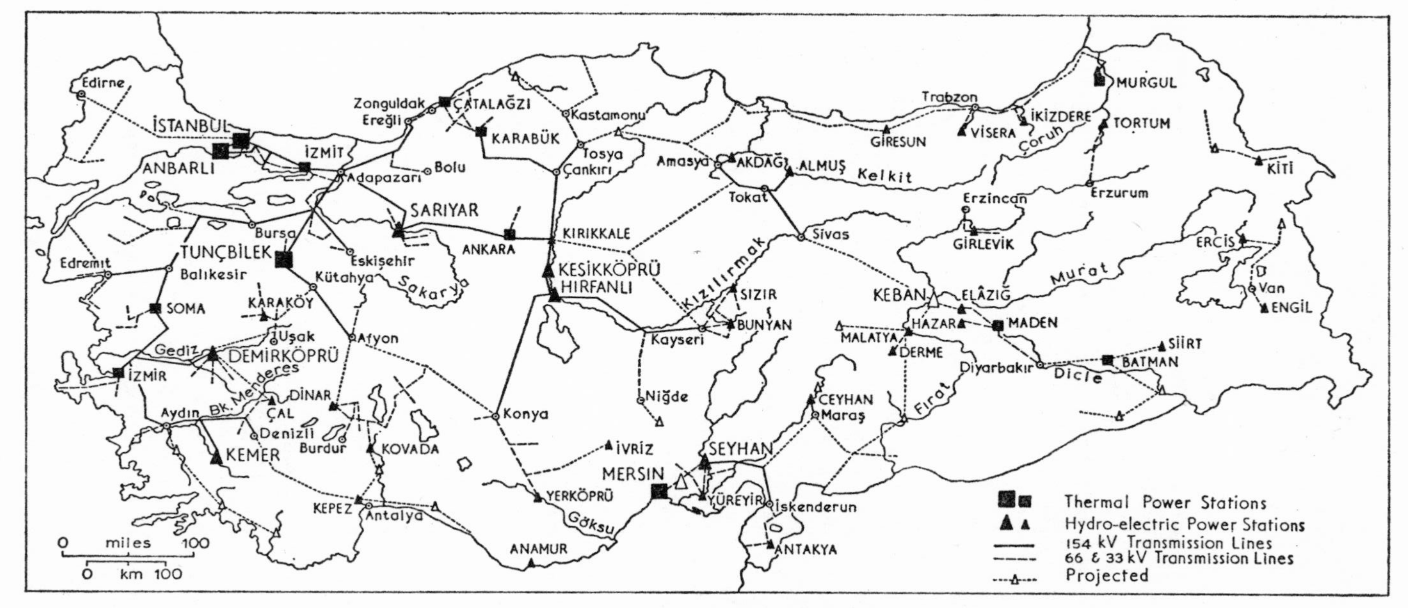

Fig. 36. Electricity generating stations and transmission lines

had risen to 44% and the amount of power generated had multiplied by 90. More than a score of small hydro-electric stations were built as well as five large ones, at Demirköprü and Kemer on tributaries of the Büyük Menderes, at Sarıyar on the Sakarya, at Kesikköprü and Hirfanli on the Kızılırmak and on the Seyhan near Adana. The largest single plant now under construction is at Keban, on the Fırat river in Elâzığ province. The Keban dam, with its planned capacity of nearly a million kilowatts, will, when opened in 1972, generate almost as much electricity in a year as is at present available from all sources. It is hoped that the widespread distribution of electricity will have fundamental effects on the economic development of the whole country. In particular it should make possible the establishment of light industries in rural areas which hitherto, owing to the lack of power, have relied almost entirely on agriculture, thus assisting such areas to achieve higher living standards. In addition, it will reduce the dependence of large parts of the country on wood and animal dung as fuel. At present, these materials account for 22 and 18% respectively of all fuel and power consumed in Turkey, compared with 28% obtained from coal and lignite, 29% from petroleum products and only 3% from hydro-electricity. Very heavy capital investment is, of course, involved in these plans. In 1967, for example, 12% of all state investment was in the electricity supply industry, a proportion second only to that devoted to transport.

Minerals (Fig. 37)

TABLE XIV

PRODUCTION OF MAJOR NON-FUEL MINERALS

	(000 metric tons)	
	1950	*1969*
Iron ore	234	2478
Chrome ore	422	682
Manganese ore	33	14
Copper (smelter production)	12	20

Turkey's iron ore resources are adequate to support the present needs of her steel industry and production has risen steadily over the past two decades. Iron-ore deposits are widely scattered, but the great bulk of the output comes from the magnetite source at Divriği, in the east of Sivas province. This is a high-grade ore with a 60–65% metal content but reserves are only sufficient to support present production for another two or three decades. The fact that a rail journey of more than 900 km (550 miles) separates the Divriği iron from the coal-mines and steelworks of Zonguldak province adds considerably to the cost of steel production. A possible alternative source of iron ore is the large but lower grade deposit around Edremit, on the Aegean coast. The chemical composition of this ore has in the past prevented its use in steel-making.

Chrome ore is Turkey's most valuable metallic mineral and production, though subject to annual fluctuations, has shown a general upward trend in the post-war period. The largest single producing centre is at Güleman, in Elâzığ province, but this is showing signs of exhaustion and its output is now exceeded by the total production from a number of smaller mines in the Fethiye district. Turkey is among the world's leading producers of chrome ore and practically the whole output is exported, much of it to

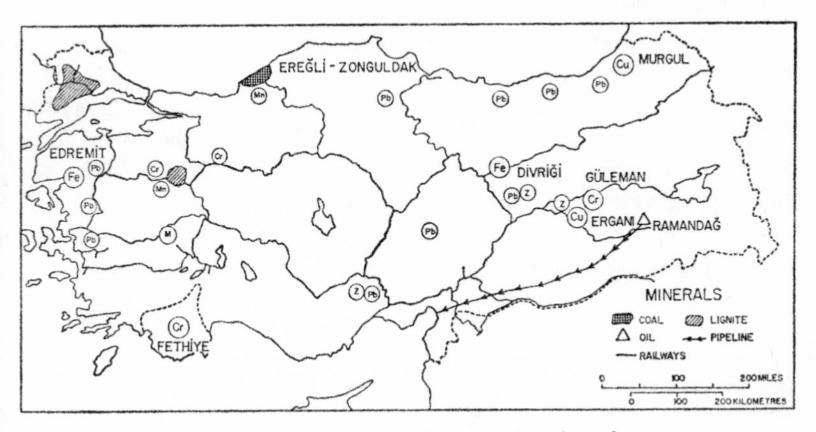

Fig. 37. Main sources of economic minerals

the United States. The volume of exports, and thus of total production, has varied a good deal from year to year. This is primarily because production costs are high and, in years when the world market price is low, the demand for Turkish chrome ore diminishes. This problem in fact applies to mineral production in general. Turkey has a considerable variety of valuable minerals, but many of them occur in small pockets, often in remote areas, so that transport and production costs are high and it is only economic to exploit them when world prices are at a high level.

In addition to chrome, Turkey is also a significant producer of copper, which is mined near Ergani in Diyarbakır province and at Murgul in the far north-east. Smelters have been established at both these places and the bulk of the metal is exported. Other minerals are of relatively minor significance. Manganese is mined near Devrek in Zonguldak province and near Kütahya. Lead-zinc ores are widespread in mountain areas and the production of zinc has risen sharply in recent years. One major source is near Keban and this may become an important centre for non-ferrous metallurgy when the hydro-electric plant is completed. Molybdenum, tungsten, bauxite, mercury and various mineral salts are all produced in modest quantities.

On balance, Turkey is reasonably well supplied with minerals, given her limited industrial development, and a few major items make a limited contribution to her export trade. In 1969 ores and metals made up about 3% of all exports by value. Whether there are sufficient reserves to support really large-scale industrialisation is, however, uncertain.

Manufacturing Industry

As has already been pointed out, in Chapter 5 (p. 90) manufacturing employs less than 8% of the Turkish labour force, despite considerable expansion over the past ten years, and manufactures amount to less than 18% of the gross national product. The distribution of the labour force among the various types of manufacturing industry is indicated by the following figures:

TABLE XV

EMPLOYMENT IN MANUFACTURING INDUSTRY

	Males		*Females*		*Total*	
	000	%	*000*	%	*000*	%
Textiles and clothing	255	28·8	36	46·8	291	30·3
Metallurgy and engineering	219	24·8	3	3·9	222	23·1
Food, drink and tobacco	139	15·7	24	31·2	163	17·0
Wood products	104	11·8	1	1·3	105	10·9
Paper and printing	23	2·6	2	2·6	25	2·6
Chemicals	29	3·3	3	3·9	32	3·3
Others	115	13·0	8	10·4	123	12·8
Total	884	100·0	77	100·0	961	100·0

As a basic element in her industrialisation plans, Turkey has recently devoted a great deal of capital investment to the expansion of her iron and steel industry, the output of which has risen from around 200 000 tons per annum in the late 1950s to over a million tons in 1969. Current plans envisage further expansion to 2·5 million tons in the late 1970s which should make the country independent of foreign sources of steel. The oldest iron and steel plan in operation is that established in 1940 at Karabük, in the Yenice valley (Fig. 38) about 100 km (60 miles) by rail south-east from Zonguldak. The site, which was reputedly selected for strategic reasons, has little to recommend it since Zonguldak coal, as well as Divriği iron must be brought to it. Nevertheless, in the late 1950s, additional installations were built at Karabük, raising its productive capacity to nearly 400 000 tons a year. A second, much smaller steel-works, producing mainly high quality, alloy steels, was opened in 1957 at Kırıkkale, 70 km (45 miles) east of Ankara. As a result of this new development, the population of Kırıkkale rose from 3000 in 1955 to 58 000 in 1965. The largest development of the 1960s has been the construction of a new, fully integrated steel works at Ereğli on the Black Sea coast west of Zonguldak. This plant, which came into production in 1965, is designed for a final capacity of more than a million tons. The more realistic location of the Ereğli plant will enable it to produce more cheaply

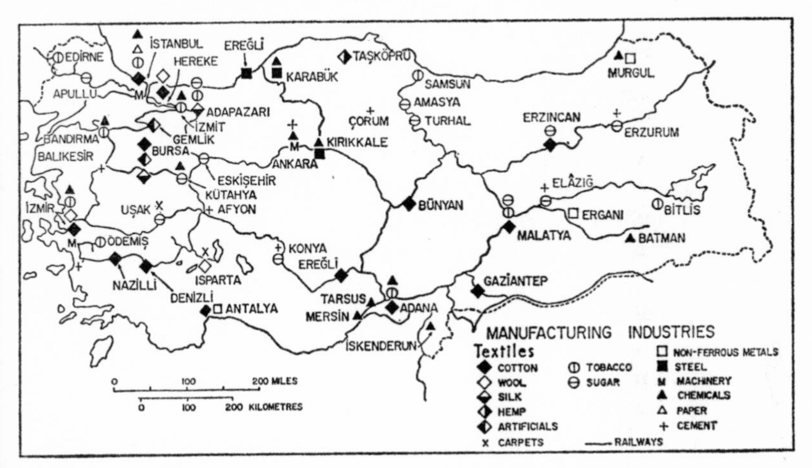

Fig. 38. Main centres of manufacturing industry

than Karabük and its coastal site will facilitate the movement of its products to other parts of the country. Work is now in progress on the construction of a further large steel plant at İskenderun, in Hatay. This, too, is designed for a productive capacity of 1 million tons and should be in operation by 1972.

In terms of employment, the most important branch of manufacturing industry is the production of textiles. In 1965 this activity engaged 120 000 workers, 20% of them women, and a further 170 000, mainly men, were employed in the manufacture of clothing. In addition to domestic spinning and weaving, carried on in the villages, there are now numerous textile mills of which roughly half are owned by the state and half by private concerns. The most important material is cotton and the output of cotton cloth has risen from 100 million metres in 1950 to nearly 600 million in 1968. Expansion of the cotton textile industry is an obvious choice as a major element in the industrialisation programme, and follows naturally on the agricultural expansion of the 1950s. All the raw material is now obtainable from within the country's boundaries. Furthermore, the development of electricity generation permits the dispersal of the cotton textile industry to areas where other forms of manufacturing are absent and where it provides welcome additional employment. The results of these factors can be seen in the present distribution of cotton mills (Fig. 38). Although the majority, particularly of those owned by private companies, are to be found in the main cotton-growing districts, such as the Adana plain and the Büyük Menderes valley, others have been established in districts where cotton-growing takes place, if at all, on a small scale only, as at Ereğli (Konya), Bünyan (near Kayseri), Erzincan and Malatya. A number of mills also exist near large urban markets as at İstanbul, İzmir and Hereke. Woollen cloth is produced on a very much smaller scale, total output amounting to only 25 million metres in 1968, and factory manufacture is confined to western Anatolia. Silk is a traditional speciality of Bursa, hemp is processed at Taşköprü in Kastamonu province and carpets, some of which are exported, are made at a number of centres in the western part of the country. The development of a synthetic fibres industry, is now in its early stages. Plant have been built at Bursa and at Gemlik on the Marmara coast, and another is under construction at Adana.

The alimentary industries forms a third major element in the industrial structure, employing about one-sixth of all manufacturing workers. Two of the most important branches are those processing tobacco and sugar beet. The former are mainly in tobacco growing areas and are often close to export facilities, but the state monopoly which controls this industry has set up a few plant in more remote districts, such as the cigarette factory at Bitlis. Owing to the bulky nature of the raw material, sugar-beet processing plant are all found close to areas in which the crop is grown. During the 1950s there was a definite government policy aimed at increasing sugar-beet production in the main cereal-growing districts. Processing plant were built in the areas considered most suitable for the production of the crop and high prices were offered to encourage the farmers to grow it. As a result of this policy, the area under sugar-beet was rapidly expanded and the output of sugar grew by leaps and bounds. Thus Turkey was transformed from a net importer of sugar to a country producing a surplus for export. Exports, have, however, run into difficulties owing to the fact that, largely because of the high prices paid to farmers, the cost of Turkish sugar has risen well above the world market price. Thus export involved a financial loss which had to be covered by government subsidy. Consequently in the past few years there has been a cut-back in production to the level required to satisfy internal demand.

A number of other alimentary industries not shown on Fig. 38 are of some local importance. Fruit and vegetable canning and the extraction of olive oil are carried on mainly in the Aegean region. The manufacture of beer, wine and spirits, a state monopoly, takes place in Ankara and other Anatolian towns as well as along the Aegean coast. The larger urban centres have modern flour mills but a large amount of milling is carried on in small, generally primitive, village establishments.

The chemical industry is very small and strenuous efforts are being made to develop it. Particular attention is being paid to the production of chemical fertilisers as a means of raising crop yields and consumption has increased tenfold over the past decade. 40% of all fertilisers are still imported, but it is hoped to reduce the proportion to 15% within the next five years. At the moment, the most important works are the phosphate plants at İskenderun and İzmit and the nitrate plant at Kütahya.

The situation in the chemical industry is representative of that in a large number of other manufacturing activities, particularly in various branches of engineering and in the production of consumer goods of all kinds. Demand for manufactured goods is small, but production is even smaller and there is a heavy reliance on imports. In the face of increasing demand and in order to achieve a more favourable balance of payments, the Turkish government has done much to encourage the investment of capital, both domestic and foreign, in the development of manufacturing industry. Thus, for example, in the past few years agreements have been made with British Leyland, Fiat, Volvo and Volkswagen for the establishment of vehicle manufacture or assembly plan in Turkey and similar developments have occurred in such diverse items as tyres, cement, plastics, glass, radio equipment and a variety of consumer goods. It is significant that the great majority of these new plant have been established along the western seaboard, particularly around the Sea of Marmara from İstanbul to Bursa, and in the İzmir district. With the important exceptions of the Black Sea coal–steel complex, the textile and chemical industries of the Adana–Hatay region and the mixed manufactures of Ankara, industry has had little impact on the remainder of the country, where mining and cotton textiles remain virtually the only sources of non-agricultural employment.

It is highly desirable that industrial development should continue along the lines established in recent years. The expansion of the agricultural processing industries can encourage increased agricultural productivity and rising exports, while the development of manufacturing will reduce imports. At the same time a broadening of the distribution of industry is also necessary if living standards are to be raised in the more remote parts of the country.

Chapter 8

COMMUNICATIONS, TRANSPORT AND TRADE

Throughout history, the development of communications in Asia Minor has been vitally affected by the facts of physical geography. Predominant among the difficulties presented by the region's physique has been that of movement between the interior and the coastal fringes, particularly those along the Black Sea and the Mediterranean. At the same time, the narrow and discontinuous nature of the coastal lowlands makes coastwise movement by land a problem, and to this day the sea remains the most satisfactory means of transport, at least for bulky goods. However, the shortest overland routes between Europe and the Middle East lie across central Anatolia, and trade along these routes has been a persistent feature. Passes through the bordering mountain ranges, of which the Cilician gates in the south-east and the Sakarya valley in the north-west are the best examples, have therefore been major lines of movement since early times. A further significant influence has been the continuing function of Constantinople–Byzantium–İstanbul as one of the old world's major trading centres at the focus of land and sea routes from many directions.

In addition to these general considerations, the topography of individual regions has important local effects on the development of routes. In the Aegean region, strongly accidental relief with a pronounced west–east trend provides a number of relatively easy lines of entry into the interior but north–south movement, except perhaps along the very irregular coastline, is difficult. In central Anatolia, on the other hand, there are few topographic barriers to movement but the more favourable soil and moisture conditions around the edges of the region have led to concentration of population and settlement so that traditional trade routes ran along the northern and southern edges rather than across the centre. The Pontic and Taurus mountain ranges, as already mentioned, are formidable barriers to any form of transport. The Pontic ranges are broken in the centre by the difficult Kızılırmak and Çekerek–Yeşilırmak valleys which provide access to the interior but in the Taurus there is no easy passageway and the Cilician Gates were used for want of anything better. In the Pontic mountains, movement parallel to the coast is possible along longitudinal valleys like those of the Çoruh and Kelkit but there is no equivalent in the Taurus. South-eastern Turkey, where plateau relief predominates, is part of the so-called 'fertile crescent' of the Middle East and has long been a zone of movement between Mesopotamia and the Levant. Finally, in eastern Anatolia, north–south movement is again very difficult and the east–west routes provided by the grain of the country encounter high passes before they reach the Iranian frontier. These routes have been of some significance for traffic westwards from Turkestan and Transcaucasia but they have never been as important as those which reach the Black Sea via the Kolkhida plain, now on the Soviet side of the boundary. All these factors are of great historical interest but have also had a pronounced effect on the form of modern transport networks.

Railways (Fig. 39)

The development of the Turkish railway system, like the more recent establishment of a road network, has been a major factor in the modernisation of the Turkish economy. Until the advent of roads it could accurately be said that only areas close to a railway line or port had any chance of being drawn into the commercial economy and of supplying their products to more than a very localised market.

The earliest railway developments took place in the last two decades of the 19th century and were largely under the aegis of foreign companies. The first line to be built within the present territory of Turkey was that from Edirne to Constantinople, which was opened to traffic in 1888. This linked the Ottoman capital with Vienna and thus with the rest of Europe, and was in fact controlled by an Austrian company. About the same time concessions were granted to British firms for the construction of lines from İzmir up the Gediz and Büyük Menderes valleys to Eğridir and Afyon respectively (the latter was eventually bought by a French company). Progress was rather slow, but by the turn of the century these lines were carrying large quantities of export produce to İzmir. By reaching Afyon, the Gediz line provided access from the Aegean coast to the Anatolian Railway. The latter, which ran from Haydarpaşa (in Scutari or Üsküdar) on the east side of the Bosphorus, via Eskişehir to Konya, was undertaken by the Ottoman government, but financial difficulties resulted in control passing first to a British and later to a German company. Significantly, Ankara was on a branch line off what was then considered the main route. These lines to Ankara and Konya marked the limits of 19th-century penetration into the interior. The only other railways were the short line from Adana to the port of Mersin, opened in 1886 by an Anglo-French company, and the line from the Caucasus to Kars and Sarıkamış, Russian-built in what was then Russian territory.

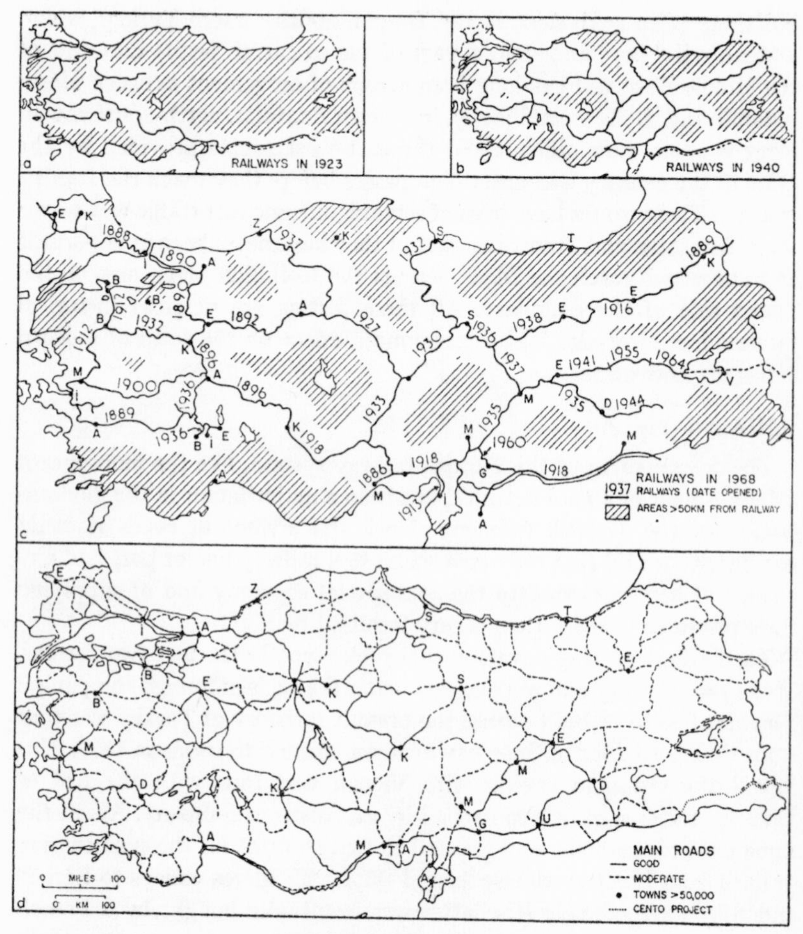

Fig. 39. Communications

In the years immediately preceding the First World War, German influence was paramount and Germany's desire to control an overland route to the Persian Gulf, rivalling the British-controlled sea route through Suez resulted in the promotion of schemes for a Berlin–Baghdad railway. Various routes were discussed, the final choice falling on one running through Konya, Adana, Aleppo, Nusaybin and Mosul. Construction began in 1906, but the line as a whole was not open to traffic until 1918. A branch to the Mediterranean at Alexandretta (İskenderun) was completed in 1913.

Thus, at its inception in 1923, the Turkish Republic possessed one major international route running diagonally across its territory from north-west to south-east with branches to Mersin, Ankara, İzmir and Bandırma (Fig. 39(*a*)). Between 1923 and 1939, most of the system was nationalised and the state railway company, T.C.D.D. (*Turkiye Cumhuriyeti Devlet Demiryolları*) undertook a fairly vigorous expansion programme (Fig. 39(*b*)). The İstanbul–Ankara line was extended eastwards through Kayseri, Sivas and Erzincan to Erzurum, where it joined the narrow-gauge railway built by the Russians from Sarıkamış to Erzurum in 1916, and an offshoot of the Berlin–Baghdad railway was carried through Malatya and Elâzığ to Diyarkbakır. These two west–east routes were linked by lines from Kayseri to Ulukışla and from Çetinkaya to Malatya. Two further lines were built from the Anatolian interior to the Black Sea coast, one running from Sivas through Amasya to Samsun, the other from Irmak (50 km/30 miles east of Ankara) through Karabük to Zonguldak. Links between western Anatolia and the Marmara and Aegean coasts were strengthened by lines from Kütahya to Balıkesir, joining the 1912 İzmır–Bandırma line, and from Afyon to Karakuyu on the İzmir–Eğridir route. The latter was provided with branches to Burdur and Isparta.

The economic difficulties of the Second World War years prevented the realisation of several major projects, notably the construction of lines from Burdur to Antalya and from Diyarbakır down the Tigris to Mosul. However, a certain amount of building continued. The Elâzığ–Diyarbakır line was extended to its present terminus at Kurtalan, on the Ramandağ oilfield, in 1944, and the line eastwards along the Murat valley from Elâzığ had reached Genç, south of Bingöl, by 1947. This line was extended to Muş by 1955 and now forms part of a broader scheme designed to provide a rail link between the CENTO countries. The Turkish section reached Tatvan, on the western shore of Lake Van, in 1964. From this point ferries will carry trains across the lake to Van itself, whence a line is now being built through difficult mountain territory to the Iranian railhead at Sharafkhaneh on Lake Urmia. This project is scheduled for completion by 1970 and, if the major construction needed in Iran does take place, it will eventually be possible to travel by rail from western Europe to India. Apart from this scheme, post-war developments have been restricted to the improvement of the existing system. These have included the replacement of the narrow-gauge Sarıkamış–Erzurum section by standard-gauge track and the construction of a line through Gaziantep to cut off the detour into Syrian territory via Aleppo. Work is also in progress on the double-tracking and realignment of the main trunk-line between İstanbul and Ankara.

The great attention paid by the Turkish authorities over the past forty years to railway construction reflects the dominant position of the railway in the internal transport system. Turkey now has a fairly well integrated but very open railway network and large areas, particularly along the Black Sea and Mediterranean coasts, lack access to rail transport. With the recent rapid development of road building it is unlikely that new railway lines will be built in the future. Attention will be concentrated on the more efficient operation of existing lines and the construction of roads to act as feeders to them.

Railways remain, by a large margin, the most important means of freight movement, particularly of bulky items. Of all freight carried by rail, coal, coke and lignite account for about 30%, other minerals for more than 20% and agricultural produce for most of the remainder, with livestock, cereals and sugar-beet as the main commodities. At 83 million, the number of passenger journeys per year is very small in relation to the size of the population, and three-quarters of these are on suburban lines, mainly around İstanbul. There appears to have been a decline in the volume of rail traffic over the past ten years and this can only mean that there has been a large increase in road traffic, though precise data on the latter are not available. With the exception of a few special passenger trains between Ankara, İzmir and İstanbul, railway travel in Turkey is slow. This stems largely from the nature of the equipment: most locomotives are still coal-fired, the majority of main lines are single-track and signalling systems are old-fashioned. Another disadvantage is the roundabout nature of some of the routes which is due to their piecemeal development. Railways now make a considerable financial loss and require thorough modernisation if they are to compete successfully with other transport.

Road Transport

The development of road transport in Turkey is still in its very early stages, despite rapid expansion during the last twenty years. In the inter-war period, investment in transport was concentrated on railway construction and roads were neglected, but since the war there has been a large road-building programme designed to link the main towns by modern highways (Fig. 39(*d*)). A fairly complete road network now exists, but only a few really major routes have a permanent hard surface. However, the majority of main roads, although unsurfaced, are well engineered and travel along them is infinitely better than was the case ten or fifteen years ago. The climate presents serious difficulties, particularly during winter, and spring washouts are common, but major routes are regularly repaired and maintained. Away from the roads indicated in Fig. 39(*d*)), movement other than by lorry or Land-Rover is virtually impossible and many villages are served only by animal-drawn transport.

Although the number of motor vehicles in use has increased fourfold over the past fifteen years, it still remains at the extremely low level of only 188 000 (1965). This includes 87 000 motor-cars, of which 34 000 are taxis, 22 000 buses and 79 000 lorries. Private cars thus number only about one to every 560 inhabitants. Lorries are used mainly over short distances between rural areas and market centres, but they may travel further where railways are lacking and are beginning to operate along routes where railways once had a monopoly. A widespread system of motor-bus services has been established by private operators: these now link many villages with urban centres and the latter with each other, and have come to rival the railways in long-distance passenger movement.

Air Transport

The Turkish State Airline, T.H.Y. (*Türk Hava Yolları*) now operates internal services between the larger towns and in 1969 carried 740 000 passengers and 50 000 tons of freight. In addition, T.H.Y. serves a number of European capitals and about a dozen foreign airlines have flights to Turkey, nearly all of them to either İstanbul or Ankara.

Sea Transport (Fig. 40)

Maritime transport includes not only foreign trade but also coastwise movement of both goods and passengers on a large scale. The latter is most significant along the Black Sea coast, where some twenty-five ports are involved, of which only the more heavily used are shown in Fig. 40. Coal and steel from Zonguldak and Ereğli, tobacco from Samsun, and a variety of agricultural products, including live cattle, from more easterly ports are shipped mainly to İstanbul for internal redistribution and for export. Manufactured goods of all kinds travel in the opposite direction. In addition there is a sizeable movement of passengers by this route which is the most efficient means of contact between the capital and the Black Sea coastlands. Coastwise movement along the Aegean and Mediterranean is on a smaller scale and there are fewer ports, of which İzmir, Antalya, Mersin and İskenderun handle most of the traffic, though there are numerous small harbours, particularly on the Aegean, which handle limited amounts of freight and passengers.

International maritime trade, which is rather smaller in volume than coastwise movement, is concentrated into a small number of ports. İstanbul handles about one-third of the shipping (2·3 million tons) and congestion has, in recent years, led to a greater use of other Marmara ports, notably İzmit (1·2 million tons). Other major centres of foreign trade are İzmir (1·2 million tons), Mersin 1·4 million tons and İskenderun (0·9 million tons). Smaller ports on the Aegean, such as Bodrum and

Kuşadası, each of which handles about 150 000 tons of shipping a year, trade mainly with Greece. Other ports have very little in the way of foreign trade. As Table XVI indicates, practically the whole of Turkey's foreign trade is carried on by sea, less than 2% (by value) moving across the land frontiers. İstanbul and other Marmara ports handle nearly half

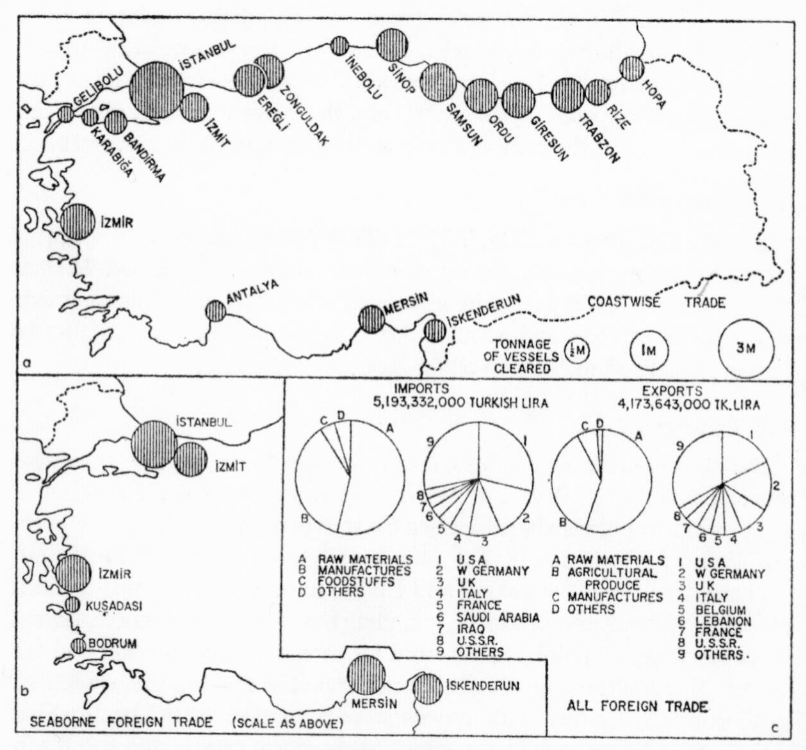

Fig. 40. Maritime trade, 1965. (*a*) Tonnage of shipping engaged in coastwise traffic cleared from each port; (*b*) tonnage of shipping engaged in foreign trade cleared from each port; (*c*) direction and commodity structure, by value, of all foreign trade

the traffic, including two-thirds of the imports but only about one-sixth of the exports. Aegean and Mediterranean ports take only one-fifth of the imports but supply nearly two-thirds of the exports. Ports along the Black Sea are of only minor significance in foreign trade.

The commodity structure of foreign trade has already been discussed in the introduction to this section. Dominant on the import side are raw materials (48%) and manufactured goods (43%), while exports consist mainly of foodstuffs (36%) and agricultural raw materials (51%).

TABLE XVI

FOREIGN TRADE (VALUE BASIS) BY ROUTE

	Imports (%)	*Exports* (%)	*Total* (%)
Istanbul and Marmara	69·4	17·0	46·1
Aegean	8·1	39·2	22·0
Mediterranean	13·3	27·0	19·4
Black Sea	5·2	12·6	8·5
Total maritime	96·0	95·8	96·0
Overland	0·1	4·0	1·6
Unallocated	3·9	0·2	2·4

Turkey's main trading partner is now the United States (Fig. 40(*c*)), which has forced West Germany into second, and the United Kingdom into third place. These three supply more than half the country's imports and take about 45% of her exports. Trade with the countries of the Middle East, except in the case of oil, is on a very small scale indeed.

Part Four

REGIONAL GEOGRAPHY

INTRODUCTION

The division of any country into regions for the purpose of geographical study presents a multitude of problems, and no such division can ever be wholly satisfactory. In the case of Turkey, we have already noted the existence of at least two sets of officially accepted regions: the standard statistical regions used particularly in recent censuses, and the regions used by the Ministry of Agriculture in the publication of agricultural data. In the present author's opinion, neither of these 'official' schemes is very satisfactory and a different one has been devised for use in the concluding

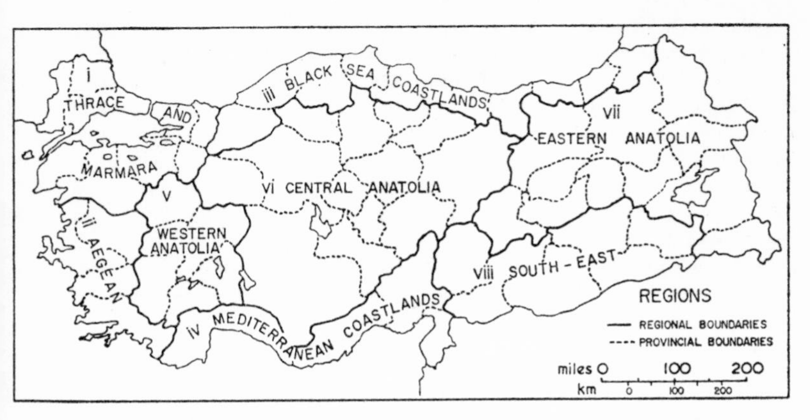

Fig. 41. The geographical regions used in Chapters 9–16

chapters of this book. All three schemes, do, of course, have strong similarities, particularly in separating the Anatolian interior from the periphery and in distinguishing between the very different fringing areas, but there are numerous differences of detail. Ideally perhaps, a regional division should have been made without reference to administrative boundaries but, because practically all the available statistical data are published by provinces, regions have been devised which group provinces together and no single province is divided between regions. Although in a few cases this results in somewhat anomalous regional boundaries, it is felt that this deficiency is more than offset by the resultant advantages, which permit the compilation of regional data of the sort displayed in Table XVII.

The scheme adopted in this text involves the division of Turkey into the following eight regions, the boundaries of which are indicated in Fig. 41.

I	Thrace and Marmara Region	V	Western Anatolia
II	Aegean Region	VI	Central Anatolia
III	Black Sea Region	VII	Eastern Anatolia
IV	Mediterranean Region	VIII	South-eastern Region

A number of important characteristics of each region are given in Table XVII.

TABLE XVII

BASIC DATA FOR EIGHT GEOGRAPHICAL REGIONS

	TURKEY	I	II	III	IV	V	VI	VII	VIII
Area (000 km²)	774·8	72·7	47·1	77·2	59·2	59·1	210·5	158·1	90·3
Area (% of total)	100·0	9·3	6·1	10·0	7·6	7·6	27·2	20·4	11·7
Population (000)	31 391	5 835	2 843	4 567	2 407	2 015	7 141	3 784	2 806
Population (% of total)	100·0	18·6	9·1	14·5	7·7	6·4	22·7	12·1	8·9
Population density/km²	40·5	80·3	60·4	59·2	40·7	34·1	33·9	23·9	31·1
Urban population (%)	34·4	51·8	39·1	19·5	39·3	26·7	35·8	22·7	31·3
Rural population (%)	65·6	48·2	60·9	80·5	60·7	73·3	64·2	77·3	68·7
Rural pop. density/km²	26·6	38·7	36·7	47·6	24·7	25·0	21·8	18·5	21·3
Sown area (000 ha)	15 555	1 932	894	1 225	1 414	1 148	5 923	1 326	1 693
Sown area (% of area)	19·6	26·5	19·0	15·6	23·9	19·4	28·1	8·4	18·7
Sown area (% of total)	100·0	12·4	5·7	7·9	9·1	7·4	38·1	8·5	10·9
Sown area (ha) per head of the rural population	0·76	0·68	0·51	0·33	0·97	0·78	1·29	0·45	0·76

Chapter 9

THE THRACE AND MARMARA REGION

This region (Fig. 42) covers a total area of some 73 000 square km (28 000 square miles) and consists of two rather distinct sections. These are European Turkey or Turkish Thrace (Trakya), and a number of provinces along the southern and eastern shores of the Sea of Marmara. The latter is some 75 km (48 miles) across at its widest part, but narrows at either end to channels less than 2 km (1·2 miles) in width which join it to the Mediterranean and Black Seas. The Dardanelles (Tk. Çannakale Boğazı) and Bosphorus (Tk. Boğaziçi) traditionally separate Europe from Asia and are ancient river channels drowned by an incursion of the sea. Straddling the Bosphorus, is İstanbul, Turkey's largest city, and the region as a whole derives much of its unity from the way in which its life tends to focus on Marmara and the Straits and in particular on İstanbul.

Relief throughout most of the region is quite gentle and the land relatively low lying. Less than one-third of the area is more than 1500 m (5000 feet) above sea level and there are extensive lowlands. Turkish Thrace terminates on its western side at the Meriç (Maritsa) river, which rises in Bulgaria and winds slowly to the sea through a broad floodplain, the lower parts of which are ill-drained and swampy. The main tributary of the Meriç is the Ergene which flows from east to west across the centre of Thrace, and the Ergene basin makes up the greater part of the district. This broad, terraced lowland, with its extensive Neogene deposits and alluvia is separated from the Sea of Marmara by the low upswelling of the Tekirdağ hills and from the Black Sea by the Istranca ranges. The latter extend eastwards to the outskirts of İstanbul and are continued, in the form of a low dissected plateau, to the lower Sakarya, beyond which the same trend-line is continued in the westernmost Pontic ranges. These hills along the Black Sea coast are one of a series of west–east trend-lines which impart a considerable variety of relief to the area immediately east of the Sea of Marmara. These trend-lines give rise in turn to the Gulf of İzmit–Lake Sapanca depression, the Samanlı range and the Gulf of Gemlik–Lake Iznik trough. Cutting northwards across this succession of ridges and basins, the Sakarya river runs in a series of gorges which carry the main road and railway from İzmit inland to Eskişehir, thus providing a major line of access to the interior of Turkey.

In the provinces of Bursa, Balıkesir and Çannakkale, the east–west

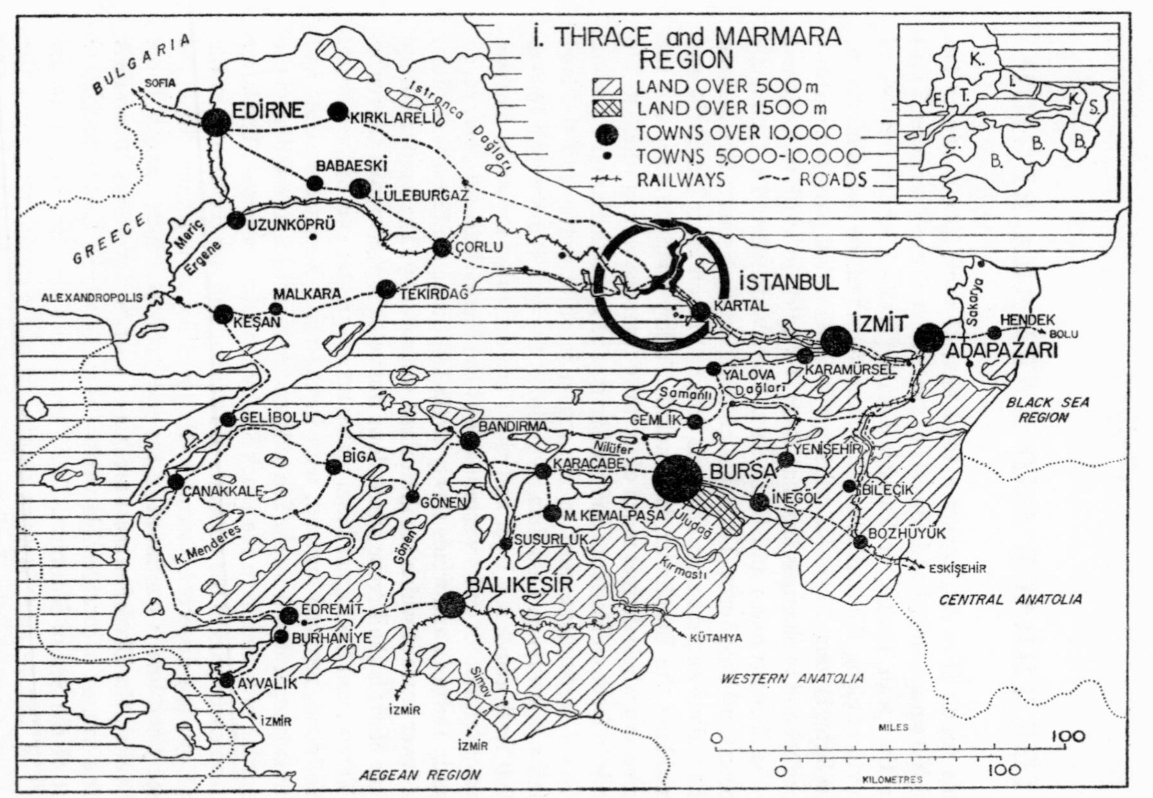

Fig. 42. The Thrace and Marmara region

trend-lines meet a south-west to north-east series which run from the Gulf of Edremit to the Sea of Marmara and control the direction of the Dardanelles. Most of Bursa and Balıkesir provinces are drained by rivers which flow north from the uplands along the southern boundary of the region. Along the Marmara coast, however, there is a line of hills some 500 m (1600 feet) high through which only one river, the Simav, has cut a passage. Immediately south of this ridge there are extensive lowlands into which flows water from the large catchment areas of the Nilüfer, Kırmastı, Simav and Gönen, and the lower areas are badly drained, particularly around the shallow lakes Manyas and Apolyont. To the west, uplands again become dominant but there is a fairly well-developed coastal plan which extends inland up the Küçük Menderes valley.* The Marmara region as a whole is bounded on its southern side by an upland rim which separates it from areas draining direct to the Aegean. Although these uplands rarely rise above 1500 m (5000 feet) there are only two passes below 500 m (1650 feet). These carry the two main lines of communication between the Marmara and Aegean regions: the Balıkesir–İzmir railway and the road to Edremit. The small lowland around Edremit, though administratively part of Balıkesir province and thus of the Marmara region should more logically be attached to the Aegean region. Only in one place does the land rise above a general summit level of 1500–1600 m (5000–5250 feet) and this is immediately south-east of Bursa, where the isolated crystalline massif of Uludağ reaches 2540 m (8330 feet).

The widespread occurrence within this region of fertile plains, the moderate winter temperatures, and the absence of serious aridity problems combine to make it one of the areas most favourable for agriculture and rural population densities are well above the national average. In this respect, there is a considerable degree of contrast between the Asiatic and European sections of the region. Thrace is the drier of the two and the natural vegetation of the Ergene plain is steppe-grassland. A high proportion of the land in this basin is under cultivation, mainly for cereals, and there is much moderate quality grazing land. Farming methods in Thrace are generally somewhat better than in other grain-growing areas of Turkey—for example, sunflower is grown widely in rotation with wheat—and yields, while by no means high, are above the national average. This permits the support of high rural densities, in places more than 50 per square km (130 per square mile). At the same time there is a constant draining of surplus population towards İstanbul.

In the sheltered lowlands to the east and south of the Sea of Marmara, where rainfall is more plentiful, agriculture is more intensive and more

* Not to be confused with the larger Küçük Menderes valley in İzmir province.

varied than in Thrace. In addition to wheat, barley and sunflower, which are the most important crops, this part of the region grows maize, tobacco and vines on a significant scale. The Edremit lowland is a major olive-producing district and the mulberry tree is widespread around Bursa. The development of productive agriculture in these lowlands has required a good deal of human effort. The natural vegetation of the surrounding hills is mixed, mainly deciduous forest, for which there is an ample rainfall, but the woodlands have been ruthlessly exploited over the centuries, causing widespread soil erosion. This has resulted in heavy deposition along the lower courses of the rivers, especially the Sakarya and Simav, and the formation of extensive swamps. During the past forty years, there has been much investment in reclamation works and colonisation of marshland where the soils, once drained, are particularly fertile. The presence of large urban markets in the region has been an added incentive to this form of development.

Although the Thrace and Marmara region is a highly productive agricultural area, it is even more noteworthy for its towns, industry and trade. More than half the population is classed as urban, a much higher proportion than in any other region of Turkey. In addition to İstanbul, which alone contains more than a quarter of the region's inhabitants, there are numerous other sizeable urban centres, including Bursa, İzmit, Adapazarı, Balıkesir and Edirne, as well as more than two dozen other towns with populations above 10 000. The region contains well over half the country's manufacturing industry, has the best-developed communications system and handles nearly half Turkey's foreign trade.

The predominance of this region in the economic life of the country is only to a limited degree the result of its natural resources. Fuel supplies are available in relative abundance from the lignite fields of Thrace and Kütahya (the latter is just outside the region) and the coal and steel of the Ereğli–Zonguldak district are easily shipped to the Marmara ports. However, it is position rather than resources which is the region's major asset. Standing, as it does, at a natural 'crossroads', the region is one through which trade has passed since earliest times and it continues to attract trade, industry and population. In recent years a large proportion of Turkey's new industrial plant, particularly that built with foreign capital, has been established on the shores of the Sea of Marmara.

İstanbul (Fig 43) merits special attention as a metropolis which has been of world importance for many centuries and which is still Turkey's largest city. The foundation of İstanbul is traditionally dated at 658 B.C., when Greek colonists established a settlement on the promontory between the Golden Horn and the Sea of Marmara, though there was an earlier Greek colony on the Asiatic shore in the district now known as

Kadiköy. A low platform some 70 m (230 feet) high, sharply dissected by a number of streams, forms the spine of the promontory and drops away steeply on either side to a coastal flat a few hundred yards wide. The Golden Horn provided a superb natural harbour and the site was protected by defensive works on the western, landward side. Successive walls were built at various dates, enclosing a progressively larger area and this process continued after the inauguration of Constantinople as capital of the eastern Roman empire in A.D. 330. The largest of these fortifications were the massive walls, some 4 miles long, built by Theodosius in A.D. 413. Practically all traces of earlier defensive works have now disappeared, but the Theodosian wall, renovated on numerous occasions, is largely preserved and to this day encloses the densely populated Fatıh and Eminönü districts (Fig. 43(*a*)). It was this site which became the capital of the Byzantine empire and was successfully beseiged by the Turks in 1453. For the next four and a half centuries, İstanbul was the Ottoman capital, until the new republican capital was shifted to Ankara. As trade expanded and population increased, the city spread across the Golden Horn into the Galata district. Although there was some settlement in that district as early as the 4th century, Galata did not become important until the 13th and 14th when it developed as the main commercial area, a function which it now performs. Further rapid growth in the 18th and 19th centuries pushed settlement up the steep slope behind the Galata shore and the residential district of Pera developed on the plateau surface. Galata and Pera together form the section now known as Beyoğlu, though the older district names are also still in use. On the Asiatic side of the Bosphorus, Üsküdar (Scutari) had a long separate existence as the ferry point at the terminus of land routes across Asia Minor.

In modern times, İstanbul has continued to grow rapidly and now has a population of 1 750 000 compared with 750 000 in 1935. That much of this growth is a product of immigration from other parts of the country is shown by the fact that, in 1965, roughly half the population of İstanbul province had been born outside that province. Of the total population of the city, about 500 000 live in the old quarters of Fatıh and Eminönü, 400 000 in Beyoğlu and the adjacent Şişli district and 300 000 in Üsküdar-Kadıköy. The remaining 550 000 live in districts which, though they have contained small settlements for many centuries have become urbanised and have been brought into the İstanbul conurbation only during the last thirty or forty years. These essentially suburban areas include Eyüp and Gaziosmanpaşa (150 000) at the head of the Golden Horn, and Zeytinburnu and Bakırköy (200 000) which represent the growth of the conurbation westwards along the Marmara shore (Fig. 43(*c*)). Beşiktaş-Sariyer (150 000) and Beyköz (50 000) face each other across the Bos-

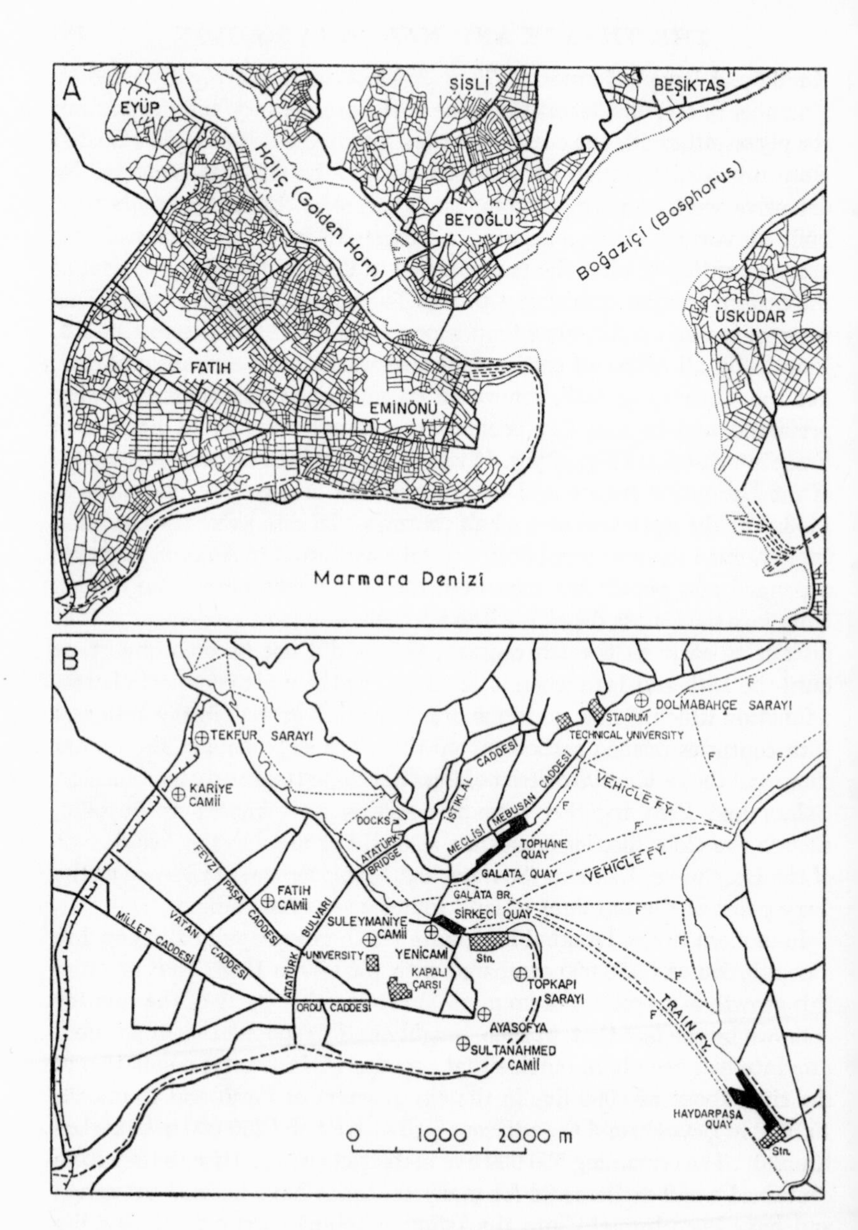
A
EYÜP
ŞİŞLİ
BEŞİKTAŞ
Haliç (Golden Horn)
BEYOĞLU
Boğaziçi (Bosphorus)
ÜSKÜDAR
FATIH
EMİNÖNÜ
Marmara Denizi
B
TEKFUR SARAYI
KARİYE CAMİİ
FEVZİ PAŞA CADDESİ
FATIH CAMİİ
VATAN CADDESİ
MİLLET CADDESİ
ATATÜRK BULVARI
ATATÜRK BRIDGE
DOCKS
SULEYMANIYE CAMİİ
UNIVERSITY
YENICAMI
KAPALI ÇARŞI
ORDU CADDESİ
İSTIKLAL CADDESİ
MECLİSİ MEBUSAN CADDESİ
STADIUM
TECHNICAL UNIVERSITY
DOLMABAHÇE SARAYI
VEHICLE FY.
TOPHANE QUAY
GALATA QUAY
GALATA BR.
SİRKECİ QUAY
Stn.
TOPKAPI SARAYI
AYASOFYA
SULTANAHMED CAMİİ
TRAIN FY.
HAYDARPAŞA QUAY
0 1000 2000 m

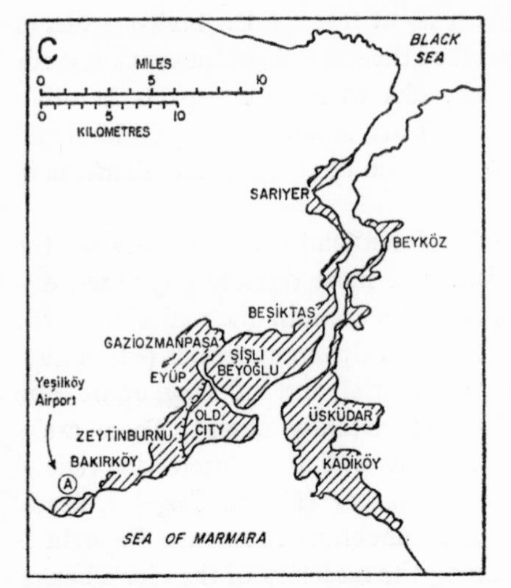

Fig. 43 İstanbul

phorus to the north of İstanbul and Üsküdar respectively. All these districts now form part of a single municipality (*belediye*). Four-fifths of the population live on the European side where the built-up area is continuous from Yeşilköy airport to Sariyer, a distance of 40 km (25 miles). Settlement is much less extensive on the Asiatic side, mainly because of the difficulties involved in crossing the Bosphorus.

The structure of the conurbation presents serious problems which stem mainly from the physical nature of the site. Flat land near sea level is very restricted, and steep slopes rise to 100 m or more on either shore. These slopes are often sharply dissected by small valleys which provide barriers to movement and make building difficult. Another and obvious hindrance to movement within the conurbation is its division by the Bosphorus and Golden Horn. The latter is now crossed by the Galata and Atatürk bridges, first built in the 19th century, which have greatly reduced the utility of the old harbour yet are inadequate as links between the old city and Beyoğlu. Numerous plans have been advanced for a road bridge across the Bosphorus, but it was not until 1970 that work on the project finally got under way. As a result, a great deal of movement between different parts of the conurbation takes place by ferry and a fleet of several dozen large motor vessels carries thousands of commuters to and from their work. Another major problem has been the close-packed nature of the older parts of the built-up area with their narrow, unplanned streets, quite inadequate to the needs of modern traffic. The intense congestion which results has been countered by the drastic expedient of driving broad arteries straight through the built-up area of the old city, a process which has involved the rehousing of many thousands of people. These boulevards which, like their counterparts in other towns, bear such names as Atatürk Bulvarı, Millet (Nation) Caddesi and Vatan (Homeland) Caddesi (Fig. 43(*b*)) form distinctive new elements in the townscape of the old city.

There are a number of noteworthy functional contrasts between the various sections of the conurbation. The most densely populated districts are Fatıh and Eminönü, which also contain the majority of the monuments of the Classical, Byzantine and Ottoman periods (Fig. 43(*b*)). These areas remain predominantly residential, and industry, apart from the small-scale, back-street variety, is virtually absent. There are a number of small modern shopping areas as well as an interesting relic of the past in the shape of the covered bazaar (*Kapalı Çarşı*). Cultural buildings include the University and numerous museums. Beyoğlu is predominantly commercial, containing the majority of the city's banks, offices and trading companies, together with modern shopping areas of a 'western' type, notably that along İstiklal (Independence) Caddesi. However, except along the waterfront, these activities have not displaced the residential function and Beyoğlu is very densely populated. Residential densities are much lower in outlying districts like Şişli and Beşıktaş which also contain such modern public buildings as the Stadium, Technical University and Hilton Hotel. On the Asian side, high density settlement occurs only in the immediate vicinity of the waterfront, and Üsküdar is much more open in plan than is İstanbul proper.

While the densely settled parts of the conurbation contain large number of small workshops, each employing a handful of artisans, large-scale factory industry is found mainly in outlying districts, notably in the area beyond the Theodosian wall, around the head of the Golden Horn and at Gultepe on the high ground behind Beyoğlu. There are now plans for the establishment of a large industrial site at Zeytinburnu. The industrial structure of the city is extremely varied. As we have already seen, İstanbul employs about a quarter of Turkey's manufacturing workers and the main activities are the alimentary, textile and engineering industries, though practically every branch of manufacturing is well represented.

İstanbul's chief function is, of course, that of Turkey's chief port and in this respect the site presents serious local difficulties which are only offset by the city's general location. In the first place, port facilities are divided among the three separate sections of Galata, Sirkeci (in Eminönü) and Haydarpaşa (in Kadiköy). The Golden Horn, once the heart of the port, is now a backwater used only by lighters and by small ocean-going vessels. This decline is due in part to progressive silting, which in modern times has been accelerated by injudicious forest clearance on the surrounding hills. The waterway is now too shallow to take large vessels and the bridges, though they can be opened, restrict access. The most important shipment point at present is Galata, immediately below the Galata Bridge, but conditions are far from ideal. The swing of the Bosphorus current against the European shore at this point gives very deep water, making the construction of quays out into the estuary prohibitively expensive, so that vessels must tie up parallel to the shore. Even with the added capacity resulting from the recent construction of the Tophane quay, only ten ships can tie up at any one time and five berths are reserved for the many passenger vessels using the port. Furthermore, the amount of flat land onshore is very restricted and, although the Tophane scheme involved the building of large warehouses, accommodation is still inadequate and landward access is very difficult. As a result, the majority of ships tie up at floating buoys offshore and are unloaded by lighter, a process which, despite the ready availability of cheap casual labour, is both slow and costly. Sirkeci quay, in the old city, has similar problems of limited space but does benefit from direct access to rail links with European Turkey and to train and vehicle ferries to the Asiatic shore. Haydarpaşa with its road and rail links to the Anatolian interior, is rapidly expanding and has the most modern port facilities of the three port areas.

The division of the port into three sections has serious disadvantages. Ocean-going vessels usually load or discharge at one point only and their cargoes must be distributed to or collected from all three, thus adding to congestion on the Bosphorus. Cargo and passenger liners, coasters, ferry-boats and lighters, to say nothing of innumerable small boats carrying fish and other wares for sale in the waterfront markets give a scene of great confusion. The Bosphorus is one of the world's most crowded waterways and its port facilities are hopelessly inadequate for the traffic attempting to use them. The result has been a marked increase, over the past decade, in the volume of trade handled by other ports, particularly in the Marmara region but also elsewhere in Turkey. There is now a plan for the construction of a new port at Zeytinburnu, on the northern shore of the Sea of Marmara to the west of old İstanbul.

İzmit, which stands at the head of the Gulf of İzmit, is now the second port of the Marmara region. In 1965 it handled 1·8 million tons of shipping (İstanbul, 5·3 million tons) including 1 million tons engaged in international trade. Its population has increased from 18 000 in 1935 to 90 000 in 1965, and continues to grow rapidly. Like so many Turkish towns, İzmit has a long history and was a port throughout the Roman,

Byzantine and Ottoman periods. In recent years İzmit has benefited greatly from its position on the main road and railway between İstanbul and Ankara. The northern shore of the Gulf, from İzmit westwards, has now become an important focus of modern industry and is the site of an oil refinery, a large thermal power station, a motor-tyre factory, cement, paper and textile factories and numerous light industrial establishments.

Adapazarı, some 40 km (25 miles) to the east, is of similar size and owes its importance mainly to its function as the marketing centre for the intensively farmed Sakarya lowlands. There is a sugar-beet factory and a number of smaller industries. The name of this city (Ada Pazar = island market) reflects both its dominant function and the fact that much of the surrounding lowland was, in the past, very badly drained: there has been much reclamation of the fertile alluvial soils over the last thirty years.

Bursa (1935: 72 000; 1965: 212 000) is the second largest city of the Marmara region and the fifth largest in Turkey. Like many ancient Turkish towns, Bursa is situated at the foot of a high mountain range, in this case the Uludağ (2543 m/8340 feet) and overlooking a fertile lowland or *ova* (*Bursa ovası*). Summer snow-melt assures the city and plain of an adequate water supply and in summer the *ova* takes on the character of an oasis. The traditional appellation of '*yeşil Bursa*' (green Bursa) points the contrast with surrounding, drier areas. The sheltered *ova*, some 8 or 9 km (5 miles) across is the scene of intensive cultivation of vegetables, fruit, maize and sunflower, though the lower, undrained parts are under marshy grazing. The mulberry tree is widely grown and there is a long tradition of silk manufacture. Highly productive agriculture and a valuable textile industry have combined to make Bursa one of the most prosperous of Turkish towns. The city dates back to classical times, was the Ottoman capital for a brief period in the 14th century and was a country seat of the Sultans until the 19th. Until quite recently, Bursa was rather isolated from the remainder of the country but in the last few years communications have been much improved. In particular, a modern motor road has been constructed to Yalova, on the Marmara coast, whence there is a fast ferry service to İstanbul. This passes through Gemlik, which is tending to replace Mudanya as the port for Bursa. Another factor which has brought added prosperity to Bursa in recent years has been the tourist industry. Improved communications, together with the growth of an urban middle class in İstanbul, have given rise to a sizeable holiday trade. Winter sports are increasingly popular and the ski slopes of Uludağ attract many enthusiasts. Bursa is Turkey's main textile centre and the production of artificial fibres is rapidly increasing. In addition, there are a number of alimentary industries.

Balıkesir (70 000) is rather remote from the main centres of economic activity in the region but occupies an important position in the communications system at the junction of the İzmir–Bandirma and İzmir–Eskişehir railways. The lowlands in the vicinity are intensively farmed and iron, lead and zinc are mined near by. The town has a mixed industrial structure with alimentary industries, cotton textiles and a cement works.

Finally, among the larger towns of the region, Edirne (50 000) must be mentioned. This city was once of much greater importance than is now the case. Founded (as Adrianople) in Roman times, Edirne was the Ottoman capital for a hundred years before the capture of Constantinople. When the Turkish empire included large parts of the Balkans, it was a major administrative centre and in the late 19th century it became a bone of contention between Greece and Turkey. Since the establishment of the Republic, Edirne has become a rather remote border town in an area which is predominantly agricultural and no major industrial development has occurred.

In addition to the major towns mentioned above, the Thrace and Marmara region is noteworthy for its large number of smaller centres. These include ports such as Çanakkale, Bandırma, Gemlik and Tekirdağ, and agricultural markets like Karacabey, Kırklareli, Lüleburgaz and Mustafakemalpaşa. Many of these centres have small industries, often recently established, such as the sulphuric acid plant at Bandirma and the tomato-paste factory at Mustafakemalpaşa, and the majority of them are now growing quite rapidly.

Chapter 10

THE AEGEAN REGION

The Aegean region (Fig. 44), which covers 47 000 square km (18 000 square miles) and has a population of 2·8 million, comprises the western seaboard from the Bakır valley in the north to the Koca valley in the south and extends inland for a distance varying between 50 and 200 km (30–125 miles). There are significant differences between a larger, northern section, made up of the three provinces of İzmir, Manisa and Aydın, and the southernmost province of Muğla.

The former area is dominated by a strongly marked east–west structural and topographic grain. In the north, the hill country which separates the Marmara and Aegean regions is drained by the Kum and Selendi tributaries of the Gediz and by the smaller Bakir system. The Gedız valley, bounded on either side by major faults is markedly asymmetrical. On its northern side, slopes are relatively gentle and there has been much dissection by tributaries, but on the south there is a very abrupt rise to the crystalline massif of the Bozdağlar, which in places exceed 2000 m (6500 feet). This, in turn, slopes steeply down to the smaller Küçük Menderes valley, which is separated by the narrow ridge of the Aydındağları from a second major trough, occupied by the Büyük Menderes. The slopes on the southern side of this feature are much gentler than those to the north and are drained by a number of major tributaries of which the largest are the Çine and Akçay. In Muğla province, which extends from the Menteşe crystalline massif eastwards into the western Taurus, relief is less orderly. Hills and mountains predominate and among them there are numerous enclosed basins, but true lowland is limited in extent, occurring mainly along the coast and stretching only a few kilometres inland. This is in marked contrast to the more northerly part of the region, where broad, flat-floored valleys penetrate to the eastern boundary.

The coastline of the Aegean region is of particular interest in that a combination of major east–west trend-lines with more localised north–south faulting has given it a highly irregular shape. As a result it consists of a series of rocky, cliff-lined promontories and peninsulas, separated by deep-set bays and gulfs. The latter receive the major rivers from the interior and these have well-developed deltas, particularly at the mouths of the Gediz and Büyük Menderes, which have extended several miles seaward since classical times. Thus the form of the coast is such that, although it provides a multitude of sheltered anchorages, sites suitable for the development of modern ports, with deep water close to firm, flat land, are few and far between. The presence of such conditions at İzmir, does much to explain that port's dominance in Aegean coast trade.

The presence of large alluvial lowlands, which are among the biggest in Turkey, the mild winters and the hot summers, combine to make this

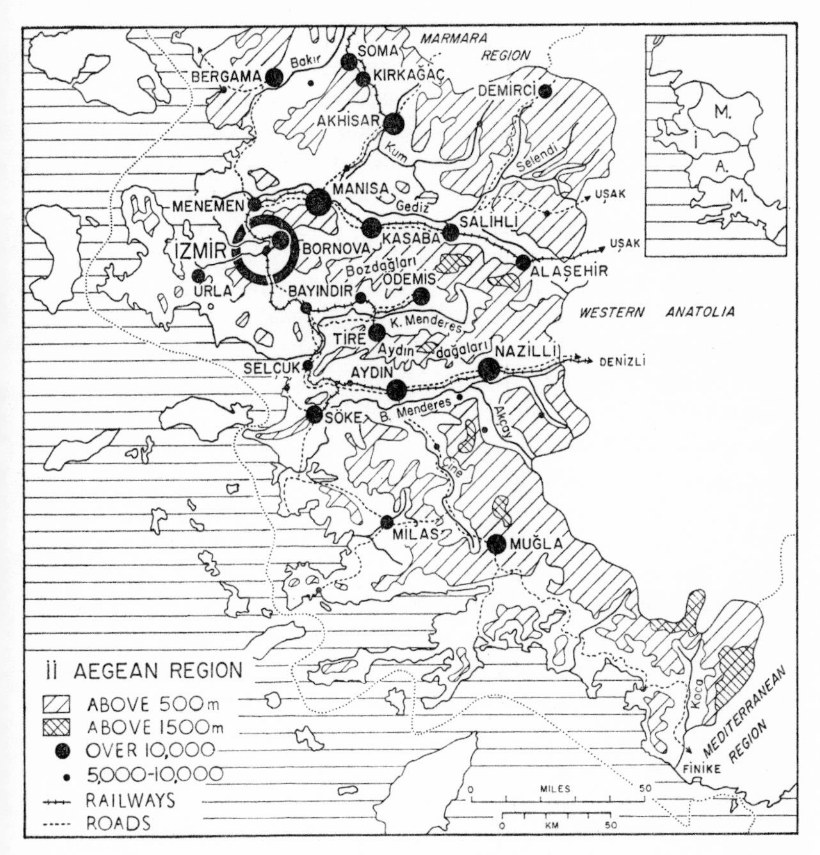

Fig. 44. The Aegean Region

a region with a high agricultural potential. The main climatic problem is summer drought, though this is neither as intense nor as prolonged as it is along the Mediterranean coast. As a result of these favourable conditions, the Aegean region produces more, in terms of value, than any other region and rural population densities are among the highest in the country. The proportion of land under cultivation, however, is slightly below the national average, partly because of the strong relief of the region but also because the 'sown area' on which this calculation is based excludes tree crops, which are of particular importance. The intensive agriculture characteristic of the region and its high productivity have not been achieved without difficulty, and the region is by no means devoid of problems for the farmer. The trough-like nature of the valleys in which the bulk of the cultivated land occurs, their very gently sloping floors and the intense erosion which occurs in the adjacent uplands lead to heavy silting, not only at the mouths of the rivers but also further upstream. Floodplains are often swampy and were in the past malarial. Thus there has been a tendency for settlement and agricultural land to develop mainly on hill-foot terraces along the valley sides and for large areas of floodplain to remain under swamp or rough pasture, used only as winter grazing by stock-rearers from the interior. Present-day patterns of settlement and communications still reflect these influences but, over the last forty years, there has been a good deal of investment in land reclamation and flood control and the cultivated area has been much extended. Several regulating barrages have been built, notably at Demirköprü on the Gediz and at Kemer on the Akçay. The Gediz delta has been reclaimed with the aid of a barrage at Menemen. The Kemer and Demirköprü dams are also used for the generation of hydro-electricity (Fig. 36, p. 131) while the Menemen and other schemes (Fig. 34, p. 122) provide irrigation water to offset the summer drought.

The increasing area of fertile alluvial farmland is devoted primarily to the production of high value Mediterranean crops, which are grown along the valleys right up to the eastern borders of the region. In particular, the Aegean region is responsible for nearly 60% of Turkey's tobacco crop, 30% of the grapes and cotton, 60% of the olives and practically all the figs. These items make an important contribution to the export trade in agricultural produce, and ease of access to the coast is a major advantage.

In contrast, the intervening uplands are for the most part infertile, though even here there are pockets of intensive farming in enclosed basins. Over wide areas, the predominantly crystalline rocks give poor, rather acid soils and, in contrast to the Marmara region, forests are not well-developed, the most common type of vegetation being a grassy scrubland. In a sense, these uplands may be looked upon as westward prolongations of the Anatolian 'plateau'. Unlike the latter, however, they remain largely uncultivated and devoted to grazing.

The dichotomy, within the Aegean region, between lowlands which are clearly Mediterranean in their climate and agriculture and uplands which are a western extension of the Anatolian interior serves to emphasise the function of the region as a transitional or link zone between maritime and continental Turkey. This linking function is facilitated by the east–west structural grain of the land and exemplified by the form of the communications network. From the Büyük Menderes valley northwards, at least, the Aegean region has a more highly developed railway network than any other. Lines run up the Gediz and Büyük Menderes valleys to join the Anatolian railway and a third important route serves the Küçük Menderes. In addition there is the useful link northwards through Balıkesir to the Sea of Marmara at Bandırma. The way in which these railways, the most heavily used in the country, converge on the port of İzmir, serves to emphasise the fact that the agriculture of the region is geared mainly to the production and export of high-value crops. As throughout Turkey, road transport has become important only during the past twenty years and the main highways tend to duplicate the rail routes already mentioned. North–south movement within the region has always been difficult, even along the coast, and it is superfluous to emphasise the significance of coastwise shipping, particularly as a link between the Aegean and Marmara ports. A modern highway now runs the length of the coast and provides a direct link with European Turkey by means of a ferry across the Dardanelles, but this is of secondary importance to rail and sea transport. In the matter of communications, there is again a clear contrast between the province of Muğla and the remainder of the region. The former is still remote, isolated, for the most part thinly populated and much less developed than the other three provinces. In Muğla, there are no railways and the only main road, still of low quality, follows a tortuous route along the coast. The small pockets of intensive agriculture, together with numerous small mining centres send much of their produce to İzmir and İstanbul by sea.

A dense population, a well-developed network of communications, thriving international trade and a tradition of urban settlement going back to classical times have made the Aegean region one in which towns are particularly numerous although, with the exception of İzmir, they are generally quite small. It is in this part of Asia Minor that the classical civilisations, particularly that of Greece, had their greatest impact. Many of the best-known classical sites, such as Pergamum, Ephesus and Telmessos are in this region and the Maeander (Büyük Menderes) and Hermus (Gediz) valleys were famed for their agricultural wealth. The Greek imprint on the region remained strong right down to the 20th century for it was the homeland of the Greek minority until the Graeco–Turkish conflict of 1919–22. As a result of the population transfers which followed, Greeks have almost entirely disappeared, but traces of the past remain in the fact, for example, that this is one of the few parts of Turkey where extensive terraced field-systems are to be found.

The region owes its wealth primarily to agriculture and trade. With the very significant exception of agricultural products such as cotton, tobacco, vines and olives, raw materials for industry occur only on a small scale. There is scattered working of lignite, manganese, lead and zinc and the eastern part of Muğla province lies within the chrome-rich zone of south-western Turkey, but there are no really large mining centres. Thus alimentary and textile industries are the main forms of manufacturing, to which a variety of other activities have been added in recent years.

The most highly developed and most densely populated part of the region embraces the Gediz, Küçük Menderes and Büyük Menderes valleys, a zone containing ten of the region's fourteen towns of more than 10 000. This zone is focused on İzmir which in turn dominates the Aegean region as a whole. Like most towns in the region, İzmir (Smyrna) was a Greek foundation and, despite its subjection to the Seljuk and Ottoman Turks, remained the main centre of Greek speech and culture in Asia Minor as well as a centre of European commercial interests until 1922. The Graeco–Turkish war, in addition to resulting in the flight or expulsion of practically the whole Greek community, caused the destruction by fire of large parts of the city. Since 1922 there has been much rebuilding and İzmir has become wholly Turkish in population. Its main function is that of Turkey's second port and although its share of imports is quite small, its exports exceed those of İstanbul and consist mainly of the agricultural products of the Aegean region and the Anatolian interior. The Gulf of İzmir is one of the best natural harbours on the Aegean coast, sheltered from the open sea by the Karaburun peninsula and free from silting owing to the northward diversion of the main channel of the Gediz and the fact that no sizeable river flows into the head of the Gulf. The original site and the main part of the city are situated on the southern side of the Gulf, where a suitable area of flat land adjacent to deep water has permitted the development of a long waterfront. Since the establishment of the Republic, and particularly since the Second World War, the city has grown rapidly and a continuous built-up area now extends around the head of the gulf to include Karşıyaka, a ship-building centre with port facilities (now part of İzmir *belediye*), and the inland industrial centre of Bornova. The total population of this agglomeration has risen from 180 000 in 1935 to 450 000 in 1965. The industrial structure of the city is a mixed one. The dominant manufactures are those processing the agricultural products of the hinterland, notably cotton and woollen textiles and tobacco but there are numerous other activities. These include fruit and vegetable canning, chemical works, cement and the manufacture of clothing, footwear and furniture.

In recent years, engineering activities have expanded rapidly and include a tractor assembly plant. There are plans for a large oil refinery. The significance of industry and foreign trade is seen in the frequent choice of İzmir, rather than İstanbul or Ankara, as the locale for industrial exhibitions and trade fairs.

The other towns of the Aegean region are small—only Manisa has a population of more than 50 000—and are essentially agricultural marketing centres and centres of alimentary and textile industries. Of recent years, tourism has assumed some importance, particularly in the Karaburun peninsula.

Chapter 11

THE BLACK SEA REGION

This highly distinctive region (Fig. 45) covers an area of 77 000 square km (30 000 square miles) and has a population of 4·5 million, giving an overall density well above the national average. Less than one-fifth of the population live in towns, however, and rural densities are higher than in any other region. The topographic grain is parallel to the coast and mountains rise steeply to heights of 1000 m or more a few miles inland. Consequently, the coastal plain is narrow over most of its length, widening out only in a few places where the larger rivers have formed deltas or where small coastal basins occur. Most of the streams draining the area are short and flow swiftly northwards to the sea, cutting sharp ravines which hinder coastwise movement. A few of the larger rivers, however, have cut back through the Pontic ranges and have developed lengthy subsequent tributaries. In the western half of the region, these flow in broad, open, high-level basins between the mountain ranges, but in the east the succession is more tightly compressed and the Kelkit–Çoruh trough is deep and narrow.

As a result of this arrangement of relief features, movement across the region from the interior to the sea is difficult almost everywhere but east–west movement is somewhat easier, the inland route comparing favourably with that along the coast. Thus coastwise movement has traditionally been by sea rather than overland and this has led to the development of an unusually large number of harbours and small ports. The coast has always been isolated from the interior. In modern times this isolation has been broken down by the construction of railways and roads across the Pontic ranges to the great benefit of such coastal termini as Zonguldak, Samsun and, to a lesser degree, Trabzon. However, long stretches of the coast still look to the Black Sea shipping route as their only reliable means of contact with the outside world.

As has already been shown (Chapter 2), the unique climate of the Black Sea region with its year-round rainfall and, at lower levels, its mild winters, is particularly favourable to agriculture and, despite the difficulties presented by the terrain, the Black Sea coastlands have become a zone of highly productive commercial farming. This applies mainly to the coastal plain, the valleys of the larger rivers and the lower hill slopes: elsewhere agriculture is on a more extensive basis and is

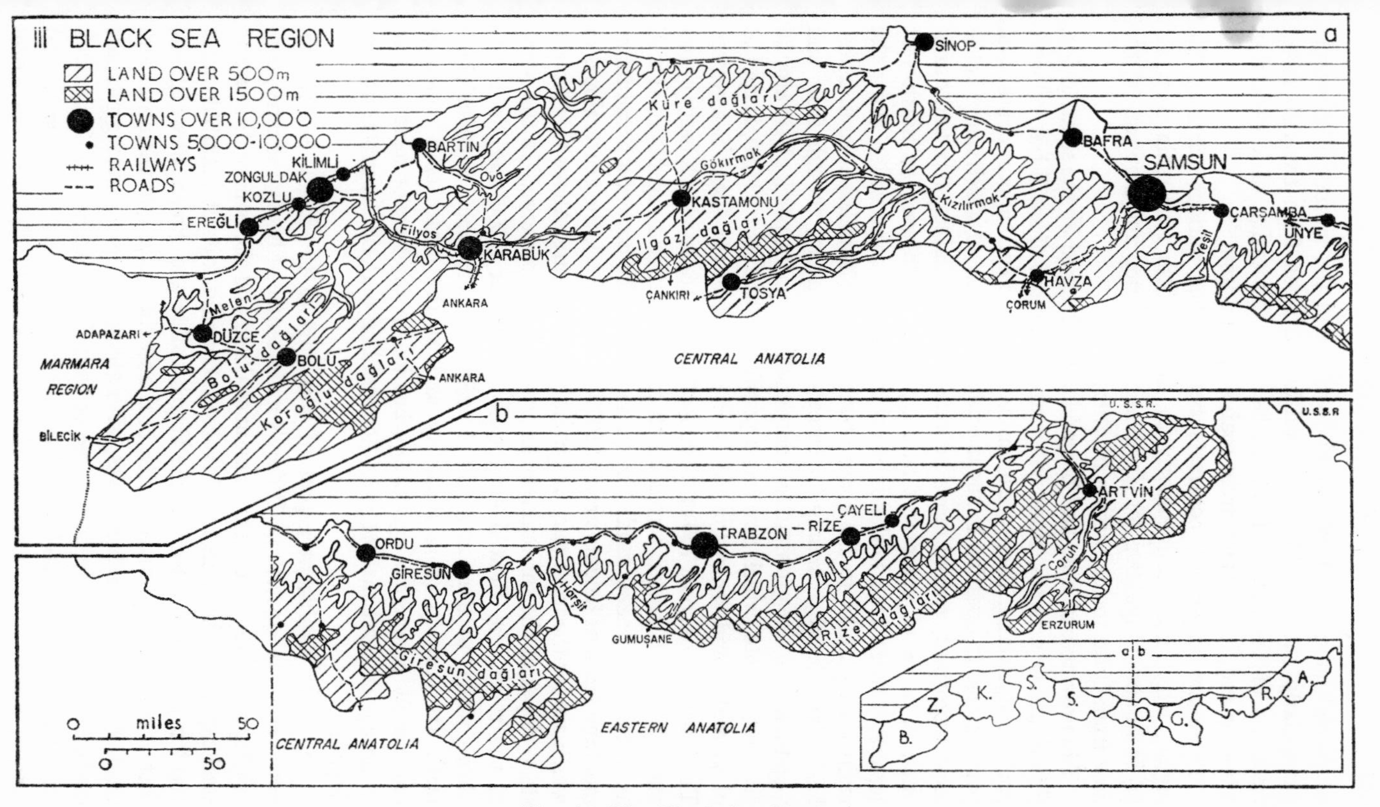

Fig. 45. The Black Sea Region

concerned mainly with cereal production and the rearing of livestock, particularly cattle. Additional wealth is derived from the rich forest resources of the region, from small-scale exploitation of a variety of minerals and, in the west, from coal, steel and iron.

There are important contrasts between the various parts of the region, which may conveniently be divided into four main sections: (*a*) Bolu and Zonguldak, (*b*) Kastamonu, (*c*) Sinop and Samsun, (*d*) the area from Ordu to the eastern frontier.

The provinces of Bolu and Zonguldak are drained by the small Melen, Filyos and Ova rivers, along which are a number of small but valuable pockets of lowland. These are intensively farmed and support dense rural populations. In addition to the ubiquitous cereals, of which maize is the most important, special crops include fruit, vegetables, flax and hazelnuts. A range of mountains running from south-west to north-west separates these true lowlands from high-level basins which carry the main road parallel to the coast about 45 km (72 miles) inland. These basins are devoted mainly to cereals and grazing, though fruit and vegetables are also grown in the more sheltered parts, particularly around the towns. Bolu, which now has a population of about 22 000, is typical of several inland centres in this western part of the Black Sea region. The town stands some 750 m (2500 feet) above sea level in a basin or *ova* about 16 km (10 miles) across which carries fruit and vegetables as well as cereals and grazing land. The *ova* is set into the floor of a broad intermontane basin at heights around 1000 m (3300 feet), the gentle slopes of which are for the most part under grain and pasture. Above this are the steep slopes of the surrounding forest-covered mountains. To the north of the town, the Bolu dağları exceed 1800 m (6000 feet) in a few places while, to the south, the Koroğlu dağları reach 2400 m (7800 feet). Its position on a routeway and at the centre of a region of moderately prosperous agriculture has led to the development of Bolu as an agricultural market with flour-milling and timber-processing industries.

The most significant aspect of this part of the Black Sea region, however, is its function as Turkey's main centre of heavy industry, containing as it does the country's main coalfield and the bulk of its iron and steel capacity. Three sites are involved: Zonguldak itself, Karabük, some 100 km (60 miles) inland in the Filyos valley and Ereğli, of which the first is concerned primarily with coal and the other two with iron and steel. The coal-mines themselves, with about a dozen operating pits, are organised into four districts, three of them in the vicinity of Zonguldak and the fourth some 30 km (18 miles) along the coast to the west, and employ about 30 000 workers. The Gelik-Kilimli, Üzülmez and Kozlu

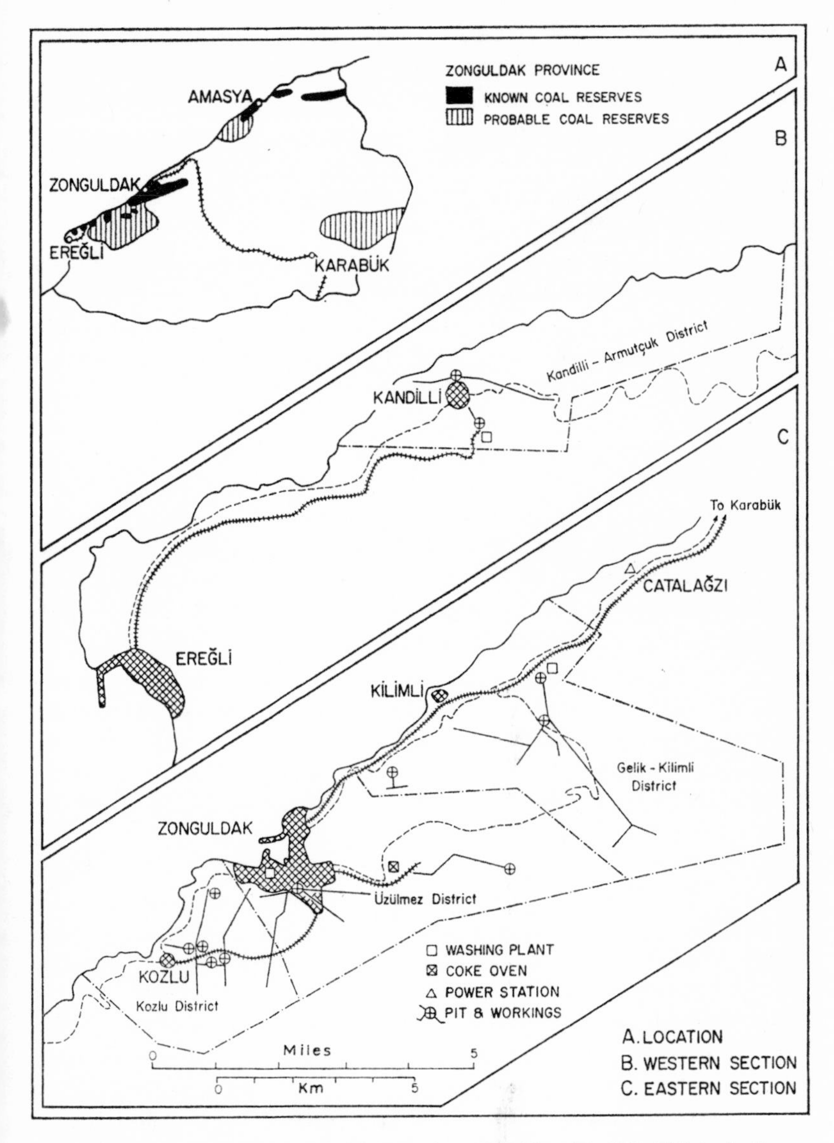

Fig. 46. The Zonguldak Coalfield. Based on Winkler, E., 'Die Wirtschaft von Zonguldak, Türkei', *Wiener Geographische Schriften*, 12/13, 1961

districts (Fig. 46) are linked to Zonguldak by rail and the Armutçuk–Kandilli area has a short stretch of railway line leading to Ereğli. Of the coal produced, about one-third is shipped from Zonguldak, mainly to İstanbul, and the remainder is divided between the coke ovens of Zonguldak, Ereğli and Karabük and the Çatalağzı power station. Attention has already been drawn to the anomalous location of the Karabük steelworks and to the recent opening of a new integrated plant at Ereğli. The latter, built on flat land at the mouth of a small river, is designed to produce steel plate, a commodity hitherto imported into Turkey. Iron is brought from Divriği in eastern Turkey, travelling by rail to Samsun and thence by boat. The movement of coal to the Ereğli site has presented some difficulties. The rail link to Zonguldak has not yet been completed and its estimated cost of 250 million *Lira* for 27 km (16 miles) of track is indicative of the great expenditure involved in industrial development along this rocky mountainous coast. For the moment, coal comes partly by the short line from Kandilli, partly by road and partly by sea. Ereğli harbour has been reconstructed and the population of the town has increased from 8000 to 18 000 in five years. It is expected eventually to reach 70 000 or 80 000 as other industries are developed. This stretch of coastline seems likely to remain the heart of Turkish heavy industry.

Beyond Bartin, a small port on the Ova river, conditions change abruptly and Kastamonu is the most thinly populated province on the Black Sea coast. The high range of the Kure dağları, rising in places to nearly 2000 m (6500 feet), runs close to the sea, leaving only a narrow coastal plain which is cut into by small, swift streams and there is no modern road. This very restricted coastal plain, intensively farmed and quite densely populated, has several small harbours and ports of which İnebolu (6000 population), the only one with a route to the interior, is the largest. The well-wooded Kure dağları, together with the higher (2500 m/8250 feet) Ilgaz dağları further inland, are both thinly settled. Between them is a broad, high-level basin, drained by the Gökırmak tributary of the Kızılırmak. This is largely under cereals and pasture, but in the lower parts fruit, vegetables and a good deal of hemp are grown. Kastamonu (24 000) has features similar to those already described in the case of Bolu. The town has grown up where the route to the coast at İnebolu crosses the interior routeway between the mountain ranges. Its small-scale industries deal with the hides, grain and timber of its district. Some 40 km (25 miles) downstream, a hemp mill has been built at Taşköprü. South of the Ilgaz dağları, a section of the Devrek valley, also tributary to the Kızılırmak, lies within Kastamonu province. It is thus technically in the Black Sea region, but its inland situation gives it a drier, hotter climate. Vines and rice are grown in the valley and there is a small textile mill at Tosya.

A further change takes place in Sinop and Samsun provinces where the Kızılırmak and Yeşilırmak break through the Pontic ranges and lowlands become more extensive. These provide better opportunities for agriculture and routes into the interior so that Samsun in particular is one of the most densely settled and highly developed parts of the Black Sea region. Sinop (13 000) has a good natural harbour, protected by a volcanic promontory but lacks direct access to the interior so that it remains of little importance. Its main function is as a trans-shipment point where goods brought in small vessels from minor ports are transferred to the larger coasters. Samsun, however, with a population of 107 000, is both the largest town and the most frequented port of the whole Black Sea littoral. Interior overland routes westwards through Kastamonu and Bolu and eastwards along the Kelkit–Çoruh trough join the north-east to south-west route from Samsun through Çorum to Ankara, while the only railway to reach the coast east of Zonguldak does so at Samsun. The town is the focus of several fertile agricultural districts including the lower valleys and deltas of the Kızılırmak and Yeşilırmak. Significantly, Samsun has developed on a sheltered bay clear of the danger of silting rather than on a river-mouth site. The deltas are by nature poorly drained, but large areas have been reclaimed and provide extremely fertile farmland which supports a large and growing rural population. Rice is grown quite extensively, but the most valuable single crop is tobacco, for which this is the only important district outside the Aegean. Tobacco from the Bafra district is renowned for its high quality. Thus the trade of Samsun includes the shipment of agricultural produce, particularly export items, to İstanbul and of iron ore from Divriği to Zonguldak and Ereğli. The more varied cargoes landed at the port are widely distributed over central and eastern Anatolia.

East of the Yeşilırmak delta, in Ordu province, high mountains again run close to the sea, reaching a height of 3000 m (9800 feet) as little as 50 km (30 miles) inland. Only eight roads cross this formidable barrier in its total length of 500 km (310 miles), and all but three of them are of very poor quality. The three roads generally considered suitable for modern traffic are those from Ordu to the Kelkit valley and thence to Sivas, from Trabzon *via* Gümüşhane to Erzurum, and from Hopa to Artvin. In contrast to the western part of the Black Sea region, there is no modern road inland parallel to the coast. Of the three trans-montane routes, the most important is that which terminates at Trabzon, which was for many centuries used as an outlet to the Black Sea for overland traffic from Persia and Central Asia. The significance of this route declined after the construction of the railway from Ankara to Erzurum in the 1930s but in recent years both the port and the road leading to it have been revitalised, largely as a result of CENTO plans for the improvement of communications between member countries. Thus Trabzon itself, after a period of stagnation, has recently undergone rapid growth, its population increasing from 42 000 in 1955 to 66 000 in 1965. The city originated as a Greek colony in the 5th century B.C. and was a trading centre in Greek, Roman and Byzantine times. With the arrival of the Turks in Asia Minor, Trabzon (Trebizond) was the capital of an independent kingdom, cut off from the shrinking Byzantine empire by the growth of Ottoman power, to which it eventually succumbed.

Other towns along this eastern part of the Black Sea coast are small but numerous. Most are minor ports and harbours which ship the products of their immediate hinterlands to the larger trans-shipment points regularly visited by coastal steamers, such as Ordu, Giresun, Trabzon, Rize and Hopa. Their proliferation indicates the primacy of water transport as a means of movement along this part of the littoral. Despite its remoteness, this part of Turkey is very densely populated and the highest rural densities in the country, 150–200 per square km (375–500 per square mile) in places, are found in Trabzon province. A wide variety of high-value crops are grown of which the hazel-nut, tobacco and tea are the most important. These, together with maize, fruit and rich forest resources, support a large population at a modest level of prosperity. In recent years, however, the rate of population growth has been well below the national average, a fact which would seem to indicate a certain pressure on resources, which is countered by a steady flow of migration westwards to İstanbul and the Marmara region.

Inland, beyond the coastal plain and the lower hill slopes, population densities fall off rapidly and the mountains are devoted mainly to forestry and the rearing of livestock, especially cattle. Small-scale mineral exploitation is carried on in this part of the region. This includes the mining of silver in Gümüşhane province (gümüş = silver) but the only really important activity in this field is the extraction and smelting of copper at Murgul in the province of Artvin.

Chapter 12

THE MEDITERRANEAN REGION

The Mediterranean region (Fig. 47) covers an area of 59 000 square km (23 000 square miles) and has a population of 2·4 million. The overall population density is thus 40·7 per square km (105 per square mile), almost exactly the same as the national average. In this respect, however, as in many others, there is a clear distinction between the western part of the region—the Antalya province—and the east, comprising the provinces of İçel, Adana and Hatay. Antalya province occupies about one-third of the total area, but has a population of 486 000, whereas the other three provinces together have 1·9 million inhabitants, nearly 80% of the regional total. The two sections have densities of 23 and 50 per square km (60 and 130 per square mile) respectively. These contrasts draw attention to the fundamental differences between the two parts of the region. Antalya province remains remote, cut off from the interior and from neighbouring coastal regions by strong relief barriers, and is as yet relatively under-developed. In the east, the physical barriers are equally formidable, but this part of the region lies across the main routeway from İstanbul through Anatolia to the Levant and the mountains are crossed by major roads and railways. The agricultural resources of Adana, İçel and Hatay are superior to those of Antalya, industry has been developed on a larger scale and the three provinces are among the most densely settled and highly developed parts of Turkey.

On the other hand, the Mediterranean region as a whole derives a certain unity from the nature of its physical environment. Landforms throughout the region show the same contrast between high, deeply dissected mountain ranges and flat or gently sloping coastal and riverine plains. Along the coast itself, rugged, cliffed sections alternate with deltaic marshes and sand bars. The dominant unifying feature is, of course, the characteristic climatic régime, more typically 'Mediterranean' here than in any other part of the country. Summer temperatures are very high and winters mild (Adana: January mean: 9·1°C/48·4°F; August mean 28·0°C/82·4°F). Annual rainfall is quite high by Turkish standards, particularly in the west, where Antalya receives 1030 mm (40·6 inches) a year, compared with 611 mm (24·0 inches) at Adana, and amounts are much higher in the mountains. Summer drought, however, is very pronounced, the months of June to September being practically

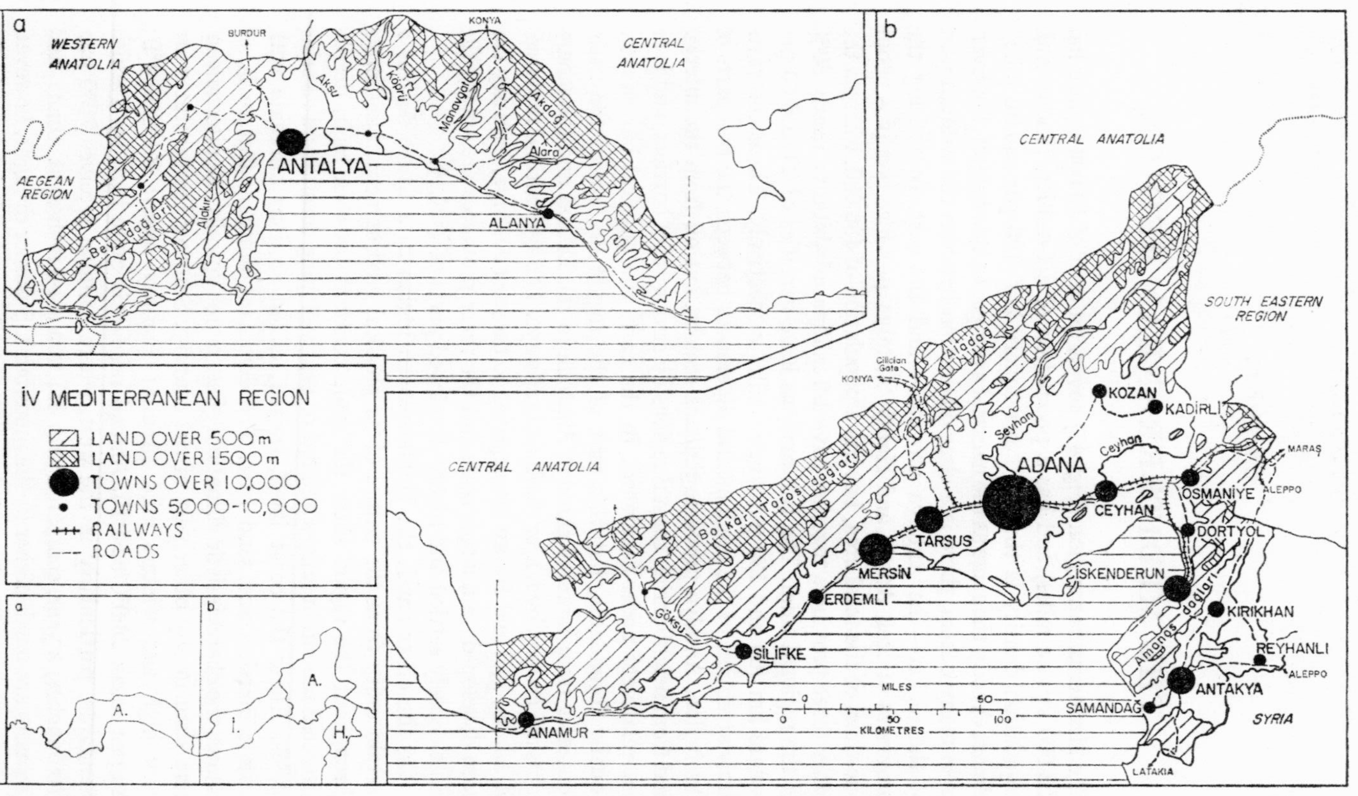

Fig. 47. The Mediterranean Region

rainless. Natural vegetation shows a distinct gradation with altitude. Maquis-type scrubland dominates the lowland while large areas of mountain country are covered with forest, which, though often degraded, is still a valuable resource. On the higher plateaux and in enclosed upland basins, grassland occurs. Temperature conditions in the lowland parts of the region are such as to permit the cultivation of a very great variety of crops and the main agricultural problem is that of organising a summer water supply. Once this is achieved, the agricultural potential is very great as has been shown by past developments in the Adana plain and plans now being put into effect in Antalya province.

In the extreme west of the region, the alignment of the Gulf of Antalya reflects the predominantly north–south trend of the Bey dağları (3086 m/10 122 feet) and adjacent ranges. Between these ranges run the deep-set valleys of small rivers like the Alakır, which form small strips of intensively farmed lowland, carrying the full range of Mediterranean crops. Along the coast, small harbours like that at Finike were, until recently, the only means of contact between these valleys and the outside world. Inland, the western Taurus contain a high proportion of limestones and karstic topography is well developed, particularly to the west of the Bey dağları. In this district there are large *polje* depressions, basins of internal drainage, some of which have been rendered highly productive by means of drainage and irrigation works. These basins, of which that developed around Elmalı is the most striking, now produce vines, fruit, cereals and sugar-beet, though winter cold prohibits the cultivation of olives or citrus fruits. Marshes and ephemeral lakes occupy the lower parts of the basins and provide summer grazing. Recent improvements to the Finike–Elmalı–Korkuteli–Antalya road have linked this part of the region to the provincial capital and provided an outlet for agricultural produce. The Elmalı and similar basins lie at heights of 1200–1300 m (3900–4100 feet) above sea level and now carry a sizeable permanent population. Elmalı is a town of some 8000 and Korkuteli has 6000 inhabitants. At higher altitudes there are many smaller basins, many of which are linked by transhumance to the Antalya plain. These high-level *ovalar*, whose villages are almost deserted in the winter months, are used in the summer by plain-dwellers who migrate there in the spring to find pasture for their flocks and to raise crops of wheat, barley and sugar-beet which they harvest before returning to the lowlands in September or October. This sort of movement is common throughout the Taurus ranges. The western part of Antalya province is a district rich in chrome ore and this mineral is extracted at a number of sites. A major check on production has been the problem of transport in an area where roads are bad and port facilities inadequate.

Recent road improvements, together with the modernisation of the port of Antalya (see below) will permit a more thorough exploitation of the chrome deposits.

The heart of the province is the Antalya plain, a triangular area between the mountains and the sea. However, the relief map is somewhat misleading in suggesting an extensive lowland, for the dominant feature of this area is a series of dry, scrub-covered karstic platforms, suitable only as very rough grazing for sheep and goats and carrying only small pockets of low-grade cultivation. Such conditions are most widespread in the western third of the plain immediately north of Antalya. The bulk of the cultivated land of the province lies in the valleys of the Aksu, Köprü, Manavgat and Alara rivers, which flow south to the sea between the spurs of the Taurus ranges, and in the alluvial coastal plain, some 10 km (6 miles) wide which runs eastwards for about 70 km (42 miles) from Antalya to the mouth of the Alara. Soils here are deep and rich, but much of the coast is fringed by a barrier of sand-dunes, which impede the natural drainage and cause problems of flooding and marsh formation.

The valleys and the coastal lowlands carry a full range of mediterranean crops, but until recently the intensity of land use was low, with most of the farmland under cereals, vines and pasture, and relatively little attention paid to tree crops. The region was greatly affected by the cotton boom of the 1950s (see p. 105) and much of the best land was placed under cotton. This had the effect of forcing cereal cultivation on to the more steeply sloping land, thus accelerating soil erosion and increasing the problems of silting and waterlogging in the plains. At the same time, the irrigation water derived from the various small irrigation schemes built in the area (Fig. 34, p. 122) was not always wisely used, while repeated crops of cotton caused soil deterioration in some places. After this 'false start', the agricultural development of the Antalya region is being put on a more sound basis by the application of a regional plan devised by F.A.O. and the Turkish Ministry of Agriculture. This aims at a more efficient use of the water resources of the area by a carefully designed system of regulating barrages and irrigation canals. A large dam has already been built on the Aksu river and others are planned. The output of high-value crops, particularly citrus fruits and vegetables, is on the increase and the total value of agricultural production from Antalya province is rising rapidly.

It has already been pointed out that, until a few years ago, the Antalya region was relatively under-developed and that this was due largely to its isolation from the remainder of the country. A number of improvements in communications have taken place in recent years. The road northwards to Burdur has been much improved and now provides an all-year route across the Taurus and the road along the coast has been reconstructed, though it is still of rather poor quality beyond Alanya. There is, however, no really satisfactory route westwards to the Aegean. The situation will be much improved by fulfilment of current plans for the development of the port of Antalya. The old harbour takes only very small vessels and larger ships have to be loaded and unloaded by lighter. Work is now in progress on the construction of a modern port which will take ships of 10 000 tons or more and this will provide an outlet both for the agricultural produce of the area and for the chrome ore of the western Taurus.

The Antalya plain was an area of advanced civilisation in classical times as witnessed by the remains of Perge, Aspendos, the port of Side and the fortress of Termessos guarding the western exit from the plain. Today, Antalya itself, founded in the 2nd century B.C., is the only town of any appreciable size. Over the past decade, the town has undergone fairly rapid development. Power is now available from the Kepez hydro-electric station and a cotton textile mill, a ferro-chrome plant and other, smaller industries have been established. These developments, together with the growing agricultural prosperity of the province and the establishment of a tourist industry, have led to rapid growth of the town, which doubled in size from 35 000 to 70 000 between 1955 and 1965. The other towns of the province are small agricultural markets strung out along the coast road. The largest of these is Alanya (12 000), a fortified site with a small harbour at the eastern extremity of the plain.

Beyond Alanya, the coastal plain disappears and as far as Silifke, a distance of about 200 km (125 miles) the mountains rise abruptly from the sea. It is this section of the coast which has long been a barrier to movement between the Antalya and Adana lowlands. Small lowland basins occur at intervals, the largest being that around the small port of Anamur (11 000). There is a major break in the Taurus ranges where the Göksu, rising to the north of the main crest-line, has cut a deep valley to the sea at Silifke (ancient Seleucia), now a town with some 12 000 inhabitants. The small delta has been reclaimed and forms a zone of intensive agriculture which extends inland up the valley floor. The modern road from Konya *via* Karaman down the Göksu valley to Silifke and thence to Mersin, takes advantage of a natural routeway across the Taurus previously neglected in favour of the traditional, though more difficult route through the Cilician gates.

North-eastwards from Silifke, there is a further stretch of coast, about 80 km (50 miles) long where the coastal plain is narrow but the mountains are set further back from the sea than in the Alanya–Silifke section. Here the main crest-line of the Taurus system reaches its greatest height of

3585 m (11 760 feet) in the Toros range. Beyond Mersin, the mountains run on in a north-easterly direction, but the coastline swings round towards the south-east. Between the mountains and the sea lie the delta plains of the Seyhan and Ceyhan rivers, one of the most extensive areas of alluvial lowland in the whole of Turkey. A series of low hills, which rise to between 300 and 600 m (1000–2000 feet) above sea level, run from north-west to south-east across the Ceyhan river east of Adana and then swing round to run parallel to the northern shore of the Gulf of İskenderun. These hills separate the Seyhan and Ceyhan deltas from the enclosed Ceyhan basin which stands about 80 m (250 feet) above sea level. The soils of both these areas are extremely fertile and temperature conditions are ideal for the cultivation of a wide range of sub-tropical crops. Throughout much of Turkish history, however, these plains have been rather thinly settled, with much of the land used only as winter pasture by nomadic stock-rearers from the surrounding hills. The underutilisation of this area was due mainly to its ill-drained, malarial nature and to the fact that much of it was flooded in the winter months and suffered from extreme drought in the summer. In modern times, and particularly over the last thirty years, a great deal of effort has gone into land reclamation. Barrages have been built across the Seyhan north of Adana and across the Ceyhan near Maraş (just beyond the eastern boundary of the region). These have served the triple purpose of controlling the flow of the rivers, providing irrigation water for the plains and generating electricity for the industries of the region. As a result, the Seyhan–Ceyhan plains have become some of the most productive farmlands of Turkey and the broad stretches of deep, level, stone-free soils have encouraged an unusually high degree of mechanisation. Development has so far been greatest in the Seyhan delta, south of Adana but the last decade has seen the process under way in the Ceyhan basin as well. A large proportion of the irrigated land is under cotton, to which the soils are particularly well suited. There remains, however, a considerable potential for further development. Large sections remain undrained and there is still much pastureland which, together with an increasing area of fodder crops, supports large numbers of livestock, including cattle. Tree crops are grown mainly at higher levels on platforms above the alluvial plain.

The region owes some of its importance to its position on the main routeway from Anatolia to the Levant and has long been the site of a number of important towns. In modern times there has been considerable industrial as well as agricultural development and several of these towns have grown rapidly. As a result the region is by Turkish standards, highly urbanised. Adana province, with 47% of the population classed as urban, is surpassed in this respect only by İstanbul, Ankara and İzmir.

Adana, with a population of 169 000 in 1955 and 290 000 in 1965, is Turkey's fourth largest city and one of the most rapidly expanding. In classical and medieval times, it took second place to Tarsus, which was then a port, but its rather more central position with relation to the Seyhan–Ceyhan plains and its function as a provincial capital have ensured its dominance of the region. The city stands on a low hill on the west bank of the Seyhan where the latter emerges from the foothills and is not only a major agricultural market but also an industrial centre of some importance. There are large cotton mills, an artificial fibres plant is under construction and there are factories processing olives, tobacco, timber and hides. River barges can reach the city, but its main outlet is through Mersin, to which it is linked by rail.

Mersin, the capital of İçel province, had a population of 50 000 in 1955 and 87 000 in 1965. It has been the main port of the Adana plain since Tarsus was silted up in early medieval times. The city has taken on a new lease of life in the modern period and its port facilities were greatly improved in the 1950s. The location of Mersin at the western end of the plain frees it from the danger of silting and its road and rail connexions with the interior give it a large hinterland. Thus, through the port pass not only the agricultural products of the Seyhan–Ceyhan lowlands but also the copper of Ergani, the chrome of Güleman and a large proportion of Turkey's oil imports from the Middle East. Industries include cotton textiles and various alimentary activities, but the most significant item is the Mersin oil refinery, the largest in the country. This was built to process crude oil imported from the Arab countries and this remains its chief function, but the refinery also handles part of the Ramandağ output, which is shipped coastwise from the pipeline terminal at İskenderun. The oil industry of the Adana plain seems likely to undergo expansion in the near future. Oil and gas have both been discovered in the area and there is a possibility that large reserves exist here and beneath the Gulf of İskenderun. Other possible future developments include the construction of pipelines to Mersin or İskenderun from the oilfields of Iraq and Iran, though no final decision has yet been taken.

Tarsus, which now has a population of 58 000, is perhaps the best-known city of this region, by virtue of its association with St Paul, and was the main port and commercial centre in classical times. For several centuries, the city was a strong point on the frontier between the Byzantine and Arab worlds and guarded the southern approach to the strategically vital Cilician Gates. Its port has been lost to Mersin and its commercial and administrative functions to Adana so that Tarsus today is primarily an agricultural market. It does, however, have alimentary industries, and a plant for the manufacture of textile dyestuffs is under construction.

Other important towns of the region include Ceyhan (41 000), market centre of the Ceyhan basin, and Osmaniye (34 000), a communications centre where road and railway to İskenderun branch off from the main route into eastern Turkey.

Immediately east of Osmaniye, the north–south line of the Amanos dağları separates the Seyhan–Ceyhan lowlands from the interior basin of Hatay province, a northward continuation of the rift valley system which runs parallel to the Levant coast. The Ası (Orontes) river, flowing northwards from Syria, turns abruptly south-westwards across Hatay to the sea and the interior basin drains southwards into the river *via* Amık Gölü. Thus Hatay province consists of a narrow coastal plain, a high mountain ridge and an interior rift-valley trough. The most noteworthy feature of the coastal plain is the port of İskenderun (Alexandretta). Traditionally the port for Aleppo, İskenderun had a population of 10 000 when it was transferred to Turkey in 1939 and now has about 70 000 inhabitants. Most of the Syrian traffic has been diverted to Latakia, and İskenderun functions mainly as an alternative to Mersin for the trade of Mediterranean and eastern Turkey. Its importance has been augmented by its choice as a pipe-line terminal and as a military centre and naval base. Current plans for the construction of a major steelworks will greatly enhance the industrial importance of İskenderun and indeed of the whole Adana–Hatay region.

The interior basin of Hatay centres on Antakya (Antioch), now a city of 58 000 with alimentary and silk and cotton textile industries. The basin itself is very fertile and produces cereals, cotton, rice, vines, fruit and tobacco, but large parts remain liable to flooding and further drainage and irrigation works are required.

Chapter 13

WESTERN ANATOLIA

This region (Fig. 48) which comprises the six provinces of Kütahya, Uşak, Denizli, Afyon, Isparta and Burdur, is a compact block of territory covering some 59 000 square km (23 000 square miles) and has a population of just over 2 million. Total population density and degree of urbanisation are both well below the national average, but rural density and the proportion of land under cultivation are both very close to the Turkish mean. Western Anatolia is bounded on one side by the Aegean region and on the other by Central Anatolia, and is, in many aspects of its geography, both physical and human, a zone of transition between the two. It forms a generally high-standing area which rises well above the level of the central Anatolian plains and, when viewed from the west, is a mountainous barrier through which routes from the coast to the interior must climb. The drainage pattern of the region is centrifugal. The western half drains towards the Aegean *via* the Büyük Menderes and Gediz rivers and tongues of land less than 500 m (1640 feet) above sea level protrude into the region along those valleys. In the south, beyond the Bozdağ, Sogut dağları and other south-west to north-east-trending ridges, drainage is to the Mediterranean via the Dalaman and Aksu systems. The south-eastern part of the region is characterised by the presence of a number of lakes. The smaller ones, like Acıgöl (Bitter Lake) and Lake Burdur, are salt and form the centres of basins of internal drainage, but the much more extensive Lake Eğridir is a freshwater lake and drains south by underground seepage through limestone rocks. In the north of the region, the rivers flowing through Tavşanlı and Kütahya are tributaries of the Simav and Sakarya respectively and thus drain to the Sea of Marmara and the Black Sea. Finally, in the western part of Afyon province there are a number of basins of inland drainage similar in all but size to those of Central Anatolia. The numerous valleys of western Anatolia form extensive areas of level or gently sloping land at heights below 1000 m (3280 feet). Above them rises a confused mass of highly dissected upland with a general summit level of 1000–1500 m (3000–5000 feet), culminating in mountain ranges which in many places rise above 2000 m (6500 feet).

The absence of any clearly marked topographic grain in western Anatolia as a whole, distinguishes it both from the Aegean region, with its clear-cut east–west trend-lines, and from Central Anatolia with its alternation of mountain and plain. One result of the relief of the region is that there is no single focal point and settlement, agriculture and industry tend to occur in a number of separate clusters. At the same time, the function of the region as a link between the Aegean and Central Anatolia is emphasised by its relatively dense network of communications and by

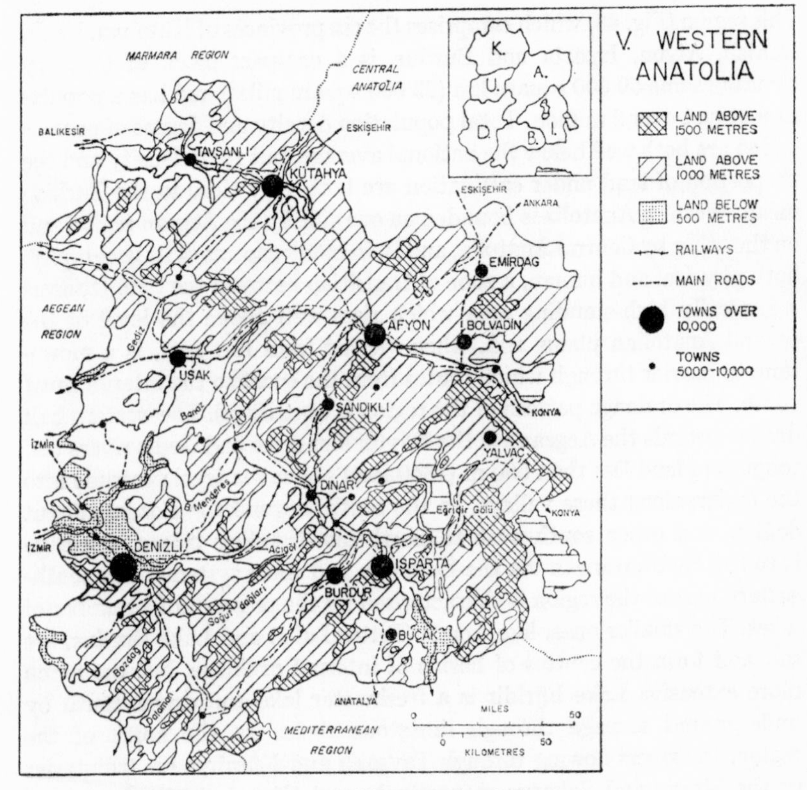

Fig. 48. Western Anatolia

the number of important roads and railways which pass through it. Three railways, ascending from the Aegean to the interior run right across the region. The most northerly of these, which is linked also to the Sea of Marmara *via* Balikesir, passes through Kütahya, *en route* from Balıkesir to Eskişehir. The central line, after climbing the Gediz valley from İzmir, runs through Uşak to Afyon and thence to Konya and the east. The Büyük Menderes line passes near Denizli and terminates at Eğridir, throwing off branches to Burdur and Isparta. At right-angles to these, and running from north to south across the region, is the Eskişehir–

Kütahya–Afyon–Burdur line which at one stage was planned to continue to Antalya, thus linking the Mediterranean with the Sea of Marmara. Modern roads now parallel the majority of these railways lines and provide additional links where necessary. Once again the most important routes run from west to east. Particularly significant are those from İzmir *via* Denizli and Isparta to Konya and *via* Uşak to Afyon. The only major north–south road is that through Afyon and Burdur. These roads and railways, it should be emphasised, were built primarily as inter-regional links, connecting Central Anatolia with the coast: only incidentally do they tap the resources of western Anatolia which, by reason of its position rather than its intrinsic importance, has a communications network superior to that of most other regions.

As has already been indicated, agricultural and industrial development has taken place in a number of separate pockets, each focused on an urban centre which is a road or rail junction and agricultural market. Thus the general pattern is one of a series of towns, each with some industrial importance, surrounded by a zone of fairly intensive agriculture. Each is separated from the others by area of low intensity land use, involving cereal growing and livestock grazing at lower levels and forestry on the higher slopes. Kütahya (49 000) is the most northerly example. Crops grown in the vicinity include cereals, sugar-beet, vegetables, fruit and tobacco and the town has a variety of alimentary industries. A noteworthy local speciality is the manufacture of pottery and china, an activity which dates back many centuries and for which the town is particularly noted. Another specialism is the making of pipes and other articles from meerschaum, which is extracted in the vicinity, and there are also carpet works, tanneries and a large chemical plant producing nitrates. Kütahya province has large deposits of lignite which are extensively worked at Tunçbilek, some 10 km (6 miles) north of Tavşanlı. These now make a major contribution to the country's energy supplies, feeding a large thermal-electric power plant which is connected to a grid system covering much of north-western Turkey. Uşak (36 000) stands at 900 m (3000 feet) on a tributary of the Büyük Menderes and has a sugar-beet factory, woollen mills and carpet works. The largest town in western Anatolia is now Denizli, the population of which has doubled over the past decade to reach 60 000. Standing only 400 m (1300 feet) above sea level, Denizli is the centre of a district where agriculture is akin to that of the Aegean region, with cotton, tobacco, vines and olives as well as cereals, vegetables and fruit. There is a long-established textile industry, now drawing its power from the Çal hydro-electric station and processing wool, cotton and flax. Burdur (30 000) and Isparta (42 000) both overlook rather dry plains which have to some extent been made productive by irrigation, and have benefited from the fact that they are railheads not only for the local area but also for the Antalya plain. Their industries include textiles, leather and the production of attar of roses. Finally, Afyon (44 000) now of growing importance as a communications centre is best known for the production of opium, from which it takes its name.

All the towns mentioned originated in classical times and have a long history of trade. In recent years a number of smaller centres have grown rapidly, notably Dinar (12 000) which is an important communications centre and the site of a hydro-electric plant.

Chapter 14

CENTRAL ANATOLIA

Central Anatolia (Fig. 49) is, by a large margin, the biggest of the eight regions, its 210 000 square km (81 000 square miles) representing more than a quarter of the total area of Turkey. Its population is slightly in excess of 7 million, and Central Anatolia is one of the less densely populated regions, yet at the same time has the highest proportion (28%) of land under cultivation. The predominance of low intensity forms of land use and the significance of the Central Anatolian grainlands to the economy of Turkey have been discussed in Chapter 6 and a general description of the physical environment was given in Part I. It should again be emphasised that there is a considerable variety of relief with an altitude range of some 1700 m (5500 feet) between the lowest basin floors, which stand between 800 and 900 m (2500–3000 feet) above sea level, and mountain peaks rising to 2500 m (8200 feet) or more. The popular use of the term 'Anatolian plateau' to describe Central Anatolia as a whole is extremely misleading since it suggests a monotony of landscape which, although it certainly exists in some districts, is markedly absent from others. Subdivision of this vast area is necessary to give some idea of the wide range of conditions to be found within it.

Sakarya Basin

The north-western part of the region, covering the province of Eskişehir and extending into northern Konya and western Ankara, constitutes the upper drainage basin of the Sakarya river and is one of the more favoured districts. East of Eskişehir, which stands close to the western boundary of the region, relief shows a pronounced grain from west-north-west to east-south-east. The broad, open plains of the Sakarya and its tributary the Porsuk are separated by rolling uplands which culminate in the peaks of the Sivrihisar and Sündiken ranges. A third mountain area, the Koroğlu dağları, forms the northern boundary of the region. The plains are extensively farmed for cereals and sugar-beet, while large areas of pasture support numerous livestock, among which sheep are of particular importance. Grain yields are appreciably higher than the average for Central Anatolia owing to the more plentiful and reliable rainfall, and this is Turkey's most important sugar-beet area. This was one of the districts which was particularly affected by the expansion of the culti-

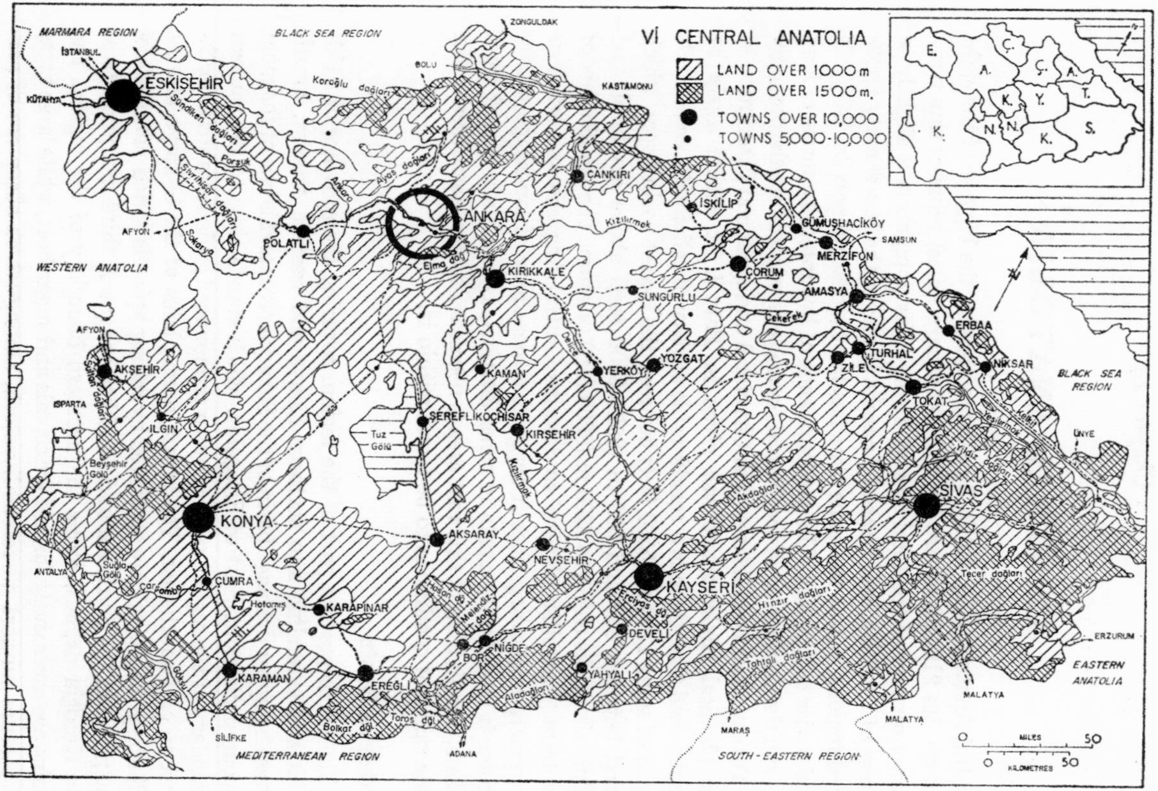

Fig. 49. Central Anatolia

vated area which took place in the 1950s, when the land under cereals in Eskişehir province increased by 83%, from 150 000 to 275 000 ha (370 000 to 680 000 acres). The area under sugar-beet more than doubled in the same period. In addition to its relatively favourable environment this part of the region has definite advantages of location, lying as it does quite close to the Sea of Marmara and at the place where the narrow defile of the middle Sakarya opens out into the broad basins along that river's upper course. In this district the ancient routeway from the east along the southern foothills of the Pontic ranges, met the diagonal route across Asia Minor from the Straits to the Levant. In modern times road and railway from the Sea of Marmara reach the interior in this area and Eskişehir stands at the junction of the 'Berlin–Baghdad' railway with the line through Ankara to eastern Turkey. Thus Eskişehir is a major focal point in the communications system and a link between the Marmara region and the interior as well as being the centre of a prosperous agricultural district. The city is now the sixth largest in the country, with a population of 173 000 and a mixed industrial structure which includes flour-milling, sugar-refining, woollen textiles, railway engineering and the manufacture of cement, bricks and tiles. Chrome ore, manganese and lignite are mined in the district in small quantities and a large hydro-electric station at Sarıyar on the Sakarya feeds power to the grid system.

Ankara District

Broad, open plains with a rather lower intensity of land use and a lower population density extend from the Sakarya eastwards towards Ankara and south towards Konya. Polatlı, a railway town of some 20 000, acts as the collecting centre for the grain and animal products of this area.

Some 50 km (30 miles) west of Ankara, relief becomes more accidented where a number of mountain masses, including the Ayaş and Elmadağ ranges, protrude southwards from the Koroğlu dağları. The Ankara river flows from east to west across this district, receiving tributaries from the mountains to the north, and this zone is the most densely settled part of the large Ankara province. In the sheltered basins which occur here, agriculture becomes more varied, with considerable areas of fruit, vegetables and vines, in addition to the ubiquitous cereals and grazing land. Near the head of the Ankara valley and close to the watershed between the Sakarya and Kızılırmak river systems, stands Ankara itself, capital of the Turkish Republic since 1923 and now a rapidly growing metropolis with a population approaching a million.

Although present-day Ankara is largely a modern city, the site has been occupied for at least three thousand years. It was an important centre in

Hittite times, a Phrygian fortress, capital of the Celtic Kingdom of Galatia and headquarters of the Roman province of the same name. The city was an administrative, commercial and military centre in Byzantine times and throughout the Ottoman and Seljuk periods. The growth of Ankara to its present size, however, has taken place mainly during the last seventy years and particularly since it was chosen as the national capital in 1923.

The general location of the city is shown in Fig. 49 and a more detailed picture of the site can be obtained from Fig. 50(*a*). The capital stands on the south side of the Ankara river, near the confluence of the Çubuk. flowing in from the north and the Hatip and İncesu streams which drain northwards from the slopes of Elmadağ. The floor of the main valley is about 1000 m wide, flat and badly drained. Above it, the hills rise, gently at first and then more steeply, away from the confluence. The old core of the city stands on a steep, rocky eminence, crowned by the Seljuk citadel (Hisar) and probably the site of earlier defensive works. This is defended by massive walls on the western and southern sides and by natural gorges on the north and east. The classical and medieval city spread out from the citadel down the slopes to the west and south, and was enclosed by a wall. The city remained small, however, until the modern period of growth which began with the arrival of the railway from Eskişehir in 1892. For the next thirty years, expansion took place mainly on the north side of the İncesu between that stream and the Ankara river. With the choice of Ankara as the national capital, growth was much accelerated and the built-up area spread rapidly southwards into the foothills of the Çal dağı.

The city still tends to be divided into two parts by the İncesu river, now canalised, and the railway running parallel to it. The northern, older part, contains the close-packed residential district of Hisar (Fig. 50(*b*)), in and around the citadel. The adjacent rocky hill known as Altındağ is now crowded with low-grade housing, mainly occupied by recent immigrants, particularly those from the eastern provinces. To the west of these areas runs the north–south spine road of Çankırı Caddesi and its modern extension into Atatürk Bulvarı. Along this street, and particularly around Ulus Meydanı (Nation Square), there has developed a modern commercial area with shops, offices and banks. Atatürk Bulvarı continues to the south of the railway line, through the Kavaklidere and Çankaya districts of the new city (Yenişehir) to terminate at the presidential palace, which overlooks the city from the south. Immediately south of the railway is the commercial centre of Yenişehir with its modern offices and shops, a district now focused on Kızılay Meydanı (Red Crescent Square), and south again are the imposing buildings of various govern-

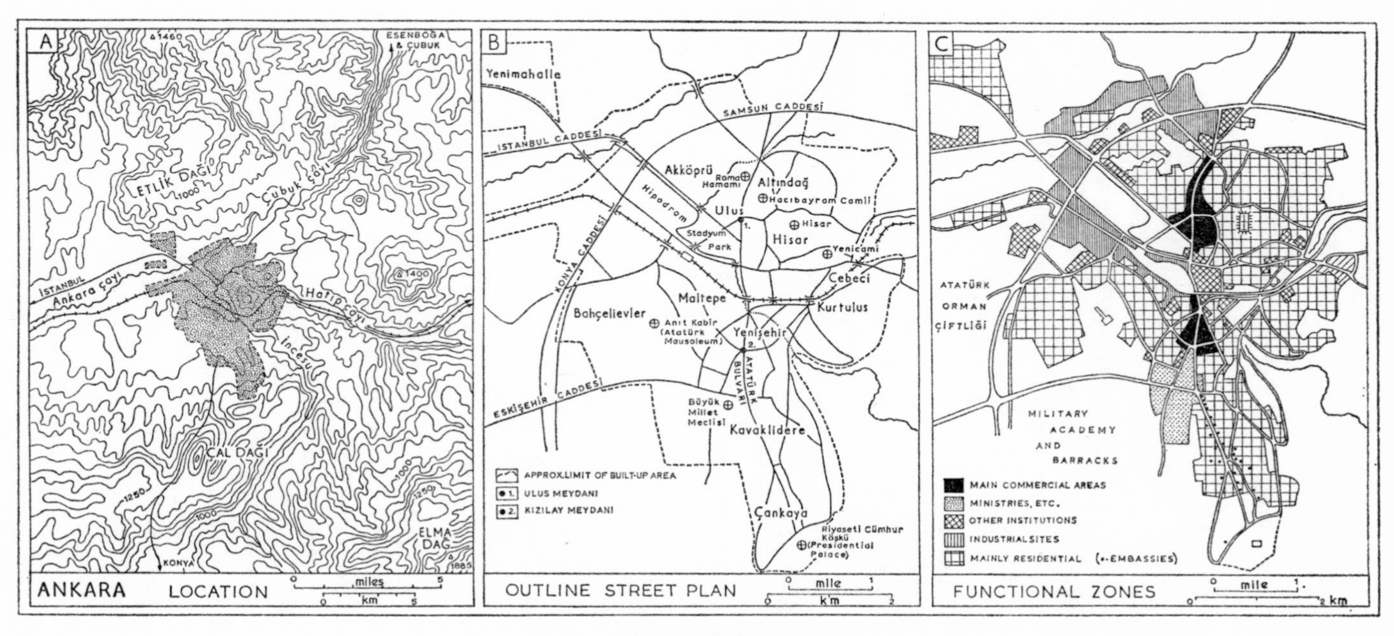

Fig. 50. Ankara

ment ministries and the National Assembly (Büyük Millet Meclisi). Middle- and high-quality residential districts have developed immediately behind Atatürk Bulvarı and these, in Çankaya district, contain the many embassy buildings. Middle-class housing development is set further back from the main road, as at Bahçelievler and Kurtulus. Industrial building has occurred along the line of the railway and this, together with the preservation of an open space containing the Gençlik (Youth) Park, sports ground and stadium, tends to perpetuate the division of the city into two parts. In recent years, a system of modern highways has been built along the western side of the city, providing exits for the İstanbul, Eskişehir and Konya roads and industries have been established on flat land along the Ankara river. Shortage of space for further development is now becoming a problem. The new roads and industrial sites, together with the experimental farm bequeathed to the nation by Atatürk (Atatürk Orman Ciftliği), the military academy (Harp Okulu) and barracks check expansion to the north and west, while steep slopes discourage growth on the southern and eastern sides. Thus new housing areas have been forced well out from the city centre and the separate residential district of Yenimahalle is likely to be followed by other similar developments. The shortage of flat land close to the centre is emphasised by the fact that the modern airport at Esenboğa is some 30 km away, on the road leading to the Çubuk reservoir from which Ankara draws much of its water. Present-day Ankara shows vivid contrasts in its urban landscape as, for example, that between the poor residential districts of the old city and the modern suburbs which would not look out of place in western Europe, or between the bazaars and small shops of the old city and the modern stores and offices of Yenişehir, now dominated by a 20-storey tower block at Kızılay Meydanı. Although predominantly an administrative and commercial city, collecting point for the agricultural produce of a large area and the site of numerous offices and educational establishments. Ankara is not without industrial importance, with its flour mills, tanneries, cement works, chemical plant and varied engineering activities.

Tuz Gölü and Konya Basins

South of Ankara, beyond the broken hill country of the Elma dağ and neighbouring ranges, is the most featureless part of Central Anatolia, the great plains which occupy the bulk of the area to the west of the Kızılırmak and north of the Taurus ranges. Low upswellings, which separate the upper Sakarya basin from the plain of the Tuz Gölü and the latter from the Konya *ova* are barely discernible as surface features. Only in a few places, notably along the northern edge of the Konya basin, do small mountain masses, mainly volcanic, protrude above the subdued relief. This is the driest part of Central Anatolia, with an annual rainfall as low as 250 mm (10 inches) in places, and the area is virtually devoid of surface streams. As a result of these adverse moisture conditions, it is also the most thinly populated part of the region, with densities below 15 per square km (40 per square mile) over large areas. Cereals and pasture occupy virtually all the farmland, with a few pockets of vines, fruit and vegetables in more favoured districts, mainly along the foot of the Taurus. The difficulties of agriculture in this area are increased by the problem of flooding in the lower parts. Despite the low rainfall, large quantities of water run into the basins from the surrounding hills and in spring large areas are likely to be submerged. In the absence of any natural outlet to these basins of internal drainage, the water is slow to clear and parts may remain waterlogged all through the summer. The obvious example is the Tuz Gölü itself which fluctuates greatly in size and may in summer be reduced to a depth of 1 or 2 feet, but similar conditions occur in the Konya basin, notably around the Hotamış swamp. Large parts of the Tuz Gölü basin, in particular remain uncultivated, partly because of waterlogging and partly because of summer drought, though the one large stream flowing into this basin has been controlled by a barrage and is used for irrigation around Aksaray. In contrast, the slightly higher land to the west and south has for the most part been put under dry-farmed cereals with some sugar-beet, since 1950.

The Konya *ova* illustrates both the problems and potentialities of the Anatolian basins of internal drainage. Conditions here are extremely dry: indeed, around Karapınar there is an area, several square kilometres in extent, of true sand desert, although only 30 km (18 miles) away the Hotamış depression is covered with water for the greater part of the year. The relief of the *ova* is such as to give an artesian structure, and wells sunk in the centre of the basin flow without pumping: unfortunately the artesian water is brackish and thus of little value for irrigation. However, the streams which descend from the Taurus do offer possibilities for irrigation and a number of schemes are in operation. The largest of these is at Çumra, south of Konya, where more than 25 000 ha (62 000 acres) are irrigated from the Çarşamba river, on which lakes Beyşehir and Suğla act as natural regulators. Inevitably, the lowest parts of the *ova* must act as sumps into which surplus water drains. Suggestions that the surplus should be removed from the basin altogether by pumping it into the Tuz Gölü seem unlikely to be put into effect owing to the enormous cost involved.

Along the southern edge of the Konya basin is a hill-foot zone where conditions for agriculture are a good deal more favourable, even without irrigation, and there is a good deal of vine, vegetable and fruit growing. This zone has also been a major routeway for many centuries and is now followed by a modern road as well as by the 'Berlin–Baghdad' railway. Along this route lie several towns. Ereğli (38 000) stands near the northern approach to the Cilician Gates and is close to the railway junction for Kayseri and Sivas. There is a hydro-electric station a short distance away at İvriz and Ereğli has a cotton textile mill, drawing its raw cotton from the Adana plain. In the plain below Ereğli is the Ayrancı irrigated area. 80 km (48 miles) to the west, Karaman (26 000) has long been of some importance as a route junction where the road down the Göksu valley to the Mediterranean leaves that along the southern edge of Central Anatolia. The largest city of the area, and the second largest in Central Anatolia, is Konya, which in 1965 had a population of 158 000 compared with 92 000 ten years previously. Under the classical name of Iconium, Konya was an important point on the route from Ephesus to Tarsus. It later became the capital of the Seljuk Kingdom of Rum and was an important administrative centre throughout Ottoman times, gaining added renown as the centre of the Mevlevi Dervish sect. Until 1923 it could generally be considered a good deal more important than Ankara. Konya's main function today is that of administrative centre for the largest province of Turkey and as a market and communications focus. Its industries are mainly concerned with agricultural products—it has a large sugar-beet factory and a number of flour mills—and its recent rapid growth is due mainly to the increasing agricultural productivity of its region. Its Seljuk and Ottoman monuments have given Konya a certain attraction as a tourist centre and its association with the Dervishes makes it a place of pilgrimage.

East-Central Anatolia

Immediately east of the Tuz Gölü, a fault-line scarp some 300 m (1000 feet) high separates the lake flats from the Kochisar uplands, which run for 150 km (90 miles) from north-west to south-east and terminate in the volcanic massifs of Hasan dağı (3253 m/10 670 feet) and Melendiz dağı (2935 m/9627 feet) north-west of Niğde. This upland forms the watershed between the interior drainage basins and the basin of the upper Kızılırmak and a continuation of the same line in a northerly direction, passing east of Ankara and west of Çankırı, separates the middle Kızılırmak from the upper Sakarya. By far the greater part of Central Anatolia to the east of this divide lies in the catchment of the Kızılırmak, Turkey's largest river, which follows a horseshoe-shaped course of more than 700 km (420 miles) before it breaks through the Pontic ranges in the province of Çorum. Only the far north-east, drained by the Yeşilırmak system and the south-east, drained by the headwaters of the Fırat, lie outside the Kızılırmak basin.

This major river rises in the north-eastern corner of Central Anatolia in the angle between the Yıldız dağları, most southerly of the Pontic ranges, and the Tecer dağları, most northerly of the Taurus folds. The upper part of the river for a distance of about 160 km (100 miles), between Sivas and Kayseri, flows towards the south-west in a series of narrow, faulted depressions between the Akdağlar and Hınzır dağları ranges. The cultivated land of this zone occurs for the most part on terraces along the valley and is devoted mainly to cereals. Lower grade cereal land and a great deal of pasture are found at higher levels and there are pockets of fairly intensive farming in some of the tributary valleys. From Kayseri westwards, another element enters the landscape in the form of a series of high volcanic peaks, including Erciyas dağı (3916 m/12 860 feet) and the Hasan dağı group. The rich volcanic soils on the lower slopes provide ideal conditions for viticulture and give rise to an area of more prosperous agriculture in the Kayseri–Niğde–Nevşehir triangle. The two major cities of the region, Kayseri (class: Caesarea) and Sivas (class: Megalopolis) both owe much of their importance to their function as foci of communications. Sivas (105 000) stands at the point where routes along the northern and southern edges of Central Anatolia converge before passing eastwards to the upper Firat, and where the railway to the Black Sea at Samsun leaves the main Ankara–Erzurum line. Kayseri (127 000) is the meeting place of railways from Ankara and Konya and is on the shortest route from the capital to Adana. In addition, both Sivas and Kayseri have links with the Mediterranean, via Malatya and Maraş respectively. Consequently, Kayseri and Sivas, which are the ninth and tenth largest cities in Turkey, are important mainly as agricultural markets and administrative and commercial centres for their large hinterlands. At Sivas, industry is almost entirely alimentary, concerned with grain and livestock products. Kayseri has undergone rather greater industrialisation in recent times. Its cotton mills are among the largest in the country and there are several sizeable engineering works. Hydro-electric stations at Bünyan and Sızır provide power and the city is also linked to the new station at Hırfanlı.

Beyond Kayseri, the Kızılırmak swings first north-west and then north to pass 50 km (30 miles) east of Ankara at Kırıkkale. In this section, the valley is wider and the plains above it are more open, but rainfall is small and agriculture is again restricted to extensive cereal and livestock production. Population densities are generally low. The 70 km (43 miles) stretch of the valley south of Kırıkkale, however, has become of considerable importance as a source of power. Large hydro-electric plant have been built at Hırfanlı and Keşikköprü and these, together with the smaller plant at Kırıkkale, are linked by high-voltage transmission lines to the Black Sea, Marmara and Aegean regions as well as to Ankara, Konya and Kayseri. Kırıkkale itself is the site of Turkey's only steel mill outside Zonguldak province. Although the main source of power is hydro-electricity, the site has relatively easy rail access to Zonguldak coal as well as to the pig-iron of Karabük. The steelworks was originally associated with an armaments factory, but it now produces alloy steels for other industries as well and there is also a copper plant. The presence of this source of metals has done much to assist the development of engineering activities in Ankara which is only 100 km (60 miles) away.

North of Kırıkkale, the Kızılırmak turns north-east and passes through an upland basin which, together with the valley of the Delice, provides better opportunities for agriculture. Here there are larger areas of cultivable land, rainfall is more plentiful and, as a result, population densities are much higher than in districts further to the south. One of the most densely populated and intensively farmed parts of Central Anatolia lies further east, across the watershed, where sheltered, well-watered basins occur in Amasya and Tokat provinces along the Yeşilırmak and its tributaries, the Kelkit and Çekerek. In these basins, cereal yields are relatively high and a good deal of land is devoted to vines, fruit and sugar-beet, and sugar-beet processing plant have been built at Amasya and Turhal. The whole of this northern zone, from Çankırı through Çorum and Amasya to Tokat is noteworthy for its general prosperity when compared with most other parts of the Anatolian interior.

Thus Central Anatolia is a region with considerable internal diversity. The west, though it does contain pockets of intensive, mixed cultivation, is dominated by the great plains, devoted to extensive cereal-growing and livestock-rearing. The east has a much more varied terrain and mountains occupy large areas so that the amount of cultivated land is much smaller. Pasture- and grainlands are still dominant but there are, particularly in the north, important pockets of much more intensive agriculture.

Chapter 15

EASTERN ANATOLIA

This (Fig. 51) is the second largest of the eight regions and covers an area of 158 000 square km (61 000 square miles). With a population of only 3·8 million, however, it is the most thinly peopled of all, with a density of only 24 per square km (62 per square mile). It is also the region with smallest proportion (8·4%) of its land under cultivation and, with the exception of the Black Sea Coastlands, has a smaller area of cultivated land per head (0·45 ha/1·1 acres) and a lower degree of urbanisation (22·7%) than any other region. These data reflect both the extremely harsh environment prevailing over most of eastern Anatolia and the prominent position of live-stock in the agricultural economy. Although the structure of the region is highly complex (see Chapter 1), relief shows a pronounced east–west trend and an alternation of mountain and plateau masses rising well above 2000 m (65 000 feet), with deep-set valleys and basins at heights ranging from 700 m (2300 feet) above sea level in the west to more than 1500 m (5000 feet) in the east.

In the extreme north, a bordering range, comprising the Gümüşhane and Rize dağları, rises above 3500 m (11 500 feet) within 30 km (18 miles) of the Black Sea coast. This formidable mountain barrier is breached in the east by the lower Çoruh and in the west by the Harşit valley, the latter forming the traditional route to the coast, though the modern road crosses a 2500 m (8200 feet) pass to reach Trabzon more directly. Immediately south of these northern ranges, lies the Kelkit–Çoruh trough, deep and narrow for most of its length but rising to an open, high-level watershed immediately west of Bayburt, where the road from Erzurum to the coast makes its way towards the head of the Harşit valley. The Kelkit–Çoruh trough is bounded on its southern side by a mountain mass comprising the Keşiş and Çimen-Kop dağları, which widens and increases in height eastwards to the Oltu valley. Beyond the Oltu, this upland opens out into the high, dissected lava plateaux of Kars province. South again, a further depression is drained westwards by the upper Fırat and eastwards by the headwaters of the Aras, the city of Erzurum standing close to the watershed between these two river systems. Towards the western edge of the region, the Fırat turns sharply to the south, cutting through the mountain barrier across its path, while in the east the Aras flows in a broad plain, forming the frontier with the Soviet Union. This

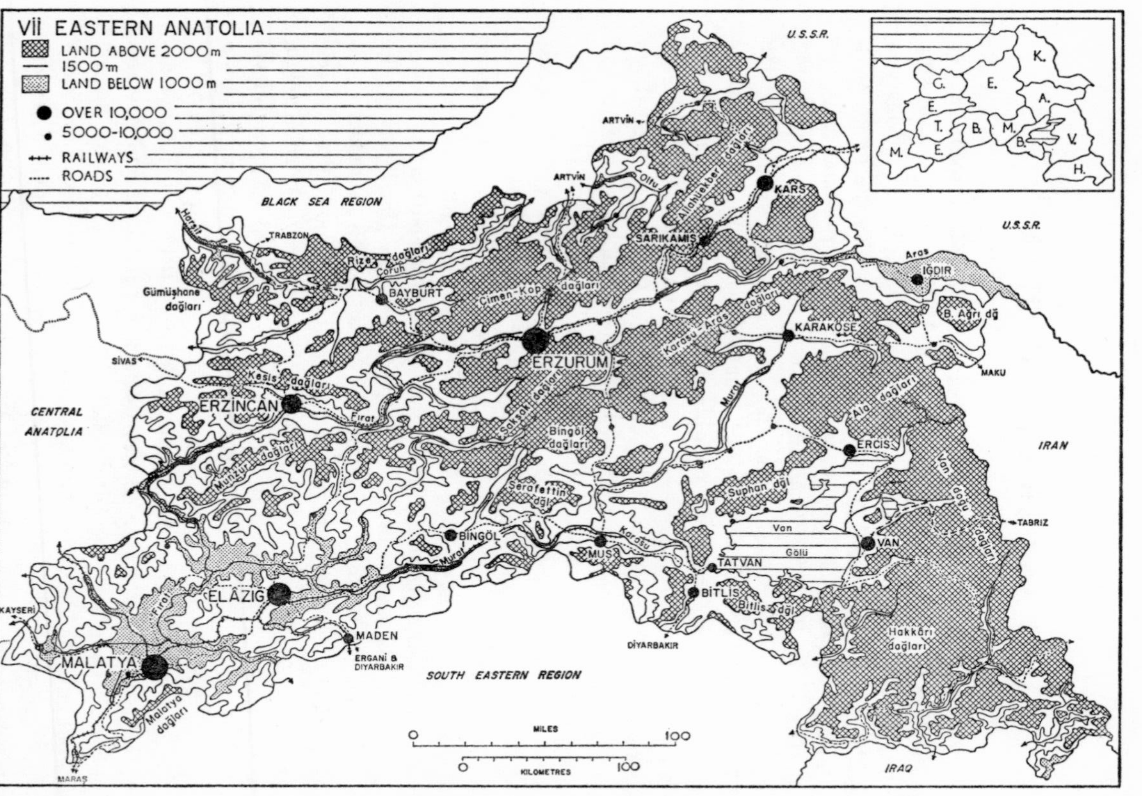

Fig. 51. Eastern Anatolia

Fırat–Aras depression is fault-bounded along much of its length and is the main west–east routeway across the region, now followed by the railway from Ankara to Leninakan in Soviet Armenia. The route is, however, by no means an easy one, for the Fırat follows a winding course and is often sharply incised, particularly in the section between Erzurum and Erzincan. The next mountain barrier to the south is, in its eastern part, a continuous upland more than 2000 m (6500 feet) high, culminating in the volcanic cone of the Büyük Ağrı Dağı (Mount Ararat: 5165 m/16 940 feet). Towards the west, however, this barrier is more broken and there are passes on either side of the Munzur dağları.

The southern half of eastern Anatolia has a more complex structure and relief and lacks the simple alternation of mountain range and valley trough typical of the northern part. In the west, the Fırat and its main tributary, the Murat, flow in broad basins less than 800 m (2600 feet) above sea level around and between Malatya and Elâzığ, before entering another narrow section from Malatya to Maden. Turkey's largest hydro-electric power plant is now under construction at Keban on a gorge section of the Fırat between Elâzığ and Malatya. Above Elâzığ, the Murat valley climbs eastwards through a succession of basins to reach Bingöl and Muş, small provincial capitals in two of the larger basins, and is followed by the railway to Lake Van. From Muş, the valley turns away northwards to Karaköse and in this section the river flows in a broad, open basin developed on lava plateaux not dissimilar to those around Kars. This basin is bounded on its south-eastern side by a series of impressive volcanic peaks (Ala dağ: 3351 m/11 000 feet; Suphan dağı: 4434 m/14 500 feet), which separate it from the basin of Lake Van. The latter, enclosed on its southern side by the faulted block of the Bitlis range, has no surface outlet, though there is probably some underground drainage to the Karasu tributary of the Murat and possibly to the small stream which flows south through Bitlis. Around Lake Van are several old shore-lines marking earlier, higher lake levels and there are a number of lacustrine flats, notably round Van and Ercis. Beyond the lake, to the east and south-east are the tangled mountain chains of Van and Hakârı provinces, where flat land is almost non-existent and population densities are the lowest in the country.

It will be apparent from the foregoing brief account of the topography of the region that eastern Anatolia offers a number of diverse landscape elements with varying possibilities for agriculture. The most favoured districts are the enclosed basins or *ovalar*, which occur at intervals along the river valleys. Most of these have abnormally low rainfall, but at the same time are subject to flooding and thus require both river control and irrigation works before they can become fully productive. When this is done, they form pockets of intensive arable farming, with fruit, vegetables, vines and small areas of cotton, tobacco and sugar-beet in addition to cereals. The largest of these basins and the most extensive irrigation works are around Malatya and Elâzığ and these provinces have about 12% of their area under crops. Similar basins, smaller in size and at greater altitudes, occur around Erzincan, Bingöl and Muş. Between the basins, rivers are usually sharply incised but above the incisions there are often broad, high-level corridors, as along the upper Murat. These carry scattered blocks of farmland, devoted almost entirely to cereals, together with large areas of pasture. In the north-east, particularly in the provinces of Kars and Ağrı, there are extensive areas of lava plateau where cultivated land is rare but which carry large expanses of fairly rich pasture and support numerous cattle. The extreme east, however, is not wholly devoid of intensive arable farming. The lacustrine flats around Lake Van carry orchards, vegetable gardens and vineyards as well as cereals, while the Aras valley, a district in which rainfall is very small, is a zone of intensive irrigated farming. In contrast, the high mountain areas are virtually devoid of cultivation and settlement but are widely used as summer pastures by the semi-nomadic valley-dwellers of the more remote areas.

The main towns of eastern Anatolia are generally situated in the more fertile basins and their actual size and importance are derived partly from the size and productivity of the provinces of which they are the capitals and partly from their position with relation to the transport network. Erzurum (105 000) has long been important as a point on the main route to the eastern frontier, as a military post and as the administrative centre of eastern Anatolia as a whole. Apart from a sugar-beet factory, there is little in the way of modern industry but the town is important as a centre for trade in livestock and livestock products. Kars (41 000) stands further to the east along the same route and is another livestock centre. Erzincan (45 000) stands at the point where the road from Sivas to Erzurum meets the railway coming up the Fırat valley. Elâzığ (80 000) is at the junction between the Tatvan line and the line from the south-east and draws added significance from the mineral resources of the district. Malatya (104 000), lying in a particularly fertile *ova*, stands where the road from Kayseri and the road and railway from Hatay, *via* Maraş reach the Fırat, and has a cotton textile industry.

Although eastern Anatolia as a whole is thinly settled and its production of crops is very small, it makes an important contribution to the Turkish economy from its minerals and livestock products. The region was probably more densely settled before the First World War when it had a large Armenian population. Its devastation and the flight of many of its inhabitants has been followed by slow recovery and it is still, both economically and socially, the most backward part of the country with a large Kurdish element which is still not wholly assimilated. Such developments as the Keban dam and the CENTO road and railway may lead to accelerated economic progress in this part of Turkey, but it will be a long time before its living standards approach those of more westerly regions.

Chapter 16

THE SOUTH-EASTERN REGION

This region (Fig. 52) has an area of 90 000 square km (35 000 square miles) and a population of 2·8 million. The proportion of land under cultivation (18·7%), the degree of urbanisation (31·3%) and the overall population density (31 per square km/80 per square mile) are all somewhat below the national average but well above the levels of eastern Anatolia.

Over most of its length, the northern boundary of the region follows the crest of a well-defined series of mountain ranges, the most southerly folds of the Taurus system, and the south-eastern region is roughly coincident with the structural block of the Arabian platform. In the west, however, the province of Maraş extends across the mountain barrier to include the basin of Elbistan, which is akin to the other *ovalar* of the Anatolian interior. South of the Taurus ranges, broad, undulating plateau surfaces fall slowly towards the Syrian frontier. Large parts of the region lie between 900 and 600 m (3000 and 2000 feet) above sea level, but in the south of Urfa province it drops to about 350 m (1150 feet). These plateau surfaces are in places interrupted by low mountain ranges which tend to follow the arcuate trend-lines of the Taurus proper, running from south-west to north-east between Maraş and Gaziantep and from west to east across Mardin province. Further diversity is derived from the presence of the Karacadağ volcanic massif, which rises to 1919 m (6300 feet) in the centre of the region. The greater part of the region is drained by the Firat (Euphrates) and Dicle (Tigris) river systems and over most of their length these rivers run in gorges cut deeply into the surface. The low rainfall of this part of the country is reflected in the fact that there are few important tributaries and many of the streams which originate within the region are intermittent, drying up completely in the intense heat of summer. Under these circumstances, irrigation, though necessary, is very difficult and the only scheme of any importance is that near Nusaybin which relies on the Çağçağ river, a small stream rising in the hills to the north-east of Mardin. Consequently, the greater part of this region is devoted to dry farming for cereals and there are large areas of grazing used by both cattle and sheep. Climate and soils are, however, favourable to viticulture which is widespread over much of the region and particularly so in Gaziantep. Like Central Anatolia, the south-east experienced a large-scale expansion of its cultivated area in the 1950s. The amount of land under cereals in Urfa province, for example, increased

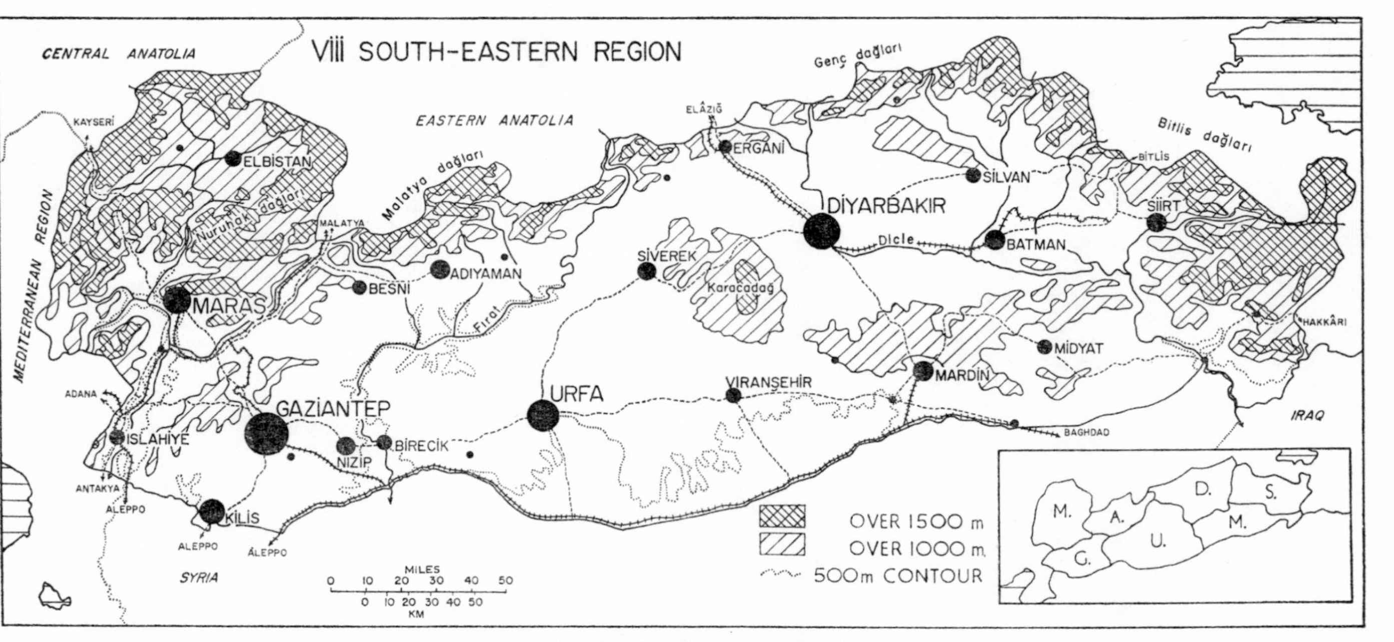

Fig. 52. The South-eastern Region

from 250 000 ha in 1950 to 500 000 ha in 1965 (60 000–120 000 acres).

There are a number of more favourable areas in the south-eastern region where the range of crops grown is wider and agriculture is more intensive. In the lowlands around Maraş for example, cotton, maize, tobacco, rice and a variety of fruits are grown in addition to wheat, barley, millet and vines. Other basins where irrigation is possible and soils are fertile include the Elbistan *ova* and the northern extension of the Levant rife valley into Gaziantep province. Agricultural productivity is also above average in the hill-foot zone below the Taurus ranges, in the Dicle valley below Diyarbakır and on the lower slopes of Karacadağ and the Mardin range. The driest area of all is Urfa province.

The region has considerable significance as a source of minerals and power. Its most important asset is the Ramandağ oilfield near Batman, where there is a refinery (see p. 130). A minor source of manganese is situated in Gaziantep province and a mineral-rich zone with chrome and copper ores occurs in the north of the region, beyond Ergani, though the actual centres of production are just across the regional boundary in Elâzığ province. The Fırat and Dicle have a considerable hydro-electric potential, none of which is yet developed though there are plans for generating stations on both rivers.

South-eastern Turkey forms part of the 'fertile crescent' of the Middle East which links Mesopotamia to the Levant coast, and although this 'fertility' is a relative matter and applies only in contrast to the Syrian desert to the south and the Taurus ranges to the north, the 'crescent' has for millennia been a line of movement between the Persian Gulf and the Mediterranean. This route is still followed by the Aleppo–Baghdad railway which has the unusual distinction of acting as the political boundary between Turkey and Syria, the tracks lying on the Turkish side.

The major cities of the region have a long history as trading centres along the fertile crescent route. Many of them have ancient defensive works, for this region was for centuries a zone of conflict, first between Persian and Byzantine and later between Turkish and Arab empires. There were large Christian minorities here until the 19th century and the region still has a Kurdish majority and a sizeable Arabic-speaking element. The towns are essentially agricultural markets and administrative centres. The largest of them is Gaziantep (160 000) which has a cotton textile industry and has grown particularly rapidly since the construction of a railway through the city to short-cut the diversion through Aleppo. Diyarbakır (102 000) has a well-preserved Roman wall and carries on small carpet-weaving and other industries. Urfa (74 000), Maraş (63 000) and Mardin (30 000) were all Roman frontier posts, but like Adıyaman (22 000) have lost much of their former importance.

FURTHER READING

There is no single volume in English on the geography of Turkey. The following titles, however, contain a good deal of valuable information.

Birot, P., and J. Dresch. *La Méditerranée et le Moyen Orient.* 2 vols. Paris: Presses Universitaires de France, 1953, 1956.

Blanchard, R. *Asie Occidentale. Géographie Universelle,* Vol. VIII. Paris: Armand Colin, 1929.

Brice, W. C. *South-West Asia.* London: University of London Press, 1966; New York: International Publications Service, 1966.

Bullard, R. W., ed. *The Middle East, A Political and Economic Survey.* London: Royal Institute of International Affairs, 1958; New York: Oxford University Press, 1958.

Clerget, M. *La Turquie, Passé et Présent.* Paris: Armand Colin, 1947.

Cressey, G. B. *Asia's Lands and Peoples.* New York: McGraw-Hill, 1951.

Cressey, G. B. *Crossroads: Land and Life in South-West Asia.* London: Pitman, 1963; Philadelphia: Lippincott, 1960.

Fisher, W. B. 'South-West Asia.' *The Changing World.* Edited by W. G. East and A. E. Moodie. London: Harrap, 1956.

Fisher, W. B. *The Middle East: A Physical, Social and Regional Geography.* London: Methuen, 1966.

Great Britain. Admiralty. Naval Intelligence Division. *Turkey.* 2 vols. London: H.M. Stationery Office, 1942, 1943.

Kingsbury, R. C., and N. J. G. Pounds. *Atlas of Middle Eastern Affairs.* London: Methuen, 1964; New York: Praeger, 1964.

Kinross, J. P. D. B. (Lord). *Turkey.* London: Thames & Hudson, 1960.

Lewis, G. L. *Turkey.* London: Benn, 1955.

Longrigg, S. H. *The Middle East, A Social Geography.* London: Duckworth. 1963; Chicago: Aldine, 1963.

Mango, A. *Turkey.* London: Thames & Hudson, 1966; New York: Walker & Co., 1968.

Oxford University Press. *Regional Economic Atlas of the Middle East and Africa.* London, 1960.

Ramazan, R. K. *The Northern Tier: Afghanistan, Iran and Turkey.* Princeton, N.J.: Van Nostrand, 1966.

Roux, J-P. *La Turquie: Géographie, Economie, Histoire.* Paris, 1953.

Roux, J-P. *Turquie.* Paris: Editions du Seuil, 1968.

Salter, C. *Introducing Turkey.* London: Methuen, 1961.

Stamp, L. D. S. *Asia: A Regional and Economic Geography.* London: Methuen, 1966.

Tanoğlu, A., S. Erinç, and E. Tümertekin. *Turkiye Atlasi* (*Atlas of Turkey*). İstanbul, 1961.

In addition the following books and articles deal with specific topics.

PHYSICAL

Baldy, C. '*Contribution à l'étude des régions climatiques turques.*' *Revue de Géographie de Lyon,* XXXV(I) (1960), 65–89.

Erinç, S. 'The climates of Turkey according to Thornethwaites's classification.' *Annals of the Association of American Geographers*, XXXIX (1949), 26–46.

Erinç, S. 'Climate types and the variation of moisture régimes in Turkey.' *Geographical Review*, XL (1950), 224–35.

Oakes, H. *The Soils of Turkey*. Ankara: Republic of Turkey, Ministry of Agriculture, Soil Conservation and Farm Irrigation Division, 1957.

HISTORICAL AND SOCIAL

Bonne, A. 'Land and Population in the Middle East.' *Middle East Journal*, V (1951), 39–56.

Brice, W. C. 'The population of Turkey in 1950.' *Geographical Journal*, CX (1954), 347–52.

Brice, W. C. 'The Anatolian Village.' *Geography*, XLIX (1955), 161–8.

Coles, P. *The Ottoman Impact on Europe*. London: Thames & Hudson, 1967; New York: Harcourt, Brace & World, 1968.

Duhamel, G. *La Turquie Nouvelle*. Paris, 1954.

Eren, N. *Turkey Today—and Tomorrow: An Experiment in Westernization.* New York, Praeger, 1963.

Fisher, W. B. 'Unity and diversity in the Middle East.' *Geographical Review*, XXXVII (1947), 414–35.

Gurney, O. R. *The Hittites*. Harmondsworth, Eng.: Penguin Books, 1952; Baltimore: Penguin Books, 1961.

Heyd, U. 'Islam in modern Turkey.' *Journal of the Royal Central Asian Society*, XXXIV (1947), 229–308.

Hostler, C. W. *Turkism and the Soviets*. London: Allen & Unwin, 1957.

Kolars, J. F. 'Bahtili: a Turkish village in transition.' *Focus on Geographic Activity*. Edited by R. S. Thoman and D. J. Patton. New York: McGraw-Hill, 1964.

Lerner, D. *The Passing of Traditional Society: Modernizing the Middle East.* Glencoe, Ill.: The Free Press, 1958.

Lewis, B. 'Democracy in Turkey.' *Middle East Affairs*, X (1959), 55–72.

Lewis, B. *The Emergence of Modern Turkey*. London and New York: Oxford University Press, 1961.

Makal, A. *A Village in Anatolia*. London, 1954.

Orga, I. *Phoenix Ascendant: The Rise of Modern Turkey*. London: Hale, 1958.

Pallis, A. A. 'The population of Turkey in 1935.' *Geographical Journal*, XCI (1938), 424–38.

Pierce, J. E. *Life in a Turkish Village*. London and New York: Holt, Rinehart & Winston, 1965.

Price, M. P. *A History of Turkey*. London: Allen & Unwin, 1956; New York: Hillary, 1961.

Rice, T. T. *The Seljuks in Asia Minor*. London: Thames & Hudson, 1961; New York: Praeger, 1961.

Robinson, R. D. *The First Turkish Republic: A Case Study in National Development*. Cambridge, Mass.: Harvard University Press, 1963.

Sarc, A. C. 'Growth of the Turkish rural population.' *Middle East Affairs*, III (1952), 71–80.

Stirling, P. 'Religious change in republican Turkey.' *Middle East Journal*, XII (1958), 395–408.

Stirling, P. 'Social ranking in a Turkish village.' *British Journal of Sociology*, IV (1953), 31–44.
Stirling, P. *Turkish Village*. London, 1966; New York: Wiley, 1967.
Taueber, I. 'Population and modernization in Turkey.' *Population Index*, XXIV (1958), 101–22.

ECONOMIC

Aktan R. 'Mechanization of agriculture in Turkey.' *Land Economics*, XXXIII (1957), 273–85.
Aktan, R. 'Problems of land reform in Turkey.' *Middle East Journal* (Washington), XX (1966), 317–34.
Craig, D. 'Anatolia: a good harvest every year.' *Ceres*, I (II), 1968.
Erinç, S., and N. Tunçdilek. 'The agricultural regions of Turkey.' *Geographical Review*, XLII (1952), 179–203.
Food and Agriculture Organisation. *Turkey, Country Report, Mediterranean Development Project*. Rome, 1959.
Helburn, N. 'A stereotype of agriculture in semi-arid Turkey.' *Geographical Review*, XLV (1955), 375–84.
Hershlag, Z. Y. *Turkey: An Economy in Transition*. The Hague: Uitgeverij Van Keulen N.V., 1959.
Kolars, J. F. 'Locational aspects of cultural ecology.' *Geographical Review*, LVI (1966), 577–84.
Menemencioğlu, N. 'The progress of Turkey.' *Progress*, XLI (1950–1), 3–13.
Nowland, J. L. 'The port of Istanbul.' *Scottish Geographical Magazine*, LXXVII (1961), 67–74.
O.E.C.D. *Turkey*. Paris, 1967.
Oram, P. A., and D. K. Jones, 'The agricultural revolution in Turkey.' *World Crops*, VII (1955), 137–42, 278–83.
Planhol, X. de. '*Expansion et problèmes de l'agriculture Turque*.' *Revue de Géographie de Lyon*, XXXV (1960), 91–103.
Shorter, F. C. *Four Case Studies in the Economic Development of Turkey*. London: Cass, 1967; New York: Kelley, 1968.
Stratil-Sauer, G. 'Cereal production in Turkey.' *Economic Geography*, IX (1933), 325–36.
Thornburg, M. W., G. Spry, and G. Soule. *Turkey: An Economic Appraisal*. New York: Twentieth Century Fund, 1949.
Tümertekin, E. 'The iron and steel industry of Turkey.' *Economic Geography*, XXXI (1955), 179–84.
United Nations. Department of Economic and Social Affairs. *The Development of Manufacturing Industry in Egypt, Israel & Turkey*. New York, 1958.
Winkler, E. '*Die Wirtschaft von Zonguldak, Türkei: eine geographische Untersuchung*. *Wiener Geographische Schriften*, 12/13 (1961).

REGIONAL DESCRIPTION AND TRAVELS

Ainsworth, W. 'Notes on a journey from Constantinople by Heraclea to Angora in the autumn of 1838.' *Geographical Journal*, IX (1839), 216–76.
Bean, C. E. 'Smyrna, ancient and modern., *Geographical Magazine*, XVII (1944), 357–63.

Chater, M. 'East of Constantinople.' *National Geographic Magazine*, XLIII (1923), 509–34.

Cornwall, J. H. M. 'A journey in Anatolia.' *Geographical Journal*, LXIV (1924), 213–22.

Douglas, W. O. 'Station-wagon odyssey: Baghdad to Istanbul.' *National Geographic Magazine*, CXV (1959), 48–87.

Hills, D. *My Travels in Turkey*. London: Allen & Unwin, 1964.

Hodgkin, R. 'Climbing in the Taurus Mountains.' *Geographical Magazine*, XVII (1945), 510–18.

Jackson, M. *The Turkish Time Machine*. London: Hodder & Stoughton, 1966.

Kinross, J. P. D. B. (Lord). *Within the Taurus*. London: Murray, 1954.

Kinross, J. P. D. B. (Lord). *Europa Minor: Journeys in Costal Turkey*. London: Murray, 1956.

Kuhn, F. 'Where Turk and Russian meet.' *National Geographic Magazine*, CI (1952), 743–66.

Marchionini, A. 'Peasants of Anatolia.' *National Geographic Magazine*, XCIV (1948), 57–72.

Mayne, P. *Istanbul*. London: Phoenix House, 1967; Cranbury, N. J.: A. S. Barnes, 1967.

Merriam, G. P. 'The regional geography of Anatolia.' *Economic Geography*, II (1926), 86–107.

Orga, I. *The Caravan Moves*. London: Secker & Warburg, 1958.

Price, M. P. 'Recent developments in Anatolia & the Caucasus.' *Journal of the Royal Central Asian Society*. XXXIV (1947), 287–98.

Ribaud, M. 'Cappadocia: Turkey's country of cones.' *National Geographic Magazine*, CXIII (1958), 122–46.

Stark, F. *Alexander's Path*. London: Murray, 1958; New York: Harcourt, Brace & World, 1967.

Stark, F. 'Landscapes in Caria., *Geographical Journal*, CXXIV (1958), 30–34, 340–6.

Stark, F. *Riding to the Tigris*. London: Murray, 1959.

Stotz, C. L. 'The Bursa region of Turkey.' *Geographical Review*, XXIX (1939), 81–100.

Williams, M. O. 'The Turkish Republic comes of age.' *National Geographic Magazine*, LXXXVII (1945), 581–616.

Wright, D. 'Trebizond and north-eastern Turkey.' *Journal of the Royal Central Asian Society*, 1946, 121–32.

Wright, I., and D. Wright. 'The Black Sea coast of Turkey.' *Geographical Magazine*, XVIII (1946), 118–25.

INDEX

Numbers in **bold** print following page references denote figure references